Tree Fruit Irrigation

A comprehensive manual of

deciduous tree fruit irrigation needs

TREE FRUIT IRRIGATION

A comprehensive manual of deciduous tree fruit irrigation needs.

Edited by
Kathleen M. Williams, Ph.D.
Thomas W. Ley

Contributors include
Preston Andrews, Ph.D.
Peter Canessa
Paul Cross
Robert Evans, Ph.D.
Michael Hepp
Terry Henderson
Ron Hermanson, Ph.D.
Thomas W. Ley
Frank Peryea, Ph.D.
Edward Proebsting, Ph.D.
Stephen Rawlins, Ph.D.
Tim Smith
Thomas Spofford
Robert Stevens, Ph.D.
Ted Van der Gulik
Michael Willett

Published by
Good Fruit Grower
Project Coordination and Design, Jim Black
Cover Design, Nancy Born
Yakima, Washington
1994

Published by Good Fruit Grower
a division of Washington State Fruit Commission
1005 Tieton Drive, Yakima, Washington 98902
509/575-2315, Fax 509/453-4880

First printing December 1994

Library of Congress Cataloging-in-Publication Data
Tree fruit irrigation: a comprehensive manual of deciduous tree fruit irrigation needs /
    edited by Kathleen M. Williams, Thomas W. Ley.
        p.   cm.
    Includes bibliographical references.
    ISBN 0-9630659-5-5 (pbk.)   : $17.00
    1. Fruit—Irrigation—Handbooks, manuals, etc. 2. Fruit-culture—Handbooks, manuals, etc.
    3. Irrigation efficiency—Handbooks, manuals, etc. 4. Fruit—Irrigation—United States—
    Handbooks, manuals, etc. 5. Fruit-culture—United States—Handbooks, manuals, etc.
    6. Irrigation efficiency—United States—Handbooks, manuals, etc.   I. Williams, Kathleen M.,
    1951-   .   II. Ley, Thomas W.
    SB357.285.T74   1994
    634'.0487'0973—dc20   94-36397
                                                                           CIP

Printed and bound in the United States of America

Preface

Water is an essential element of all living organisms. Deciduous fruit trees need water for both tree growth and fruit production. If water is a limiting factor in tree growth, the effects are quickly observed in the reduction of growth and fruit size.

The environment directly affects water utilization by deciduous fruit trees. The influential factors include light, soil type and moisture status, humidity and temperature. The nutrition of fruit trees depends directly on the water status of the trees. If water is limiting, key elements for growth and development will not be available to the fruit trees and perhaps fruit itself.

There are other environmental concerns affecting water management of fruit trees. The political implications of using water efficiently are clearly present; the tree fruit industry must face a complex set of issues directly related to availability and quality of irrigation water. Agricultural runoff into ground water sources as well as surface water systems is a concern that the public has expressed. Utilization of agricultural chemicals and nutrients demands careful attention to not only the method of irrigation, but also the longterm effects of the application method.

In the Part I of this book, the whole tree physiology as related to nutrient and water relations is discussed. The soil-water interface and how this affects the tree and fruit growth and development is also covered.

Part II covers all aspects of irrigation scheduling from elaborate computer model systems to a simple "checkbook balance" method. Of particular note is a deficit irrigation method as drought management strategy.

Regulations and the environmental concerns which affect the use of irrigation water are discussed in Part III. The "Best Management Practices" concept for protecting the environment is discussed in relation to tree fruit production and efficiency of irrigation.

Finally, the design of efficient irrigation systems and delivery methods is covered in Part IV. Systems which are capable of both irrigation and cooling or frost protection are discussed. Pump design systems are included are part of this section. High density orchard systems and irrigation design are also included in this section.

This book will serve as a reference for fruit growers, orchard consultants and extension and research personnel interested in tree fruit irrigation.

Gratitude is expressed to all the contributors to this book, to my co-editor Tom Ley, and to the tireless cooperation of the Good Fruit Grower staff.

Kathleen Williams,
editor

TABLE OF CONTENTS

PART 4, System design considerations

PART ONE

Plant, soil and water relations

Dynamics of water and solutes with soil and plants

Stephen Rawlins, Ph.D.
Research Soil Scientist
USDA/ARS, Washington State University, Prosser

To understand how water moves within the soil-plant-atmosphere continuum, it's necessary to define a few terms. A minimum number of factors governing water flow should be examined to see how they interact in a typical irrigation cycle, and then some major processes governing water flow in soil should be explored.

Gravitational potential

Water and the chemicals it carries are seldom at equilibrium in the soil-plant-atmosphere system. Liquid water is pulled downward by gravity, but it is also pulled downward as well as in other directions by adsorptive forces arising from soil particle surfaces. The gravity force, which causes water to move from high elevations to low elevations, can be expressed in terms of the gradient (change per unit length) of the gravitational potential of the water. The term *potential* refers to the *potential energy* of the water. The higher the water is above some reference elevation, arbitrarily defined as zero potential energy, the higher the potential energy or gravitational potential of water. Potential energy of water can be expressed per unit *weight* of water, which gives it the dimension of length. For gravitational potential this is the same as the familiar term

gravity head. The length is the distance above or below a plane arbitrarily defined as zero. If the point in question is above this plane, its gravitational potential is positive. If it is below, its gravitational potential is negative.

Water potential can also be expressed as energy per unit *volume* of water, which can be expressed in the familiar units of pressure: atmospheres, bars or pascals. Expressed as energy per unit *mass* of water, water potential has units such as Joules/kg.

Matric potential

The adsorptive force causing water to move in soil can also be expressed in terms of the gradient of a potential energy. In this case the potential energy is called the *matric potential,* because it arises from adsorptive forces of the soil *matrix.* This force allows one to blot ink with a blotter, or pick up spilled water with a dry towel.

The drier the towel (or soil) the more force it exerts in picking up the water. Matric potential, as with all water potential components, can be expressed in terms of head, pressure or energy per unit mass. Expressed as a head (length), the length is that of a theoretical column of water hanging from a porous membrane, such as a porous ceramic tensiometer cup, in contact with the soil water, that is just long enough to balance the adsorptive forces pulling the water into the soil. (In this case the pores in the membrane are considered to be large enough to allow solutes to pass, but not soil particles.) Because the column is hanging, that is it is measured downward from the point of insertion of the tensiometer into the soil, matric potential is always negative for soil not fully saturated with water. If matric potential is expressed in pressure terms, the pressure is that of the water inside the tensiometer cup, which is less than atmospheric, and therefore, is negative.

For any given soil, the drier it is, the more negative is its matric potential. Water always moves from high (less negative) matric potential to low (more negative) matric potential in the soil. It is the matric potential gradient that causes water to move upward from a water table, a process called capillary rise. Zero matric potential is equal to atmospheric pressure. For unsaturated soils, water in the soil is normally in contact with a continuous gas phase that connects with the atmosphere, so it is impossible for matric potential to be positive.

But in cases where this gas phase is not continuous, because of a confining layer, pressures can build up as the result of the weight of the soil above, even though the soil is unsaturated. This creates the equivalent of a positive matric potential — often called the *overburden* potential.

Water within a *confined* aquifer can also be under positive pressure, *pressure potential,* which gives rise to upward, artesian, movement through soil where the confining layer is discontinuous. This gives rise to saline seeps in many areas of the world. Of course, water in pipelines, and below unconfined water tables, usually has a positive pressure potential. Below the surface of an unconfined water table the pressure potential is exactly equal to the gravitational potential, resulting in no potential gradient to cause flow.

Hydraulic potential
Water moves in the soil in response to the *hydraulic potential*—the algebraic sum of the gravitational, matric and pressure potentials. Because the pressure potential is normally zero in unsaturated soil, only the gravitational and matric potentials contribute to flow. Water flows from high hydraulic potential to low hydraulic potential, just as heat flows from high temperature (thermal potential) to low temperature.

Hydraulic conductivity
The rate of water flow, just as the rate of heat flow, depends not only upon the potential gradients, but also on the conductivity of the medium. The heat conductivity of most materials is essentially constant with temperature, so the rate of heat flow is proportional to the temperature gradient. The water or *hydraulic conductivity* of soil, on the other hand, is not constant, but varies greatly with soil water content. This occurs because liquid water can flow only through liquid-filled pores. As a consequence, the hydraulic conductivity of soil decreases drastically (as much as a million-fold!) as the soil water content decreases from saturation to the wilting point of plants.

Dynamics of flow for an irrigation cycle
To illustrate how all of these factors interact, consider a typical irrigation cycle. Assume a uniform soil which is initially relatively dry— matric potential = -1 bar (-33 ft. of head). Water applied at the surface is pulled downward by gravity, but a much larger force pulling water into the soil results from adsorption forces. The low (negative) matric potential of the dry soil results in a high matric potential gradient, which far exceeds the gravitational potential gradient.

This force is initially very large because of the sharp boundary between wet and dry soil. This short distance between wet and dry soil results in a large gradient, resulting in a large force. Although the gradient can only be determined by taking the derivative of the matric potential-distance curve, if the distance is short, its order of magnitude can be estimated by dividing the difference in matric potential between points by the distance between them. For example, if the boundary between wet soil and dry soil is 0.1 foot, the matric potential difference between the saturated soil and the dry soil of -33 feet is dissipated across a distance of 0.1 foot, resulting in a large potential gradient, of the order of -330 feet per foot. The, gravitational potential gradient is always unity: one foot per foot. The force resulting from the matric potential gradient is, therefore, initially about 300 times the force resulting from the gravitational gradient. As water infiltrates, the wetting zone spreads out, and the combination of the reduced matric potential gradient and the reduced hydraulic conductivity through the longer transport zone result in a decreasing infiltration rate. If irrigation is continued long enough, the matric potential gradient becomes small, leaving only the gravitational gradient. In this case the infiltration approaches a constant value equal to the saturated conductivity of the soil.

Once irrigation ceases, water begins to move out of the root zone by three pathways: 1) by continued downward redistribution into the soil beneath by adsorption into drier subsoil or by the gravitational pull, 2) movement into plant roots and stems to leaf surfaces, where it passes through the leaf stomata into the atmosphere—a process called transpira-

tion; and, 3) through the soil to the surface, where it moves into the atmosphere—by evaporation. The first process can result in storage of water in soil below the root zone, which later moves back up along a matric potential gradient, or it can lead to permanent loss through deep percolation. The combined processes of transpiration and evaporation are called evapotranspiration (ET).

Transpiration results in decreased water (potential) within the plant, which extends to its roots, causing water to be extracted from the soil. This decreases the matric potential of the soil at the root surface, resulting in a matric potential gradient that moves water from the soil to the root surface. As water is extracted, the hydraulic conductivity of the soil near the root decreases, requiring the water potential within the plant to decrease to maintain a constant flow of water. At some point, as plant water pressure decreases, the leaf stomata close, decreasing the transpiration rate.

Likewise, direct evaporation of water from the soil surface also results in a matric potential gradient, moving water directly through

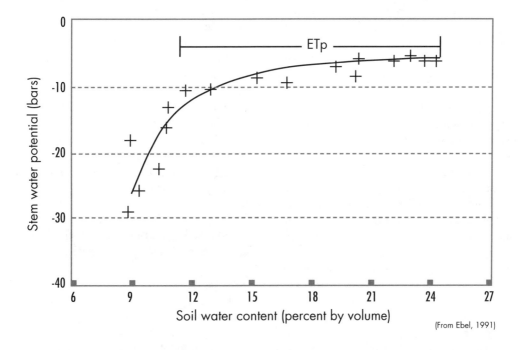

(From Ebel, 1991)

FIGURE 1. Stem water potential of apple as a function of soil water content of Warden sandy loam soil.

the soil to the surface. When the soil is wet, the rate of extraction of water from the soil by both roots and through direct transport to the surface is usually limited only by the amount of radiant energy from the sun. If the incoming energy is constant, the ET during this phase is also constant, and is often referred to as the *constant rate evapotranspiration phase.* The evapotranspiration during this phase is referred to as the *potential evapotranspiration* (ET$_p$).

As a consequence of both decreasing soil hydraulic conductivity and leaf stomata closure, as extraction continues the point is reached where water cannot be supplied either to the plant roots or to the soil surface at a rate sufficient to maintain evapotranspiration at the potential rate. Because evapotranspiration decreases with time during this period, it is often referred to as the *falling rate evapotranspiration phase.*

Figure 1 shows the effect of decreasing hydraulic conductivity of the soil on the stem water potential of apple trees as water is extracted from Warden sandy loam soil. The inflection point in the curve at about 12 percent water content corresponds to the transition from potential evaporation to a decreasing rate. Eventually the soil dries out so much that the plants growing within it wilt, even after the sun goes down. The soil water content at this point is called the permanent wilting point.

The relative importance of transpiration and evaporation in extracting water from the soil profile depends on the extent of root growth into the soil, and the proportion of the soil surface shaded by the crop canopy. Because a newly planted crop has only a few shallow roots, and the leaves shade only a small part of the soil surface, evaporation is the dominant process responsible for water extraction from the profile. For a fully mature crop, with a deep extensive root system, and with a closed canopy (where all of the soil is shaded), only a small part of the water extracted is in the form of soil evaporation.

Before concluding this overview of a typical irrigation cycle we need to consider what happens to solutes in the irrigation water. Initially solutes move freely with the liquid water within the soil, but they are stopped at either the plant root surface or a site of evaporation. Thus, solutes tend to accumulate within the root zone and at the soil surface. As the solute concentration of the soil water increases, its *osmotic potential* decreases. Osmotic potential is important primarily where water must move through semipermeable membranes, such as exist in roots, that restrict the movement of solutes. Plants, therefore, must extract water not only against the forces resulting from the gradients of the matric and gravitational potential, but also from the osmotic potential gradient. In addition to the osmotic effect, some specific ions can be toxic to plants.

Osmotic potential, like matric potential, can also be expressed in terms of energy per unit weight or as a length of a hanging water column. The only difference is that in this case the theoretical membrane connecting the water column to the soil water does not allow solutes to pass. Zero osmotic potential occurs when the water is free of solutes. It decreases (becomes more negative) as the solute concentration of the soil water increases. Of course, like other components of the water potential, osmotic potential can also be expresses as energy per unit volume or pressure, or as energy per unit mass.

Coping with salt in the root zone requires not only a knowledge of its origin, but also an understanding of some basic physical, chemical and biological principles dealing with its transport and interaction with the soil and crop. Salinity control at the farm level consists basically of providing both an increment of irrigation water in addition to evapotranspiration to leach salts from the root zone and a place to dispose of the leached water.

Basic soil properties and effect on water transport and storage

Soil texture

Soil texture is a measure of the size distribution of the primary mineral particles making up the solid soil matrix. These particles are classified into three categories with the following diameters: clay, 0 to 0.002 mm; silt, 0.002 to 0.02 mm; and sand, 0.02 to 2.0 mm. Clay particles have about 1,000 times as much surface area per unit mass as do coarse sand particles. Because the adsorptive forces responsible for the matric potential of soil arise at these soil surfaces, fine textured soils—those dominated by clays—hold water far more tightly at any given water content than do coarse textured soils—those dominated by sand. This fact is reflected in the difference in their water retentivity, as will be discussed below.

Fine textured soils *that are not aggregated* have much smaller pores for water to flow through, resulting in relatively low hydraulic conductivity at high water content.

Soil structure

Soil structure is a measure of the degree of aggregation of primary particles into larger, secondary units. These secondary units can range from small aggregates to large blocks, or peds, separated by permanent cracks, or zones of weakness in the soil. Both organic and inorganic compounds in the soil serve as cements to bind primary soil particles into more or less stable aggregates. Forces from freezing and thawing as well as wetting and drying are among those responsible for moving the particles together to form aggregates.

Because the binding forces act at soil surfaces, fine-textured soils tend to form aggregates more readily than course-textured soils. As a consequence their total pore space is typically greater. Figure 2 shows this relationship. Fine-textured soils often develop large cracks and channels through which water, air, and plant roots can penetrate into the soil profile. Sandy soils, on the other hand, frequently comprise single grains, having essentially no structure, and can form dense compacted layers through which plant roots penetrate poorly.

Because soil structure mainly affects the larger pores in the soil, its effect on hydraulic conductivity is mainly in the very wet range. In the dry range, hydraulic conductivity depends more on soil texture.

Highly aggregated soils have good tilth. They drain quickly in the spring, plow easily, and crumble into a uniform seed bed, without large compact clods.

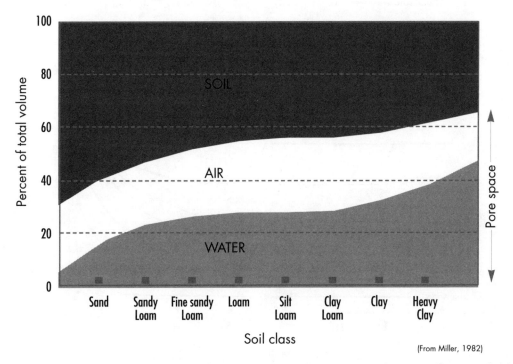

(From Miller, 1982)

FIGURE 2. Typical distribution of soil, water, and air on a volumetric basis at field capacity as related to soil texture.

Soil water retention

The amount of water held by a soil as a function of matric potential is often referred to as its soil water characteristic curve. Figure 3 shows such curves for several soil samples of varying texture. Note that the water content reaches a maximum when all of the pore space within a soil is filled with water. The water content of the coarse sand decreases quickly in response to the application of only slightly negative matric potential. The clay, on the other hand, retains a high soil water content even at matric potentials as low as -16 bars, about the permanent wilting point. The high water content even at the wilting point illustrates the fact that even though the clay soil holds more water, it is not necessary available for use by plants.

Available water

The amount of water available for crop use is the difference between the water content that exists immediately after infiltration, when most drainage has ceased (field capacity), and the water content when plants can no longer extract water (wilting point). Fine-textured soils have low available water-holding capacity because both the field capacity and the wilting point are high. Coarse-textured soils have low available water-holding capacity because both the field capacity and the wilting point are low.

It is important to note that although the field capacity and the wilting point often occur near the matric potentials of -0.3 and -15 bars, they can vary substantially from these values for different soils. The wilting point is reached when the water content and hydraulic conductivity of the soil are too low to maintain sufficient water flow to the plant roots to maintain plant turgor. Experiments show that this can vary over a wide range — from a negative matric potential value of only a few bars to tens of bars for different soils and different crops. But, as can be seen in Figure 3, the amount of water released from the soil below a negative matric potential value of a few bars is so slight, that it makes little difference which value is used in the calculation of available water.

Field capacity

The upper limit of available water, the field capacity, is a different matter. Because the soil

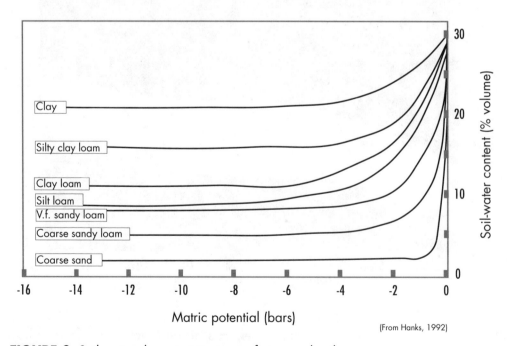

(From Hanks, 1992)

FIGURE 3. Soil water characteristic curves for several soils.

water characteristic curves are very steep in this range, only a slight difference in the matric potential can result in a large difference in water content. But more importantly, the quantity of water held at field capacity is not a function of the properties of the surface soil only, but of the entire soil profile. So it is impossible to select a single value for the matric potential that corresponds to field capacity for any soil sample.

Field capacity can never be estimated accurately by any laboratory measurement on a soil sample. It must be measured in the field by following the water content of the soil after a heavy irrigation. Soils with subsoils that impede deep drainage have much higher field capacities than soils that are uniform with depth.

Also, some soils do not have a clearly defined field capacity. Although for coarse textured soils drainage tends almost to cease a day or two after infiltration, for some fine textured soils it can continue for weeks. Calculations of available water for these soils must include an estimate of this deep drainage.

The concept of available water-holding capacity is most useful for dry land agriculture, or for manual irrigation systems, where each application incurs an additional labor expense.

In dry land agriculture, where the crop is grown on stored water, it is important to know how much water is available, for example, to determine how much fertilizer should be applied. Likewise, where an additional cost is incurred for each irrigation, there is reason to minimize the number of irrigations by depleting as much stored water as possible. But for solid-set, or automated irrigation systems it is seldom advisable to maximize the use of stored water between irrigations. Irrigation scheduling in these cases is based more on the steady replacement of evapotranspired water than on filling the soil profile to capacity, and depleting it as far as possible. Because knowledge of the available water-holding capacity in these cases is important mainly in determining the minimum frequency of irrigation, it need not be determined accurately.

Applications of principles

Water and solute flow trajectories with different irrigation systems

Different irrigation systems cause important differences in the patterns of water and solute flow. One-dimensional systems are those that apply water uniformly to the soil surface, so that the only component of flow is downward. Sprinklers and flood irrigation systems can fit into this category. Sprinkler systems can be operated to apply water at a rate that is less than that which can be accommodated by soil infiltration, so that water never stands on the soil surface. This is a *flux-controlled* system, because with no opportunity for water to flow over the soil surface, the uniformity of infiltration is equal to the uniformity of application. As long as the application rate is less than the rate of infiltration that can be accommodated by the slowest spots, non-uniformity of soil properties do not affect the uniformity of infiltration.

The uniformity of infiltration with flood irrigation, on the other hand, is largely controlled by soil properties. Only the opportunity time—the time water stands on the soil surface—is controlled by the irrigation system. With such systems, non-uniformities resulting from differences in soil texture, soil structure, cracks, root holes or gopher holes control the uniformity of infiltration.

Two-dimensional irrigation systems are those that apply water in a line, such as a drip hose or a furrow. Drip lines can be operated as flux-controlled systems, but furrows cannot, for the same reasons stated above. Two-dimensional systems do not move solutes uniformly downward through the profile. Solutes move with the water, which is downward under the line source, but is lateral and upward between. This can have advantages and disadvantages. Among the advantages is that nitrate fertilizer need not be leached by deep percolating water. If the fertilizer is applied between the irrigation lines, the two-dimensional water flux pattern will tend to keep it there. A disadvantage of two-dimensional irrigation is that non-nutrient solutes, in the irrigation water, for example, are not leached uniformly from the root zone.

Typically, the quantity of solutes that accumulate in the root zone from a single irrigation season is not sufficient to cause any problems. Solutes can then be leached during the winter either by rainfall, or, if necessary, by installing portable sprinkler irrigation systems.

Three-dimensional irrigation systems apply water at points within the field. Only closed conduit systems, such as drip, spray or bubbler systems, can do this; surface irrigation systems cannot. The dynamics of flow away from a point applicator are similar to those for a line source, except solutes move to the soil surface in a ring surrounding the point of application rather than in a line. Bubbler systems that flood a surface reservoir under each tree in an orchard can qualify as three-dimensional systems at a distance scale equal to the tree spacing.

Water infiltration below the ponded water reservoir will be controlled soil properties, and, therefore, will not be uniform. But as long as the quantity of infiltrating water during each irrigation is small compared to the water-holding capacity of the root zone, nonuniformities in infiltration can be compensated for by natural adjustments in root distribution pattern that prevent water from escaping by deep percolation. Anyone who has dug up a leaky sewer line knows that tree roots grow toward water.

A fourth class of irrigation—subirrigation—is one-dimensional if it is from an elevated water table, but can also be two- or three-dimensional if water is applied from buried drip lines or drip emitters. In both cases, water movement is from the bottom up, which allows for no leaching of the root zone. Alternative means for leaching must be employed to maintain salt balance.

Field water and solute balances

Both irrigation water requirements and leaching requirements must be established to maintain appropriate water and solute balances in the field. As discussed earlier, and as will be discussed in more detail in other chapters, irrigation water requirements are established to replace evapotranspired water at a sufficiently frequent interval to avoid serious plant water stress. For sandy soils with low water-holding capacity, this may require daily irrigation during the peak water-use period. The important factors that must be considered, in addition to soil water-holding capacity, are the evapotranspiration rate and the uniformity of irrigation. Usually, managers want to apply sufficient water to ensure that adequate water is applied to those areas that otherwise receive the least amount. This means that with non-uniform systems, other areas receive more than enough, which ends up as deep percolation.

Solute balance does not have to be maintained on a continuous basis unless irrigation water is extremely saline. For most water sources in the Pacific Northwest, it is only necessary to assure solute balance on a seasonal or longer interval. In fact, deficit irrigation, the practice of under irrigating by a small amount to move water slowly beneath the root zone upward for use during the season, usually causes no salinity problems, as long as solutes are pushed back down by leaching during the winter.

Deficit irrigation is an important strategy for preventing nutrient leaching during the growing season. If irrigation is sufficiently frequent, and the deficit is small, crops experience no water stress. Especially where water tables are shallow, however, care must be taken to assure an overall downward flux of water, at least on an annual basis. But even with very saline water tables, the root zone can be maintained adequately free of solutes with little excess water for leaching, if a downward, but small water flux gradient is continuously maintained. Rarely is it necessary to apply more than a few percent extra irrigation water on an annual basis to maintain an adequately leached root zone, if the root zone is uniformly leached.

REFERENCES

Ebel, Robert Charles. 1991. *Apple Tree and Fruit Response to Drought Stress,* Ph.D. Thesis, Department of Horticulture and Landscape Architecture, Washington State University.

Hanks, R. J. 1992. *Applied Soil Physics: Soil Water and Temperature Applications,* Springer-Verlag, New York, 175 pp.

Miller, Dave E. 1982. "Physical Characteristics of Soils as they Relate to Irrigation and Water Management," pp 3-28 in *Water Management and Irrigation of Tree Fruits: Proceedings of the Short Course–1982,* Washington State University, Cooperative Extension, Pullman, Washington.

Understanding water and nutrient uptake

Frank J. Peryea, Ph.D.

Associate Soil Scientist and Horticulturist

Tree Fruit Research and Extension Center, Washington State University, Wenatchee

Nutrient uptake by fruit trees can occur through both roots and leaves. Under most conditions, root absorption of nutrients found in the soil is the dominant means by which trees acquire nutrients. Root activity and nutrient supply from the soil are directly influenced by the moisture content of the soils. Understanding the complex relationships between roots, soil, water, and nutrients is therefore essential to optimize mineral nutrition in fruit trees.

Root morphology and structure

Roots serve several functions in fruit trees. They provide anchorage, helping to keep the tree from toppling over in strong winds and when bearing heavy loads of fruit. Roots absorb water and nutrients from the soil and conduct them to the stem. Roots are important storage organs for nutrients, being a particularly important reservoir of stored nitrogen during the winter.

Roots also synthesize phytohormones, including cytokinins, gibberellic acids, ethylene, and abscisic acid, which can influence tree and fruit growth and physiology. They also excrete other organic compounds that change the chemistry of the soil immediately outside the root (the rhizosphere), thereby influencing soil nutrient availability and the activity of soil microorganisms and roots of other plants.

The morphology of roots is complex. Figure 1 illustrates the structures encountered as one moves radially from the outside to the center of a root. Figure 2 shows the root structures encountered as one moves longitudinally from the tip towards the trunk.

Root development and distribution in fruit trees

Newly developed fruit tree roots initially are white. After about three weeks in summer or longer in winter, natural browning of the cortex spreads from the older regions towards the tip. The cortex then decomposes. After the loss of the cortex, secondary thickening occurs in some roots that become part of the perennial root system. The tree root system therefore is composed of roots of different types, ages, sizes, and life histories.

At maturity, the apple root system consists of a horizontal scaffold of major roots that radiate from the trunk and produce both vertical roots that descend to deeper soil horizons and highly branched roots that exploit the more superficial soil. The exact form of the root system and root distribution is influenced by many variables, including soil type, irrigation practices, planting density, root-stock, and tree species. Examples include:

1) frequent light irrigations encourage superficial rooting;
2) disking encourages root growth below the tillage zone;
3) under arid conditions, roots of irrigated trees are restricted to the area wetted by the irrigation water;
4) roots tend to proliferate in parts of the soil which have greater water and nutrient availability;
5) pear roots have a more vertical structure than do apples; and
6) densely planted trees have more horizontally compact root systems with a higher proportion of the root volume deep in the soil profile.

Transport of water and nutrient into roots

Water and solutes in the soil solution move radially into roots through apoplastic or symplastic pathways *(Figure 1)*. The apoplastic pathway consists of movement within the spaces between cells and is usually terminated at the Casparian strip in the walls of the endodermal cells. There are some leaky areas, in the meristematic zone at the root tip and in basal portions of roots where lateral roots penetrate the endodermis. Calcium and magnesium tend to move apoplastically in roots.

The symplastic pathway consists of penetration into plant cells through the cellular membrane and subsequent movement from cell to cell through plasmodesmata, tiny tunnels that connect the cytoplasm (cell sap) of neighboring cells *(see Figure 3)*. Nutrients must enter the symplastic pathway before they

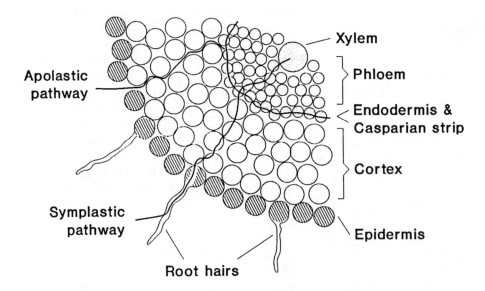

FIGURE 1. This figure illustrates the radial transsection of a root showing apoplastic and symplastic pathways. Definition of structures follows:

ROOT HAIRS = transitory single-cell structures that increase root contact with soil particles and increase absorption of water and nutrients
EPIDERMIS/RHIZODERMIS = outer cell layers from which root hairs develop; usually colonized by microorganisms
CORTEX = outer portion of root between vascular stele and epidermis
ENDODERMIS = inner part of cortex; usually one cell-layer thick
CASPARIAN STRIP = suberized (corky) band of tissue that forms around the endodermal cells, creating a barrier to extracellular movement of water and nutrients from the cortex to the vascular stele
STELE/VASCULAR BUNDLE, consists of the following structures:
    Pericycle = cells surrounding the phloem and xylem
    Phloem = tubular vessels that transport metabolites from shoot to roots
    Xylem = tubular vessels that transport water and solutes from roots to shoot

can be transported to the shoot. Water, nitrogen, potassium and phosphorus tend to move symplastically in roots. Newly formed roots and root hairs contain more plasmodesmata than older roots, which accounts in part for their ability to absorb and transport nutrients more rapidly.

Nutrients must cross through the cell membrane to enter the symplastic pathway. This is done through passive or active transport processes *(Figure 4)*. In passive transport nutrients are more concentrated on one side of a membrane (i.e., they have more potential energy) than the other, and thus diffuse without additional energy inputs from a higher to a lower chemical potential environment (downhill transport). Water, calcium, and magnesium tend to be passively transported. In active transport, dissolved nutrients move through a membrane against a concentration gradient, that is, from a lower to a higher energy environment (uphill transport). This requires physiological ion pumps or carrier systems, which often select for certain nutrients, and requires the plant to expend energy to acquire nutrients. Potassium, phosphate, sodium, and nitrate are actively transported.

Water and nutrients that enter the symplastic pathway bypass the barrier of the Casparian strip and enter the stele, where they are released into the xylem by leakage from the stelar cells. The water and nutrients are then transported up into the shoot in the xylem fluid.

Water and nutrients can be taken up by all portions of the root system. White roots of cherry appear to be more efficient than woody roots at taking up water and potassium *(Figure 5)*. Woody roots of cherry are more efficient than white roots at taking up calcium while

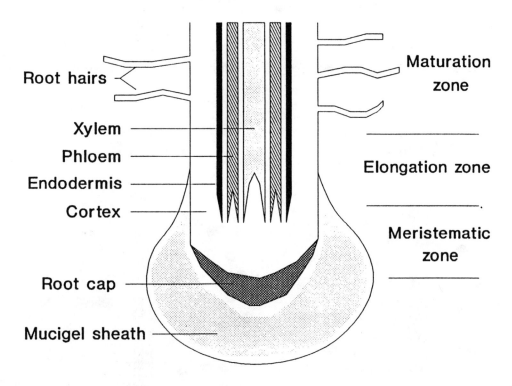

FIGURE 2. This figure illustrates longitudinal transsection of the apical portion of a root. Definition of structures follows:

MUCIGEL SHEATH = noncellular mucilaginous film secreted by the root cap; coats the outside of root tips
ROOT CAP = protective cell layer on root tip that produces hormones that cause roots to grow downward
MERISTEMATIC ZONE = tip of root where cells are formed
ELONGATION ZONE = area behind meristematic zone where newly formed cells expand
MATURATION ZONE = area behind elongation zone where newly formed and expanded cells differentiate
 into root structural components

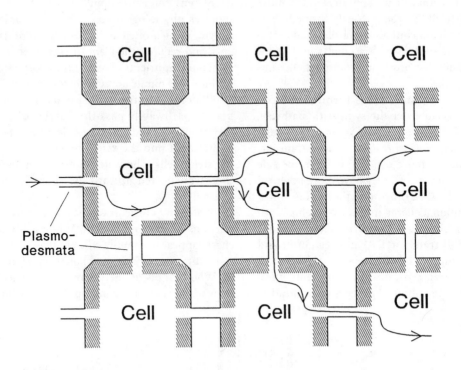

FIGURE 3. This illustrates symplastic flow of nutrients between cells via plasmodesmata.

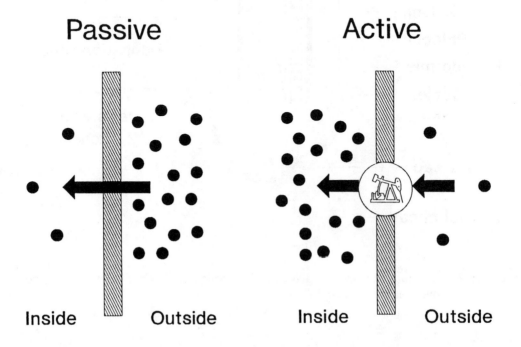

FIGURE 4. This illustrates passive and active uptake of nutrients across root membranes.

apple roots show little difference *(Figure 5)*.

Phosphorus uptake is generally similar for white and woody roots of cherry except right at the root tip where the uptake rate is very high *(Figure 6)*. Although deposition of suberin in the Casparian strip prevents water and nutrient movement through the endodermis, suberin that is deposited in bark tissue on woody roots appears to be sufficiently discontinuous that it does not form a substantial barrier.

Transport of absorbed nutrients out of roots and up to stems and leaves appears to differ between white and woody roots, with white roots being more efficient.

Fruit tree roots grow periodically, with early (May) and late season (August-September) peaks, often before and after fruiting *(Figure 7)*. Total annual growth of white roots decreases with tree age *(Figure 8)*. The contribution of different root types to nutrient uptake will depend on the relative amounts present, inherent rates of absorption, contact with the surrounding soil, and the differential effects of environmental variables on the different root types. Soil-root contact, which is essential for adequate water and nutrient uptake, appears to be better with woody roots than with white roots. Because brown roots can make up 15 to 100 percent of the root length of young fruit trees, depending on the time of observation, they are important as absorbing structures.

Supply of water and nutrients by the soil

Soil moisture influences the rate of nutrient uptake principally because it affects the rate of nutrient supply by the soil and the rate of root extension. The ability of a root surface to absorb nutrients is usually not limiting. Because the density of fruit tree roots in soil is lower than that of other crops, they may be more sensitive to moisture-related interruption of nutrient availability from the soil. On the other hand, fruit tree root systems tend to extend deeper into subsoils where nutrients may continue to be available even if the topsoil dries out.

Nutrients in the soil are supplied to plant

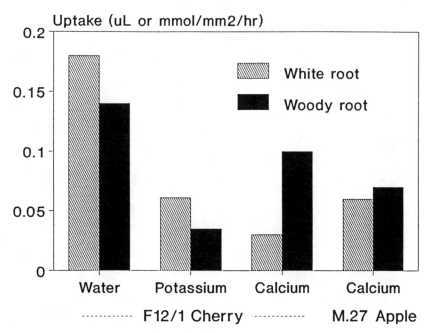

(from Atkinson, 1979)

FIGURE 5. Water potassium and calcium uptake rates by white and woody roots of a F12/1 cherry and M.27 apple rootstock layers.

roots by three mechanisms: root interception, mass flow, and diffusion. Root interception is the absorption of nutrients directly encountered by root surfaces as roots grow through soil *(Figure 9a)*. Root interception is believed to account for a very small proportion of total nutrient uptake by most crop plants (<1%); however, it may be more important for fruit trees because the lower density of fruit tree roots in soil (amount of roots per volume of soil) reduces the ability of mass flow and diffusion to deliver nutrients to the root surfaces.

Mass flow is the movement of nutrients through the soil to root surfaces in the convective flow of water caused by absorption of soil water by roots *(Figure 9b)*. The amount of

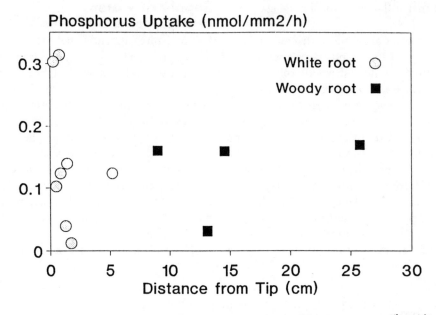

(from Atkinson, 1983)

FIGURE 6. Phosphorus uptake rates by white and woody portions of F12/1 cherry root.

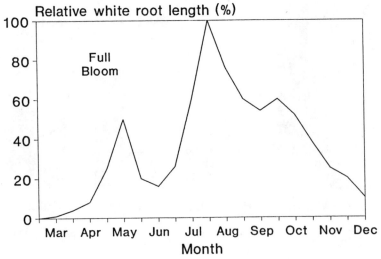

(from Adkinson, 1983)

FIGURE 7. Relative length of white roots for Worchester/MM.104 apple trees during 1961.

nutrient movement by mass flow is related to the amount of water absorbed and the nutrient concentration of that water. Mass flow is capable of supplying all of a tree's needs for calcium, sulfur, and magnesium, and part of the demand for nitrogen. The rate of ion movement to the root by mass flow depends on the rate of water uptake, which in turn is affected by climate and soil moisture content. Meteorological factors that enhance transpiration, such as high temperatures and low relative humidity, increase nutrient movement by mass flow because of increased water absorption by roots. If the roots take up water faster than the nutrients dissolved in the water, the nutrients will accumulate at the root surface. This can be observed in tree fruit roots grown in calcareous soils or with irrigation water that contains high levels of calcium and bicarbonate. Dissolved calcium concentrations in the rhizosphere increase until lime (calcium carbonate) precipitates out as hard white crusts on the roots.

When root interception and mass flow do not supply the root with sufficient quantities of a particular nutrient, continued uptake reduces the concentration of available nutrients in the soil at the root surface. This in turn causes a concentration gradient perpendicular to the root surface (low at root, high in bulk soil), with nutrients subsequently diffusing along the gradient toward the root surface *(Figure 9c)*. The distance for diffusive nutrient movement through the soil is usually in the range 0.1 to 15 mm (0.04 to 0.625 inches). Only nutrients within this soil zone contribute to diffusive nutrient supply to the root. Nutrient diffusion rates decrease with decreasing soil moisture and temperature and with increasing soil bulk density. Ion diffusion may become negligible at soil moisture levels that are still adequate for normal plant growth. Plants receive most of their phosphorus and potassium, and part of their nitrogen, by diffusion.

Drought

As a plant transpires, it withdraws water from the soil immediately adjacent to the root. Water from the bulk soil moves in to replace it. If the rate of water withdrawal by the root system exceeds the rate of resupply by the bulk soil, then the soil around the roots will become drier than the bulk soil and flow of water into the root will decrease. A reduction in water flow rate decreases the amount of nutrients being delivered to the root surface by mass flow.

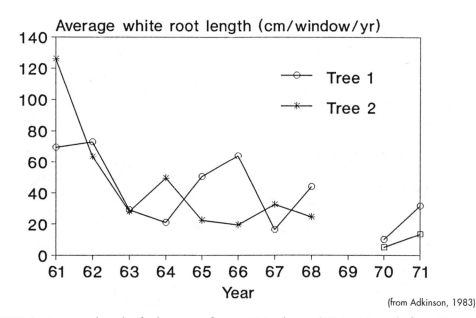

(from Adkinson, 1983)

FIGURE 8. Average length of white roots for two Worchester/MM.104 apple from May to October of the indicated years. Trees were allowed to fruit in 1970 and 1971.

As soils dry, the amount of water in soil pores decreases. This reduces the effective pore cross-sectional area through which nutrients can diffuse and increases tortuosity, the length of the inter-connected pore pathways through which nutrients move from the bulk soil to the roots *(Figure 10)*. In addition, as the water film on soil particles becomes thinner, nutrients are forced to move more closely to surfaces of soil particles and are more likely to be slowed down by electrostatic interactions with the surfaces.

In addition, both soil particles and plant roots tend to shrink as soils dry, which may cause them to pull apart and further reduce water and nutrient uptake.

Tree roots will not penetrate into soils where water is unavailable, eliminating root interception as a mechanism for obtaining nutrients.

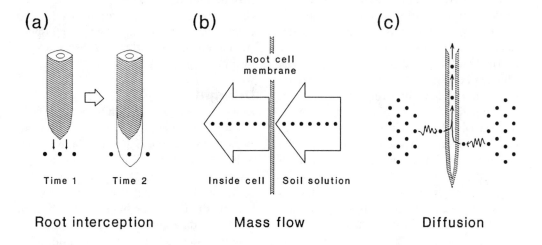

FIGURE 9. Mechanisms for supply of soil nutrients to roots.

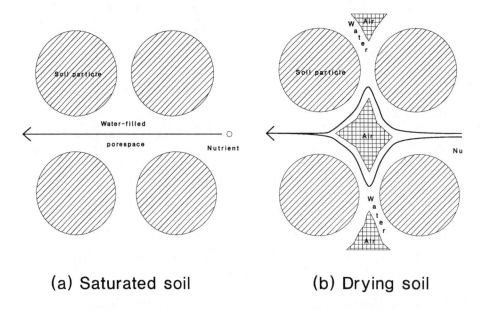

FIGURE 10. As the soil dries nutrients must travel an increased pathlength (tortuosity).

Waterlogging

An important factor restricting root development is the oxygen content of the soil. Roots and many microorganisms require oxygen for respiration. Oxygen normally diffuses from the atmosphere into the soil where it can be used for respiration by roots and microorganisms. Waterlogging reduces the oxygen supply in soils by filling up pores with water instead of air and decreasing both the amount of oxygen that the soil can hold and the rate at which oxygen can diffuse from the atmosphere into the soil. Lack of oxygen (anoxia) impairs root respiration and, consequently, active uptake of nutrients. Surface crusting and poor soil structure (compaction) may also impede diffusion of oxygen into the subsoil. Tree roots will not penetrate into soils where aeration is limiting.

Potentially phytotoxic substances, including ethylene, sulfide, cyanide, carbon dioxide, organic acids, and iron, are produced in waterlogged soils because of anaerobic metabolism. If these compounds accumulate to high levels, they can injure plant roots. Anoxia also impairs production of essential phytohormones by the roots.

Temporary anoxia as a result of sudden high water content, e.g., from excessive rainfall or irrigation, can create local oxygen deficiency, especially in summer when respiration is high and the roots are most sensitive. Large parts of the root system in deeper layers may be killed, with a resulting loss of water and nutrient absorption capacity (see Figure 11).

In addition to direct effects on root uptake of nutrients, considerable amounts of nitrogen can be lost from waterlogged soils by denitrification (conversion of nitrate to gaseous nitrogen compounds) and by leaching in drainage water.

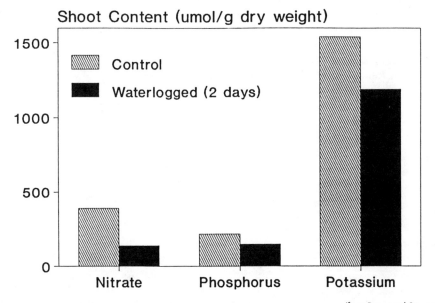

(from Drew and Sisworo, 1979)

FIGURE 11. Reduction of water and nutrient uptake by barley seedlings in waterlogged soil.

REFERENCES

Atkinson, D. and S.S. Wilson. 1979. "The growth and distribution of fruit tree roots: some consequences for nutrient uptake." p. 137-150. In D. Atkinson, J.E. Jackson, R.O. Sharples, and W.M. Waller (eds.) *Mineral nutrition of fruit trees,* Butterworths, London.

Atkinson, D. 1983. "Root growth, tree mineral nutrition and the soil environment." p. 1-25. In R.G. Stevens and R.B. Tukey (eds.) *Tree fruit nutrition.* 1983 Shortcourse Proceedings, Washington State University Cooperative Extension, Pullman, Washington.

Drew, M.C. and E.J. Sisworo. 1979. The development of waterlogging damage in young barley plants in relation to plant nutrient status and changes in soil properties. *New Phytol.* 82:301-314.

Physiology of water-related stresses in fruit trees

Preston K. Andrews, Ph.D.

Assistant Horticulturist

Department of Horticulture and Landscape Architecture, Washington State University, Pullman

Light, temperature, nitrogen and water are major environmental factors affecting the productivity of fruit trees. Orchardists manage light by various manipulations of the tree canopy; temperature by site selection, frost protection and evaporative cooling; nitrogen by fertilizer applications; and water by irrigation.

Observation of precipitation patterns and natural vegetation indicates the aridity of a region and the need for irrigation. There are striking regional differences in these characteristics within Washington State. As one travels east from humid western Washington, where abundant, relatively well-distributed precipitation supports dense forests, and crosses the Cascade crest, a semi-arid region with seasonal drought is entered, characterized by chaparral and sparsely-forested river valleys such as the Wenatchee and Okanogan. Traveling south and further east, an arid region of consistent drought is entered, characterized by desert shrubs and the absence of native trees such as occurs in natural areas of the Yakima Valley and Columbia Basin. The relationships between precipitation patterns and vegetation types result from the effects of water stress on physiological processes, and in those regions where tree fruit crops are pro-

duced, illustrate the prevalence of drought and the urgency of irrigation.

Drought is defined here as a meteorological event that is a combination of restricted water supply caused by insufficient precipitation and enhanced rates of water loss because of high evaporative demand, resulting in limited soil moisture and reduced productivity. Depletion of soil moisture results in insufficient water readily available for the physiological processes essential for plant growth. A quantitative definition of drought was proposed that is based upon the ratio of precipitation (substitute irrigation) to evapotranspiration (Transeau, 1905).

Without irrigation, the "greening" of the central Washington State desert that began with the Highline and Sunnyside canals of the Wenatchee and Yakima river valleys at the turn of the century, would not have been possible. Following this initial phase of water development came a period where great improvements in irrigation technology made possible a shift from high-volume furrow irrigation and impact sprinklers to low-volume microsprinkler and drip systems. More recently, improved understanding of the water needs of fruit trees, sophisticated methods of micrometeorological measurement, and programmable irrigation controllers have made possible scientific irrigation scheduling that can significantly improve the efficiency of water use. Unfortunately, a large portion of our water distribution system is still grounded in the past.

Plant water relations

Water in a fruit tree is in continuity with water in the soil and water vapor in the atmosphere. Soil water is absorbed by roots, transported throughout the tree via the xylem vessels, then lost to the atmosphere as water vapor through transpiration from the leaves, and finally returned to the soil as precipitation or irrigation. The status of water in this soil-plant-atmosphere continuum can be expressed in terms of its activity or energy. This measure of water status is referred to as water potential, which is defined as the free energy of water that is potentially available to do work relative to pure water. Water potential (Ψ_{water}) may be comprised of four components and is expressed as:

Equation 1:
$$\Psi_{water} = \Psi_{pressure} + \Psi_{solute} + \Psi_{matric} + \Psi_{gravitational}$$

where $\Psi_{pressure}$ is the pressure potential or turgor, Ψ_{solute} is the solute or osmotic potential, Ψ_{matric} is the matric potential, and $\Psi_{gravitational}$ is the gravitational potential. These components of Ψ_{water} are expressed in units of pressure such as pascals (Pa) or bars, where 1 MPa (megapascal) = 10 bars (=145 psi). Both $\Psi_{pressure}$ and Ψ_{solute} contribute to Ψ_{water} in fruit trees. Pressure potential represents the hydrostatic pressure in plant cells that causes them to enlarge. If a plant is turgid, $\Psi_{pressure}$ will be positive, but if a plant is flaccid, $\Psi_{pressure}$ will be zero or sometimes negative. Solute potential results from dissolved molecules and ions present within the interior of cells, is always negative and is important in a plant's ability to tolerate water stress. The Ψ_{solute} is also a component of soil Ψ_{water} because, like the cell sap, soil water is a solution with dissolved molecules and ions. The Ψ_{matric} is always negative and is a very important component of soil Ψ_{water} also. It accounts for the attractive forces

between water molecules and the surfaces of soil particles. The $\Psi_{gravitational}$ is usually positive, but it is only important in very tall trees where it results from the effects of gravity caused by differences in height.

Plant water status also may be expressed in terms of water content, which is the relative volume of water present in the tissue compared to saturated or fully turgid conditions. Relative water content may have a greater regulatory effect on physiological processes such as photosynthesis than Ψ_{water}. Water potential, however, indicates the direction of water movement in the soil-plant-atmosphere continuum. It is always negative and water always moves from regions of higher Ψ_{water} (i.e. less negative) to regions of lower Ψ_{water} (i.e. more negative). This difference in Ψ_{water} is the driving force that moves water through the soil, into the roots, through the xylem, into the fruit, and out of the leaves to the atmosphere.

Water stress

The definition of plant water stress depends somewhat on the perspective of the observer. Orchardists view water stress in terms of reductions in yield and fruit quality, while a tree fruit physiologist views it in terms of loss of turgor and inhibition of physiological processes, which lead to reduced growth. Water stress develops when water lost through transpiration exceeds water absorbed by the roots for a long enough period of time so that the water content of the tissue is significantly decreased and turgor is lost. Thus, water stress develops when transpiration from the leaves exceeds absorption by the roots for sufficient time to decrease cell enlargement and disrupt essential physiological processes.

An economic analogy can be applied to this definition of water stress, where excessive withdrawals (i.e., transpiration) and inadequate deposits (i.e., absorption) lead to deficits. For example, excessive transpiration may occur during hot, dry weather, whereas reduced absorption may occur when the soil is cold in the spring or fall.

In moist soil, water absorption is controlled largely by the rate of transpiration because there exists little resistance to uptake by the roots. Water absorbed by the roots is pulled up through the xylem vessels by the tension that is exerted on these continuous columns of water by water that is evaporating from the leaves. These columns of water usually have sufficient internal cohesion to maintain them intact. Transpiration from the leaves is regulated by stomata, which are tiny pores whose apertures open or close depending on the turgor of the two guard cells that bound them *(Figure 1)*. The size of the stomatal apertures regulate the rate of water loss by transpiration. In fruit trees, these are present only on the bottom surface of the leaves, and in apple may number 170 to 600 stomata per mm^2 (110,000-385,000 stomata per inch^2) (Slack, 1974; Beakbane and Mujamder, 1975).

On a hot, sunny day, the transpiration rate of a well-watered tree increases rapidly in the morning, and since water is removed first from the leaves, their Ψ_{water} declines *(Figure 2)*. The rate of transpiration increases when sunlight is more intense and when the air is drier. Wind increases the transpiration rate when the stomata are open or when solar radiation is reduced during cloudy weather. This is because wind disturbs the boundary layer of relatively calmer air that surrounds a leaf or orchard canopy, decreasing the resistance of

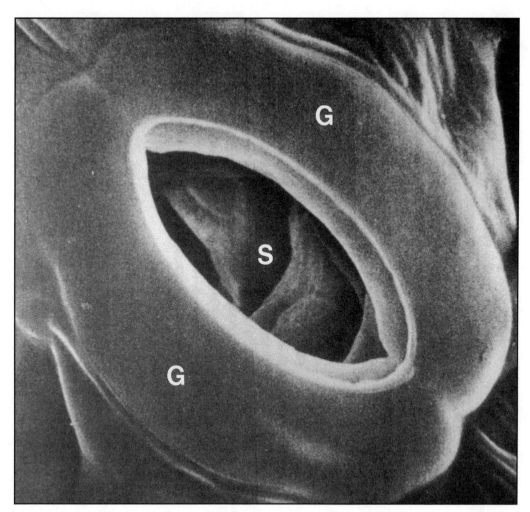

(From Troughton and Donaldson, 1972)

FIGURE 1. Electron micrograph of a stomate (S) (plural = stomata) and guard cells (G) on the lower surface of a cucumber leaf, magnified 7,900X.

transfer of water vapor from the leaves to the atmosphere. The amount of water transpired by an orchard canopy also increases seasonally as the leaf area develops from bud break in spring to full canopy in summer.

The transpiration rate usually recovers by evening, but certainly by the next morning *(Figure 2)*. Overnight recovery occurs because the stomata close at night, reducing the transpiration rate to nearly zero. When transpiration begins in the morning, water stored in

the trunk and fruit is borrowed to contribute to the maintenance of water status in the leaves for photosynthesis. This water storage or capacitance of the trunk and fruit results in shrinkage of these organs during the day *(Figure 3)*. Water initially may be borrowed from stems closer to the leaves before the more distant trunk. Most stem shrinkage of apple was caused by water being borrowed from the bark and not from the xylem (Brough, et al, 1986). The capacitance of a mature fruit

TABLE 1. The absorption of water by white, unsuberized and woody, suberized F12/1 Mazzard cherry roots (From Atkinson and Wilson, 1979).

| | Absorption per unit | |
| | Length | Surface Area |
Root type	(µl H$_2$O/mm/hr)	(µl H$_2$O/mm^2/hr)
White, unsuberized	0.42±0.12[z]	0.18±0.04
Woody, suberized	0.51±0.26	0.14±0.01

[z] = Standard error of the mean.

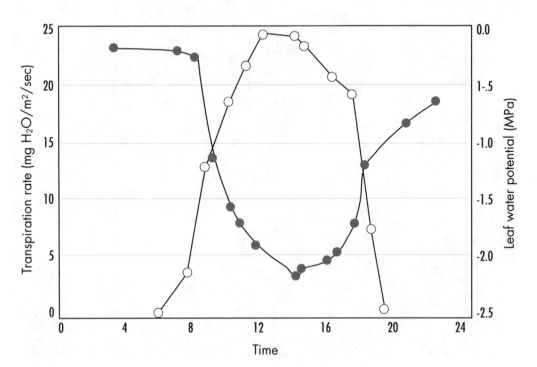

FIGURE 2. Transpiration rate (white circle) and leaf water potential (grey circle) of irrigated Cox's Orange Pippin apple trees on typical sunny days in England.
(Transpiration rate redrawn from Landsberg and Jones, 1981, based on unpublished data of D. B. B. Powell. Leaf water potential redrawn from Goode and Higgs, 1973)

tree is not great. Only two hours of storage capacity *(Figure 2)* were estimated for a nine-year-old apple tree transpiring at 20 mg H_2O/m^2 leaf area/second as the Ψ_{water} decreased 2 MPa (Landsberg, et al, 1976).

As soil begins to dry, water absorption by the roots is reduced because of the increased resistance to water movement through drying soil as the continuity of water between the soil particles and roots declines. As the soil Ψ_{water} declines, the gradient in Ψ_{water} between the roots and soil decreases, reducing the driving force for water movement.

In contrast to many herbaceous plants, water absorption through the woody, suberized roots of the F12/1 Mazzard cherry rootstock was as great as through young white roots *(Table 1)*. This highlights the importance of the woody roots of fruit trees in water absorption. Uptake of nutrients also is reduced by water stress, however, the relative absorption of specific nutrients may be different. For example, the ratio of calcium to potassium absorbed by M.9 apple roots increased as soil

Ψ_{water} decreased (Tromp, 1980).

In the early stages of soil drying, roots nearer the surface are often exposed to drier conditions than deeper roots where the soil is more moist. Therefore, roots near the surface may dehydrate sooner or meet soil that is more difficult to penetrate than deeper roots. To communicate and integrate the effects of a drying soil to the aerial parts of the plant, roots near the surface may produce a signal that is translocated through the xylem. There is evidence that this signal is chemical in nature and that it may act prior to reduced water supply in controlling the stomatal aperture, transpiration rate, leaf water status and growth (Davies and Zhang, 1991). Root signals have been inferred in apple trees during soil drying (Gowing, et al, 1990).

With increased soil drying, midday water deficits are often severe enough to cause temporary wilting, stomatal closure, decreased photosynthesis, and excessive shrinkage of plant organs. As water stress increases in the tree, the resistance to water movement

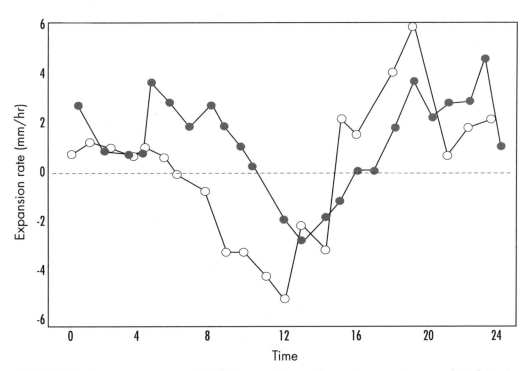

FIGURE 3. Changes in trunk girth (white circle) and fruit diameter (grey circle) of Cox's Orange Pippin apple trees on a typical sunny day in England.

(Same date as transpiration rate shown in Fig. 2. Redrawn from Landsberg and Jones, 1981, based on unpublished data of D. B. B. Powell)

through the xylem increases. This increased resistance is caused by cavitation and embolism of the columns of water in the xylem vessels (Tyree and Sperry, 1989). Cavitation occurs when a water column ruptures as its tension surpasses its capacity for internal cohesion. Cavitation leads to embolism, which is the formation of air bubbles in the xylem vessel that blocks sap flow. While there is evidence that some cavitation occurs even in well-watered grapevines during periods of rapid transpiration (Schultz and Matthews, 1988), the degree of blockage increases significantly as soil dries.

During severe drought, absorption of water by all parts of the root system declines and transport of water through the xylem is significantly blocked by cavitation and embolism so that replacing water lost by transpiration becomes very difficult. Seasonal drought can result in extremely low leaf Ψ_{water}, as illustrated by nonirrigated peach trees that experienced the 1977 drought in Washington

State *(Figure 4)*. Such extreme water stress results in complete stomatal closure, negligible photosynthesis and severe wilting. Eventually the permanent wilting point is reached when the plant cannot recover from the water deficit. Death of a fruit tree from drought is rare, although severe consequences to yield and fruit quality can occur (Proebsting and Middleton, 1980).

Effects of water stress

Water stress results in decreased cell water content and $\Psi_{pressure}$, which leads to reduced cell enlargement and growth. Growth is very sensitive to water stress because a minimum $\Psi_{pressure}$ is necessary for cell expansion. The Ψ_{water} also declines during water stress, which affects the movement of water in the soil-plant-atmosphere continuum.

Growth

Decreased leaf area and premature setting of terminal buds result from water stress. In

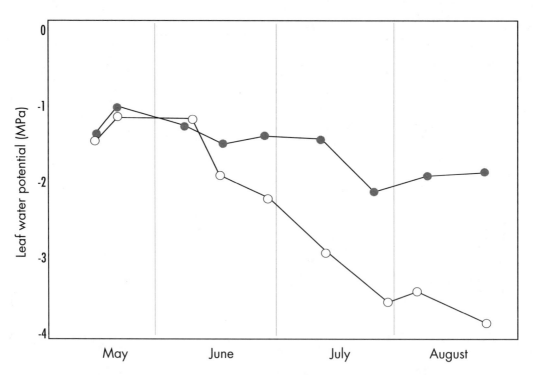

FIGURE 4. Seasonal changes in leaf water potential of irrigated (grey circle) and non-irrigated (white circle) 30-year-old Elberta peach trees growing in the Yakima Valley, Washington, during the 1977 drought.
(Redrawn from Proebsting and Middleton, 1980)

M.16 apple rootstock, water stress reduced leaf area by 50 percent compared to well-watered trees (Maggs, 1961). Besides the daily, reversible shrinking and swelling of bark and fruit, seasonal water stress reduces the number and size of xylem vessels (Kozlowski, et al, 1991). It is well-known that the diameter of the xylem vessels produced during the spring is larger than in the summer. Small diameter xylem vessels with smaller pit pores in their walls are less vulnerable to cavitation and embolism (Tyree and Sperry, 1989). The change from large- to small-diameter xylem vessels can be accelerated by water stress or delayed irrigation. Therefore, delayed irrigation in the spring may confer some protection against debilitating water stress later in the summer. Indeed, the threshold Ψ_{water} for cavitation in unstressed M.9 apple rootstocks was higher (-0.9 MPa) than for rootstocks that were pre-stressed (-2.5 MPa) (Jones and Peña, 1987).

While the roots are usually the last organ to be water stressed because they are closest to the source of water, stress that develops in the leaves and shoots eventually is transmitted to the roots. Reduced root growth in drying soil decreases water and nutrient absorption. The percentage of growth that is partitioned to the roots, however, usually increases during water stress at the expense of new shoot growth (Maggs, 1961). This response allows the tree to improve its balance between water absorption by the roots and water loss from the leaves.

Reproductive growth is usually more sensitive to water stress than vegetative growth. It is commonly observed that fruit size is reduced by water stress. This occurs when water deficits reduce the rate of cell enlargement during the rapid stage of fruit growth. Flower bud initiation, differentiation and maturation may be susceptible to water stress occurring between mid summer and fall. The number of peach fruit buds produced per unit shoot length on nonirrigated trees exposed to the 1977 drought

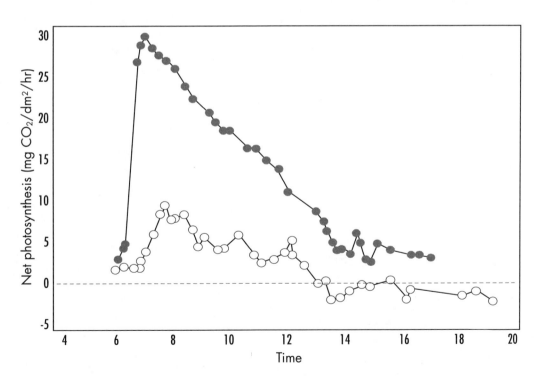

FIGURE 5. Net photosynthesis of fully expanded leaves of irrigated (grey circle) and droughted (white circle) 30-year-old Bartlett pear trees growing at Tatura, Australia.

(Redrawn from Kriedemann and Canterford, 1971)

in Washington State were reduced over 60 percent compared to irrigated trees (Proebsting and Middleton, 1980). Fruit set also is sensitive to water stress. The fruit set of nine-year-old Cox's Orange Pippin apple trees grown in England was reduced 65 percent for trees receiving no rain or irrigation from March to June and 35 percent for trees receiving only rain, compared to well-irrigated trees (Powell, 1974). Flower abscission may be increased and pollen viability may be decreased by water stress (summarized by Jones, 1992).

Stomatal behavior

Generally, stomata open in light or in response to a low CO_2 concentration within the leaf and close in darkness or when guard cells lose turgor caused by water stress. As stated earlier, some stomatal closure may occur even in well-watered trees at midday during hot, sunny weather. Exposure to dry air also causes stomatal closure of turgid leaves. The stomatal apertures of M.7 apple rootstock leaves closed as the deficit in vapor pressure between leaf and air increased from

0.60 to 2.45 kPa (Fanjul and Jones, 1982). This level of vapor pressure deficit is not unlike those occurring in central Washington during the summer. Under extreme water stress, stomata close as leaf Ψ_{water} decreases.

The plant growth regulator abscisic acid (ABA) promotes stomatal closure during water stress. Large increases in ABA concentrations have been measured in water-stressed apple leaves (Davies and Lakso, 1978). Abscisic acid is synthesized both in leaves and root tips during water stress. Root-synthesized ABA is transported in the xylem stream to the aerial parts of the plant, signaling soil drying. While other endogenous compounds may function as root signals in drying soil, root-synthesized ABA has been most studied and currently is the best candidate for fulfilling this role (Davies and Zhang, 1991).

Photosynthesis

Photosynthesis can be reduced by water stress either caused by stomatal closure or damage to the photosynthetic apparatus. Severe daily decreases in photosynthesis are caused by

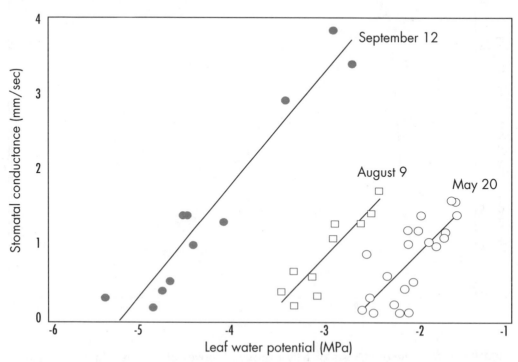

FIGURE 6. Seasonal changes in the relationship between leaf water potential and stomatal conductance of 10-year-old McIntosh apple trees growing in Geneva, NY, on May 20, Aug. 9 and Sept. 12, 1977 (Redrawn from Lakso, 1979).

early stomatal closure. Significantly reduced net photosynthesis occurred in 30-year-old Bartlett pear trees even when minimum leaf Ψ_{water} of irrigated (-3.0 MPa) and drought-stressed (-3.3 MPa) trees were not appreciably different (*Figure 5*). Damage to the photosynthetic apparatus may occur during long-term water stress. In addition, respiration may increase when leaf temperature rises after stomatal closure, thereby reducing net photosynthesis.

Leaf senescence and abscission
During severe water stress, leaves may prematurely senesce and abscise. During rapid dehydration, leaves may wither but remain attached, with abscission occurring upon rewatering (Kozlowski, et al, 1991). Premature abscission is often more common in older leaves, with younger leaves being retained. Premature leaf senescence during drought probably results from complex interactions between growth regulators, nutrients and carbohydrates produced during photosynthesis.

Nonirrigated peach trees that experienced the 1977 drought in Washington State began to defoliate in early August and were completely defoliated by September 10 (Proebsting and Middleton, 1980). Nonirrigated trees in which all the scaffold limbs were removed 1.5 meter above the ground (dehorned) in spring 1977 retained leaves longer than trees that received only a light dormant pruning, and they exhibited more normal growth in 1978.

Physiological, biochemical processes
Numerous physiological and biochemical processes are sensitive to water stress (summarized by Jones, 1992; Kozlowski, et al, 1991). Cell division, growth and cell wall synthesis are reduced. Although specific mRNAs and proteins may exhibit increased synthesis, photosynthetic enzyme activity and chlorophyll formation are decreased. Respiration also is decreased by water stress; however, it is usually less sensitive than these other physiological and biochemical processes.

Beneficial effects
In regions where air pollution is prevalent, leaf injury may be decreased if stomata close because of a mild water stress, thereby restricting entry of the air pollutant. Water stress also can increase the proportion of thick-walled xylem elements which may result in stiffer branches. Perhaps one of the most beneficial effects of mild water stress is reduced vegetative growth. This benefit has been capitalized on by an irrigation management practice called regulated deficit irrigation, which is based on the observation that different stages of vegetative and fruit growth vary in their sensitivity and response to soil water deficits.

Research in Israel and Washington State demonstrated that regulated deficit irrigation during early fruit growth increased yields and reduced vegetative growth of apples (Assaf, et al, 1974; Proebsting, et al, 1977). Similar results were found for peaches and Bartlett pears grown in Australia (Mitchell and Chalmers, 1982; Mitchell, et al, 1989). Additionally, significant reductions in seasonal water use were achieved.

Drought tolerance
Droughts may be tolerated to various degrees by structural or physiological adaptations that either avoid or postpone dehydration or enable the tree to tolerate dehydration without serious injury. For natural plant populations, drought tolerance signifies survival. In a horticultural context, however, production of higher yields of marketable fruit is a better indication of drought tolerance than mere survival.

Mechanisms that avoid or postpone dehydration include: 1) drought escape, 2) efficient water absorption and transport systems, and 3) control of transpiration. Drought escape is not applicable to woody perennials because it refers to plants that rapidly complete their life cycles during periods of favorable soil moisture. The principal mechanisms that promote tolerance of dehydration include: 1) turgor (i.e. $\Psi_{pressure}$) maintenance and 2) protective compounds.

Avoidance of dehydration
One of the most effective safeguards against drought is the development of a deep, extensive root system that can obtain water from a

large volume of soil or from a deep water table. Indeed, during water stress it is common for plants to increase the relative mass of roots to aerial parts. Of course, there is a cost to develop an extensive root system in terms of photoassimilates that otherwise could have been used for fruit growth. For nursery stock, however, a capacity to generate new roots is essential for establishing a successful planting.

The symbiotic role of mycorrhizal fungi in nutrient absorption is well established. Apple seedlings have been shown to depend on mycorrhizal fungi for optimal growth (Hoepfner, et al, 1983; Miller, et al, 1989). Enhanced seedling growth has been accompanied by improved uptake of phosphorus, copper and zinc (An, et al, 1993). Mycorrhizae also may improve water absorption and increase drought tolerance. Mycorrhizal infection of plant roots increases the effective surface area of the root system for water absorption, resulting in improved plant water status. Whether the improved water status is a result of direct uptake of water by the mycorrhizae, modified phosphorus content or production of growth regulators is unclear (see Krikun, 1991).

There is evidence that as the surface soil dries, water can be transferred through the roots from deep, moister soil to the drier surface soil. Experiments with sagebrush (*Artemisia tridentata* Nutt.) indicate that water absorbed by deep roots in moist soil moves upward through the roots, is released by roots in the upper soil profile at night, and is stored there until it is reabsorbed by the upper roots the following day (Caldwell, et al, 1991).

This phenomenon is called hydraulic lift. It is thought that this self-irrigation of the surface soil by roots may improve nutrient uptake in the more nutrient-rich and better aerated upper soil layers, prevent fine root death in the deficit-prone surface soil, and prolong the activity of mycorrhizae and other soil microorganisms. Increased water loss by evaporation from the surface soil also may ensue.

Hydraulic lift may reduce the production of chemical signals from the surface roots by delaying water deficits in the soil, thereby permitting the continuation of photosynthesis and growth. While hydraulic lift has not been examined in fruit trees, sugar maple trees in forests of the northeastern United States exhibit hydraulic lift that benefits the shallow-rooted understory plants growing in association with them (Dawson, 1993).

Plant adaptations that conserve water may prevent detrimental dehydration either by conserving soil water or by reducing the transpiration rate so that resistances to water transport do not become excessive. Soil drying may be accompanied by an increase in the proportion of root surface that is suberized (Kozlowski, et al, 1991). Suberization may not reduce the uptake of water (*see Table 1*) but may reduce efflux of water from the roots. Most water conservation mechanisms occur in the leaves, however.

Water loss is reduced by increased wax accumulation on the cuticle of leaves in response to intense sunlight and dry air. The responsiveness of the stomata is critical to the prevention of water stress, whether resulting from the hydraulic effects of decreased water content and turgor or because of chemical root signals transported to the leaves. Reduced transpirational water loss also occurs from leaves with very small, sunken stomata, with lower stomatal density per unit leaf area, and by accumulation of wax in stomatal antechambers.

Another response to water stress and bright sunlight is an increase in leaf thickness which increases photosynthesis relative to transpiration. Slower leaf expansion during water stress reduces the transpiring leaf area, but also reduces the effective photosynthetic surface. Reduced absorption of solar radiation can delay dehydration by reducing leaf temperature. Leaves with lower water content may reflect more light than leaves with higher water content. Leaf hairs also tend to increase the reflectance of leaves. The leaf surface exposed to sunlight sometimes is reduced by changes in leaf orientation relative to the sun.

Exposure to excessive sunlight also is reduced by wilting of older, less photosynthetically-efficient leaves or by leaf folding which can significantly reduce transpiration. Although reductions in transpiring leaf surface by premature senescence and shedding of leaves is a symptom of severe drought, it also is a drought-tolerance adaptation that may assure survival. Unfortunately, the relative contribution of these water-conserving mechanisms to the drought tolerance of fruit trees is unknown.

Storage of water in plants is another method for postponing dehydration during drought. Use of stored water to replace water lost by transpiration is responsible for shrinkage of fruit, trunk and stems (*Figure 3;* Brough, et al, 1986). Utilization of stored water reduces the severity of midday water deficits, permitting photosynthesis to continue for longer periods of time each day. Extended use of water stored in fruit will reduce fruit size, however. If water is borrowed from the xylem, increased cavitation may result, increasing the resistance to water flow through the xylem vessels. In apple, however, most of the water is borrowed from the bark rather than the xylem (Brough, et al, 1986).

Antitranspirants are used to reduce transpiration, either by closing stomata, coating the foliage with a water-impermeable film, or increasing the reflection of sunlight from the leaves. Compounds that close stomata include ABA, which when sprayed on apple trees caused stomatal closure, reduced transpiration and increased Ψ_{water}. Its effects were only temporary, however, and did not increase yield (Goode, et al, 1978). Film-forming compounds, such as silicone and latex emulsions and plastic films such as polyvinyl chloride, also are rarely effective or long-lasting.

Unfortunately, because the molecular weight of CO_2 is larger than H_2O, all films are less permeable to CO_2, resulting in greater reductions in photosynthesis than in transpiration. A five percent wax emulsion sprayed on cherry trees at 11 and 25 days before harvest, however, increased fruit diameter at harvest about one mm (an increase from 11 1/2- to 11-row fruit size) (Uriu, et al, 1975). Increasing the reflection of sunlight from leaves by applying materials such as kaolinite may lower leaf temperatures and decrease transpiration (Jones, 1992). The chief usefulness of antitranspirants is for getting nursery trees past transplant shock.

Tolerance of dehydration

As drought intensifies, the capacity of mechanisms that avoid or postpone dehydration is overcome and trees must possess other mechanisms that maintain physiological activity as water content or Ψ_{water} decreases. Maintenance of turgor occurs when the solute concentration of cells increases in response to water stress. This process is called active osmotic adjustment if the decrease in Ψ_{solute} is caused by the accumulation of additional solutes beyond what would occur solely by concentrating existing solutes during dehydration. Full turgor maintenance, which occurs when the decrease in Ψ_{solute} equals the decrease in Ψ_{water} (*Equation 1*), is observed over a limited range of Ψ_{water}. Even partial turgor maintenance can be advantageous, however. While inorganic ions, especially K^+ and Cl^-, can contribute to osmotic adjustment, certain compatible organic solutes tend to be more important.

In addition to active osmotic adjustment, there is also the passive concentrating of solutes that occurs as cells dehydrate. Active osmotic adjustment of 0.2-0.4 MPa between sunrise and midday has been measured in leaves of nonirrigated Cox's Orange Pippin trees in England, along with an equivalent amount of passive adjustment caused by cell dehydration (Goode and Higgs, 1973). Active osmotic adjustment between July and September was 0.5 MPa. The capacity of apple leaves to adjust osmotically was greater in mature, fully expanded leaves than in immature leaves near the shoot tips (Lakso et al, 1984).

Turgor maintenance by osmotic adjustment should permit stomatal opening, photosynthesis, leaf expansion, root growth and water absorption to lower Ψ_{water} than otherwise would be possible. The effect of osmotic adjustment is implied by the increased capacity of the stomata of apple leaves to conduct water vapor at lower Ψ_{water} as seasonal water stress increased (*Figure 6*). The increased stomatal conductance resulted in higher net photosynthetic rates (Lakso, 1979). Osmotic adjustment also may assist in postponing leaf senescence and in protecting meristems of water-stressed plants.

Decreased cell size commonly occurs with drought and may help in maintaining turgor (Cutler, et al, 1977). An increase in cell wall elasticity maintains turgor at low Ψ_{water} as effectively as osmotic adjustment.

A number of compatible organic solutes have been found to effectively protect proteins and membranes from desiccation injury, even when they accumulate to high concentrations where inorganic ions would be toxic. These compatible solutes include a number of sugars, sugar alcohols (e.g., sorbitol, prevalent in fruit trees) and amino acids (e.g., proline).

It has been suggested that bound water may contribute to dehydration tolerance (Vertucci and Leopold, 1987). Bound water refers to water that is so tightly fixed to a matrix, such as cell walls, membranes or proteins, that its thermodynamic properties differ from those of the bulk water. Since dehydration injury may be attributed to disorganization of the fine structure of membranes and organelles (Hincha, et al, 1987), bound water may protect these structures. There also is evidence that free-radical damage is an important factor in desiccation injury. There are reports that differential expression of antioxidant systems that scavenge free radicals in plants may contribute to drought tolerance. The importance of changes in the pattern of protein synthesis during water stress, such as the accumulation of proteins called dehydrins, is uncertain and has not been examined in woody plants.

Although the capacity to tolerate dehydration is important to the survival of natural vegetation and fruit trees during prolonged drought, it is less important than avoidance or postponement of dehydration where the profitability of fruit trees is concerned. Many mechanisms that enhance survival during drought decrease productivity. The ideal tree involves a balance between water conservation and productivity. To optimize tree fruit productivity, the ideal tree should maximize its photosynthesis and conversion of photoassimilates into fruit relative to the amount of water available. It is of no use for a fruit tree merely to have a high efficiency of water use if the water supply is nonlimiting. Such efficiency in a fruit tree would not be ideal if it lost some of its potentially available water to a faster growing cover crop.

Drought hardening

It is well-known that plants previously subjected to mild water stress usually suffer less injury during transplanting and soil water deficits than plants not previously stressed. Hardening, whether of mature or nursery trees for transplanting, involves many of the mechanisms described above. The chief effects of hardening are increased root-shoot ratios, production of thicker leaves, increased leaf cutinization and wax deposition, osmotic adjustment, and more responsive stomatal behavior. These adaptations are a fruit tree's first defense against water stress.

REFERENCES

An, Z. Q., T. Shen and H.G. Wang. 1993. "Mycorrhizal fungi in relation to growth and mineral nutrition of apple seedlings." *Scientia Horticulturae* 54: 275-285.

Assaf, R., B. Bravdo and I. Levin. 1974. "Effects of irrigation according to water deficit in two different soil layers, on the yield and growth of apple trees." *J. Hort. Sci.* 49: 53-64.

Atkinson, D. and S. A. Wilson. 1979. "The root-soil interface and its significance for fruit tree roots of different ages," pp. 259-271. In J. L. Harley and R. S. Russell (eds.) *The soil-root interface*. Academic Press, London.

Beakbane, A. B. and P. K. Mujamder. 1975. "A relationship between stomatal density and growth potential in apple rootstocks." *J. Hort. Sci.* 50: 285-289.

Brough, D. H., H. G. Jones and J. Grace. 1986. "Dirunal changes in water content of the stems of apple trees as influenced by irrigation." *Plant, Cell Environ.* 9: 1-7.

Caldwell, M. M., J. H. Richards and W. Beyschlag. 1991. "Hydraulic lift: ecological implications of water efflux from roots," pp. 423-436. In D. Atkinson (ed.) *Plant root growth: An ecological perspective*. Blackwell Scientific Publ., Oxford.

Cutler, J. M., D. W. Rains and R.S. Loomis. 1977. "The importance of cell size in the water relations of plants." *Physiologia Plantarum* 40: 255-260.

Davies, F. S. and A. N. Lakso. 1978. "Water stress responses of apple seedlings: Changes in water potential components, abscisic acid levels and stomatal conductances under irrigated and non-irrigated conditions." *J. Amer. Soc. Hort. Sci.* 103: 310-313.

Davies, W. J. and J. Zhang. 1991. "Root signals and the regulation of growth and development of plants in drying soil." *Annu. Rev. Plant Physiol. Plant Mol. Biol.* 42: 55-76.

Dawson, T. E. 1993. "Hydraulic lift and water parasitism by plants: Implications for water balance, performance, and plant-plant interactions." *Oecologia* 95: 565-574.

Fanjul, L. and H. G. Jones. 1982. "Rapid stomatal responses to humidity." *Planta* 154: 135-138.

Goode, J. E. and K. H. Higgs. 1973. "Water, osmotic and pressure potential relationships in apple leaves." *J. Hort. Sci.* 48: 203-215.

Goode, J. E., K. H. Higgs and K. J. Hyrycz. 1978. "Abscisic acid applied to orchard trees of Golden Delicious apple to control water stress." *J. Hort. Sci.* 53: 99-103.

Gowing, D. J., W. J. Davies and H. G. Jones. 1990. "A positive root-sourced signal as an indicator of soil drying in apple, *Malus x domestica* Borkh." *J. Exp. Bot.* 41: 1535-1540.

Hincha, D. K., R. Höfner, K. B. Schwab, U. Heber and J. M. Schmitt. 1987. "Membrane rupture is the common cause of damage to chloroplast membranes in leaves injured by freezing or excessive wilting." *Plant Physiol.* 83: 251-253.

Hoepfner, E. F., B. L. Koch and R. P Covey. 1983. "Enhancement of growth and phosphorous concentrations in apple seedling by vesicular-arbuscular mycorrhizal." *J. Amer. Soc. Hort. Sci.* 108: 207-209.

Jones, H. G. 1992. *Plants and microclimate. A quantitative approach to environmental plant physiology.* Cambridge University Press, Cambridge.

Jones, H. G. and J. Peña. 1987. "Relationships between water stress and ultrasound emission in apple (*Malus domestica* Borkh.)." *J. Exp. Bot.* 37: 1245-1254.

Kozlowski, T. T., P. J. Kramer and S. G. Pallardy. 1991. *The physiological ecology of woody plants.* Academic Press, Inc., San Diego.

Kriedemann, P. E. and R.L. Canterford. 1971. "The photosynthetic activity of pear leaves (Pyrus communis L.)." *Aust. J. Biol. Sci.* 24: 197-205.

Krikun, J. 1991. "Mycorrhizae in agricultural crops," pp. 767-786. In Y. Waisel, E. Amram and U. Kafkafi (eds.) *Plant roots: the hidden half.* Marcel Dekker, New York.

Lakso, A. N. 1979. "Seasonal changes in stomatal response to leaf water potential in apple." *J. Amer. Soc. Hort. Sci.* 104: 58-60.

Lakso, A. N., A. S. Geyer and S. G. Carpenter. 1984. "Seasonal osmotic relations in apple leaves of different ages." *J. Amer. Soc. Hort. Sci.* 109: 544-547.

Landsberg, J. J., T. W. Blanchard and B. Warrit. 1976. "Studies on the movement of water through apple trees." *J. Exp. Bot.* 27: 579-596.

Landsberg, J. J. and H. G. Jones. 1981. "Apple orchards," pp. 419-469. In T. T. Kozlowski (ed.) *Water deficits and plant growth, Vol. VI.* Academic Press, New York.

Maggs, D. H. 1961. "Changes in the amount and distribution of increment induced by contrasting watering, nitrogen, and environmental regimes." *Annals of Botany* 25: 353-360.

Miller, D. D., M. Bodmer and H. Schuepp. 1989. "Spread of endomycorrhizal colonization and effects on growth of apple seedlings." *New Phytol.* 111: 51-59.

Mitchell, P. D. and D. J. Chalmers. 1982. "The effects of reduced water supply on peach tree growth and yields." *J. Amer. Soc. Hort. Sci.* 107: 853-856.

Mitchell, P. D., B. van den Ende, P. H. Jerie and D. J. Chalmers. 1989. "Responses of Bartlett pear to withholding irrigation, regulated deficit irrigation, and tree spacing." *J. Amer. Soc. Hort. Sci.* 114: 15-19.

Powell, D. B. B. 1974. "Some effects of water stress in late spring on apple trees." *J. Hort. Sci.* 49: 257-272.

Proebsting, E. L., Jr. and J. E. Middleton. 1980. "The behavior of peach and pear trees under extreme drought stress." *J. Amer. Soc. Hort. Sci.* 105: 380-385.

Proebsting, E. L., J. E. Middleton and S. Roberts. 1977. "Altered fruiting and growth characteristics of Delicious apple associated with irrigation method." *HortScience* 12: 349-350.

Schultz, H. R. and M. A. Matthews. 1988. "Resistance to water transport in shoots of *Vitis vinifera L.*" *Plant Physiol.* 88: 718-724.

Slack, E. M. 1974. "Studies of stomatal distribution on the leaves of four apple varieties." *J. Hort. Sci.* 49: 95-103.

Transeau, E. N. 1905. "Forest centers of eastern North America." *Amer. Nat.* 39: 875-889.

Tromp, J. 1980. "Mineral absorption and distribution in young apple trees under various environmental conditions," pp. 173-182. In D. Atkinson, J. E. Jackson, R. O. Sharples and W. M. Waller (eds.) *Mineral nutrition of fruit trees.* Butterworths, London.

Troughton, J. and L. A. Donaldson. 1972. *Probing plant structures.* McGraw-Hill, New York.

Tyree, M. T. and J. S. Sperry. 1989. "Vulnerability of xylem to cavitation and embolism." *Annu. Rev. Plant Physiol. Plant Mol. Biol.* 40: 19-38.

Uriu, K., D. Davenport and R. M. Hagan. 1975. "Preharvest antitranspirant spray on cherries. Part 1. Effect on fruit size." *Calif. Agric.* 29(10): 7-9 (Oct.).

Vertucci, C. W. and A. C. Leopold. 1987. "The relationship between water binding and desiccation tolerance in tissues." *Plant Physiol.* 85: 232-238.

PART TWO

Irrigation scheduling and management

Strategy development for managing drought

Ed Proebsting, Ph.D.
Horticulturist
Irrigated Agriculture Research and Extension Center, Washington State University, Prosser

The threat of inadequate water for irrigation of fruit trees is chronic in the Pacific Northwest. There are many reasons for this, most of them well documented. People in the fruit industry are increasingly conscious of the possibility that some orchards will not receive enough water in any given year. It is important that growers understand about management of orchards under drought stress in order to develop individual strategies that will help the orchard survive the severe conditions that could occur.

Drought years are filled with uncertainty about how much water will be available and when. Strategies must be flexible. To be flexible, decision makers must understand all components of the soil-plant-atmosphere environment as well as the whole water-delivery system.

This chapter has three sections dealing with the soil, the atmosphere, and the plant, particularly under water-short conditions. Drought management strategies will revolve more around obtaining additional water and conserving the water that is available than with conditioning trees to produce or survive without water. Results of research conducted at the Irrigated Agriculture Research and Extension Center (IAREC) in Prosser, Washington, are the basis for this chapter.

The Yakima Valley faced a serious threat of curtailed water delivery in 1977. In response, IAREC researchers began a series of field experiments directed at answering some of the dramatic questions that were asked at that time.

RESPONSE TO DROUGHT

In the spring of 1977, the fruit-growing community learned that the Roza District, a large junior water district in the lower Yakima Valley, could be drastically short of water and that water might not be delivered at all. One of the first unknowns was how trees would respond to very severe drought. They knew that trees would wilt if they were to become too dry, but had no data on trees left for extended periods without water. Drought periods are expected in nonirrigated areas, but these areas did not provide the information scientists needed.

In most cases, nonirrigated orchards are in relatively high-rainfall areas and the drought is neither severe nor prolonged. In marginal areas, trees adapt to low water conditions and perform marginally. Neither of these situations are the same as denying water to the intensively irrigated orchards of central Washington. What happens to trees previously grown under luxury consumption of water when they are suddenly deprived of any irrigation throughout a long, hot central Washington summer?

Over the past 15 years, IAREC researchers have observed the performance of peach, pear and apple trees that were not irrigated. They have also looked at cherry and prune trees that received as irrigation 15 percent of evaporation from a Class A pan, adjusted to the canopy area of the tree. From these observations they can provide a generalized description of how fruit trees respond to severe drought in central Washington.

These experiments were done with trees on three to four feet of soil with good moisture-holding properties. Some orchards in central Washington grow on very little soil. If denied water for a full season, these trees will be subjected to much more severe drought than those on deeper soils.

Vegetative effects

The first symptom, of course, is wilting. Wilting in woody plants is not always a distinct symptom, but it becomes apparent in time. Near, or perhaps before, the time of wilting, terminal growth stops. The readiness of the shoot to stop growing relates to its vigor. Rapidly growing shoots in the spring flush of growth are more likely to continue growth than the same shoots a month later when they have naturally slowed.

Wilting is followed by leaf chlorosis, which precedes partial defoliation. During the tests, researchers did not observe complete defoliation during the growing season. The few remaining leaves stayed on the tree in the fall

longer than leaves on normally irrigated trees. Apple trees with a heavy crop retained their leaves longer and showed less chlorosis than did trees with a light crop.

In the year following the drought, pears and cherries died back from the periphery of the tree. New, vigorous growth emerged from the trunk and lower scaffold area of the trees. Peripheral wood tended to remain weak. Cherry scaffold branch surfaces that faced southwest sunburned and died. Enough good tissue on the shaded side survived to keep the branches alive and productive. Some 30-year-old peach trees died but other than that no trees of any other species were lost.

Fruiting effects

The first really important response to water deficit is that fruit growth slows down. If water is not restored right away, this response is reflected in smaller fruit at harvest.

Apple fruit quality and storage quality have been difficult to assess definitively. Severe drought destroys the value of the fruit through its effect on size and juice content (*Table 1*). Beyond that, in marginal situations, effects have not been large or consistent. Water deficit certainly increases sugar and reduces water content. In the trials, there seemed to be no effect on apple maturity, though maturity was not studied intensively. (Maturity of peaches was delayed substantially in one situation.)

There seemed to be less scald development on dry trees but the effect of drought was much less than the effect of fruit maturity on scald (*Table 2*). Bitter pit seemed to be serious in moderately droughted trees harvested early

TABLE 1. Effect on apple quality of varying periods of drought before harvest.

		Date of last irrigation							
	None	5/29	6/15	6/29	7/13	7/27	8/10	8/24	9/7
Wt./fruit (lb)	.16	.28	.38	.35	.41	.38	.38	.42	.38
Sol. solids (%)	19.5	16.8	14.4	13.6	12.5	12.6	11.8	12.2	11.5
Firmness (lb)	23.5	21.5	21.0	21.0	20.5	20.5	21.5	20.0	20.5
Water content (%)	74	76	80	81	81	82	82	82	82
Starch (rating)	2.7	2.8	2.6	2.4	2.2	2.2	2.2	2.4	2.0

but was absent from trees harvested two weeks later. Fully irrigated trees developed little bitter pit, seriously droughted trees developed none. We found no firm evidence that drought affected the rate of fruit softening in storage.

In the year following the drought, after full irrigation had been restored, severely droughted trees failed to bloom or did not bloom normally. Most interesting were apples that doubled. Severity of the effect ranged from almost no differentiation, showing only a calyx sepal on the side of fruit, to nearly fully formed fruit attached to the main fruit. Effects on the following year's fruiting accompanied only the most severe drought treatments.

Trees probably will not die

Throughout all these drought experiments the only trees that died were 30-year-old peach trees that already were in poor vigor from accumulated winter injury over many years. This is good news but must be tempered by the knowledge that, in the event of no water for some districts in central Washington, there may well be more severe drought imposed on trees than scientists could develop in their experiments.

The trees in this work were generally on good soil with good water-holding capacity and root development throughout the soil profile. They started the year with the profile full of water. They were surrounded by irrigated crops, permitting potential water move-ment under the experimental orchard through cracks in the underlying basalt layer. Any source of additional water, even if minor, can temper the effect of drought.

In a severe drought there will be big differences in response between orchards and within orchards. The biggest difference will be in the amount of stored water available to the trees. That will equate mostly to the depth of soil and its water-holding capacity. Where it took two months after the water was shut off to develop drought symptoms in the experiments, researchers have seen severe symptoms develop in two weeks on shallow soil spots in commercial orchards. There will be management differences, particularly in the amount of water stored in the soil profile from the previous year and, perhaps, in how well the soil profile is explored by roots. There will be less chance in a real drought emergency for subsoil moisture to be a factor because there will be no water in the canals.

MINIMUM WATER NEEDED

One of the most dramatic questions that is asked in the years when there will be no water is, "I have found a source of water and a tank truck. How much water does it take to keep a tree alive?" The answer is very complex. It requires answers to many other questions.

"How much water can the tree reach with its root system?" This question asks how much water is in the profile, how much in the subsoil, and how well roots are distributed.

TABLE 2. Scald, bitter pit and firmness of Delicious apples harvested at two maturities and stored until May 23, as affected by a drought gradient.

					Date of last irrigation				
	None	5/29	6/15	6/29	7/13	7/27	8/10	8/24	9/7
Scald (%)									
9/12 harvest	6	26	24	50	51	60	62	64	74
9/27 harvest	0	0	5	1	6	6	0	8	10
Bitter pit (%)									
9/12 harvest	0	0	7	4	13	8	20	5	4
9/27 harvest	0	0	0	0	0	0	0	0	0
Firmness (lb)									
9/12 harvest	18.6	16.2	12.4	11.8	11.4	11.6	11.2	10.8	10.8
9/27 harvest	13.8	12.1	11.5	11.2	11.4	11.5	11.4	11.2	11.0

"How far apart are the trees planted?" Wider spacing makes more soil, and therefore more water, available to the tree. This is why non-irrigated orchards are planted at wide spacings.

"How much injury is tolerable?" If it is necessary to have a marketable crop in the drought year, the answer would be much different from having the tree survive and return to full cropping after two or three years.

"How big is the tree canopy?" A large, older cherry tree uses much more water than a dwarfed apple tree. Water use is reliably related to the size of the tree canopy.

IAREC scientists did some experiments in the 1970s that were directed at this question (*Table 3*). Young apple trees, irrigated by trickle or sprinkler at the rate water was used by the orchard, used very little water in their first year. The cover crop in the sprinkled block was the principal water user in the early years of the orchard. Even by the seventh year, when the trees filled their allotted 10 foot by 15 foot spacing, the trickle irrigated trees were using only half the water the sprinkled trees were getting.

To answer the question of people who want to tank water to the trees, researchers calculated the amount of water the trees under trickle used by month as the trees grew older (*Table 4*). In July, when the trees were seven years old, they used 18 gallons of water a day. Smaller trees and less-demanding months used less.

These rates of application did more than just keep the trees alive. By the standards of most central Washington growers, the trickle-irrigated trees in this experiment were mildly stressed for water. Under these conditions the trickle-irrigated trees did not grow as much as the sprinkled trees, but they produced substantially more fruit that was equally as large.

In another experiment, scientists tested the amount of water, applied by trickle, that was needed to keep prune and cherry trees alive (*Table 5*). Cherry trees that were watered at 100 percent of pan evaporation used an average of 88 gallons per tree per day during June, July and August. Prune trees on the survival rate of 15 percent evaporation used only six gallons per tree per day.

Cherry trees on the maintenance level of 50 percent evaporation performed satisfactorily showing no effect on the current season crop nor in the following season. The prune trees at 50 percent evaporation had more drop and smaller fruit in the year of the drought but were normal the following year.

TABLE 3. Water application to young apple trees planted 10 feet by 15 feet.

Year	Trickle	Sprinkle	Pan evaporation
	(acre inches per acre per year)		
1	1	23	36
3	5	26	34
5	13	31	34
7	18	36	36

TABLE 4. Water application to trickle irrigated apple trees (10 feet by 15 feet) by month.

Year	June	July	August	September
	(gallons per tree per day)			
1	0.6	0.8	1.0	0.6
3	3.4	4.8	4.2	3.8
5	8.4	12.2	13.1	6.8
7	15.0	18.3	11.0	9.7

Cherry trees were damaged at 15 percent evaporation and had lower yields the year after the drought with other effects persisting beyond that. Prune trees at 15 percent evaporation recovered quite normally. No trees died.

In the final analysis, the most important factors in determining survival of crops and orchards will be the amount of water that is available, if some water is available all season, and how well conservation measures are implemented. Water saving by manipulating the plant will not be nearly as important as finding more water, especially for the latter half of the season.

MONITORING DROUGHT STRESS

If water is short and close management of irrigation at the orchard is required, then one should understand and monitor the soil-plant-atmosphere system. It is useful to check soil moisture regularly but it is much more useful if it is done in connection with recording evapotranspiration and with regular observation of tree and crop performance. It is most useful if a permanent record of all three components is kept so that trends and changes can be observed and interpreted throughout the season.

Soil

Another chapter will discuss measuring soil water content. Remember that soil moisture varies drastically within an orchard. It varies with soil type, with depth, with distance from the tree, and with presence or absence of a cover crop. Soil water is only significant if tree roots can get to it. A good method of measuring soil water content should be selected, but more importantly, the soil moisture in the orchard must be sampled thoroughly.

Atmosphere

Atmospheric conditions are important. The response of the tree to any level of soil moisture is conditioned by the kind of weather. It is clear that a tree with insufficient soil moisture will be much more affected by a clear, hot, dry day then by a cool, cloudy, moist day. Atmospheric conditions can be monitored easily through the Washington State University Public Agricultural Weather System (PAWS).

Plant

The connecting link between soil and atmosphere, and really the only reason there is concern about either of those factors, is the tree. In spite of its importance, researchers know less about the plant than they do about either the soil or the atmosphere in the drought relationship. How the plant responds to drought is the bottom line. Besides that, the plant is a sensitive integrator of all the physical forces from the soil and the atmosphere that act on it.

Growers can observe when leaves wilt, turn yellow and drop. This is a good indication that serious trouble is starting. But there are ways to measure changes in the plant well before trouble starts.

It is now possible to measure how the tree is reacting to the soil and atmosphere in several ways. Scientists can measure water potential in the plant, which relates well to soil water potential and to atmospheric water potential *(Figure 1)*. Plant water potential varies widely diurnally and within the tree and reflects also the soil moisture within the root zone.

Note that stem water potential does not change too much with drier soil until two-thirds to three-quarters of the available soil moisture is used. Note also that while there is still enough soil moisture, the stem water

TABLE 5. Water appied during June, July and August to mature cherry and prune trees at normal (100%E), maintenance (50%E) and survival (15%E) rates.

Species	100%E	50%E	15%E
		(gallons per tree per day)	
Cherry	88	47	13
Prune	48	24	6

potential varies little on days of low vapor pressure deficit in the atmosphere. On days with high vapor pressure deficit, lower stem water potential was measured even with sufficient moisture in the soil.

Researchers calculated a Stress Day Index by multiplying the stem water potential by the number of days represented by each stem water potential measurement. This number accounts for both the intensity of the stress (stem water potential), and the duration of the stress. Figure 2 shows a close linear relationship between the Stress Day Index and fruit size.

Scientists can measure stomatal conductance, which relates to photosynthesis, or they can measure photosynthesis directly. They can measure the difference in temperature between the leaf and the air, which depends on stomatal conductance, and this can be sensed remotely. Finally, they can measure growth of plant parts, very sensitively if desired.

Fruit growth is a sensitive and economically significant way to observe the effect of drought on the plant *(Figure 2)*. One of the

first symptoms of drought stress is reduced growth rates. Fruit growth rate was chosen as a drought indicator because it responds quickly to drought stress, because fruit size is an important quality factor and is easy to measure, and because people in the industry know quite a bit about fruit growth rates through the practice of fruit thinning.

Many growers are familiar with the work of Jack Batjer (around 1960) when he established a standard apple fruit-growth curve with tables to estimate fruit size at harvest from fruit size at any time during the summer. This information is used to help evaluate the hand thinning that is needed. It can just as well be used to help evaluate the effect of drought.

By measuring fruit size of a large number of apples at least weekly, a growth curve for the season can be established to compare with the standard curve developed by Batjer. If the growth rate becomes slower than normal, and the evapotranspiration and soil moisture measurements indicate drought, one can be sure that the crop has been affected. If water is available, now is the time to apply it. Similarly,

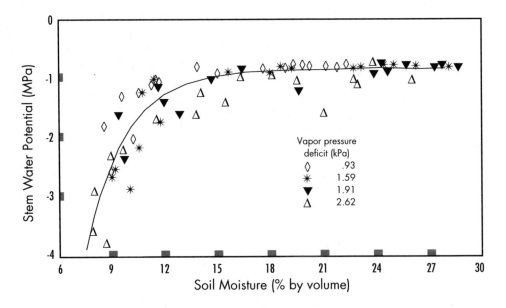

FIGURE 1. Stem water potential of apple trees as affected by soil moisture and atmospheric vapor pressure deficit. The more negative the stem water potential the more severe the drought stress felt by the plant. The higher the vapor pressure deficit the drier the air.

the size data can be used to help adjust thinning to compensate for smaller fruit induced by drought.

Figure 3 illustrates the effect of crop load on fruit-growth rates compared with the standard rate from the fruit thinning tables. A heavy crop load reduces the growth rate of individual fruit. This is one reason trees are thinned. When water is withheld *(Figure 4)*, the growth rate slows compared with the standard curve, regardless of crop load. When water was restored in mid-August, growth resumed at a more rapid rate than before and fruit size ended at nearly the same size as if the drought had not occurred.

These figures illustrate the point that fruit size and growth rate can be used to monitor the effect of drought, that some of the size lost to temporary drought can be regained, and that it is very important to have water available during the end of the season when the fruit is finishing.

As with soil-moisture measurements, it is also important in evaluating plant responses to sample the orchard carefully and thoroughly, particularly around drought-susceptible areas. This means choosing a method that can be done quickly. Evaluation stations, where both soil and plant characteristics are measured, permit one to evaluate all the factors in the drought problem as they relate to each other.

ORCHARD PRACTICES TO AID DROUGHT SURVIVAL

There are not very many choices of things we can do to help trees perform normally without water. Researchers have tried several practices that might help trees survive. Mostly they have undesirable aspects that put them into the desperation category. One difficulty is that a decision about what needs to be done must be made before it is known what the water situation will be in July or August.

Reduced cropping

If it is known that the orchard, or part of the orchard, will be seriously short of water, growers can thin more heavily than normal. This can be done almost any time but is most effective if done at bloom and is decreasingly effective from then on. The operation simply acknowledges that the trees will get dry and fruit growth will be reduced. To maintain fruit in the desirable sizes one must grow less fruit. These decisions can be helped by the fruit-growth curve measurements suggested above.

Figure 5 illustrates that with low Stress

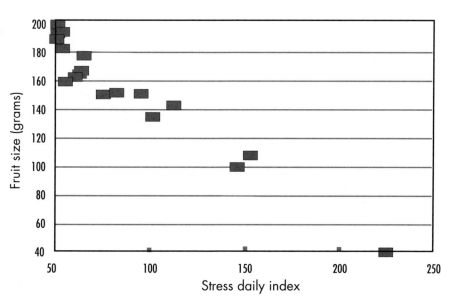

FIGURE 2. Relationship between apple fruit size and Stress Day Index.

Day Index the trees respond to thinning with much larger fruit. The effect of thinning diminishes as the stress becomes more severe, vanishing with very severe stress.

Researchers also have good indications that heavy thinning early will help trees survive, if the drought is that serious. Since failure to flower is a drought effect, heavy, early thinning might help with return bloom, although IAREC researchers have no data to show that this is so.

Severe pruning

The most remarkable response by trees in all the drought studies researchers did was to dehorning type pruning. They did this initially on peaches and pears, later on apples. The rationale at the time was to reduce the evaporating surface, thereby conserving soil moisture a little longer. It did that but also did more.

The trees were dehorned in May, when there still was plenty of moisture in the soil. Naturally, they grew very vigorously. It was believed that the tender, vigorous growth would be injured seriously when it ran out of water. It was not. In all cases, on peach, pear and apple, these trees retained their leaves much longer than normally pruned trees. In most cases, they held their leaves throughout the season.

The effect of several pruning treatments on the relationship between fruit size and Stress Day Index shows parallel size decrease with increasing stress for all treatments (*Figure 6*). Dehorning in April increases apple fruit size for any given level of stress. So does a severe pruning done by removing selected scaffold branches, when done in April. This treatment would be easier to bring back into production the following year than would be dehorned trees. When done in July, severe pruning slightly decreased fruit size.

Most interesting here is the effect of adding supplemental nitrogen to the dehorning treatment. Nitrogen had a major effect in this experiment, less so in other experiments, perhaps because of difficulties getting it into the root zone in a drought year, perhaps because of an interaction with the dehorning.

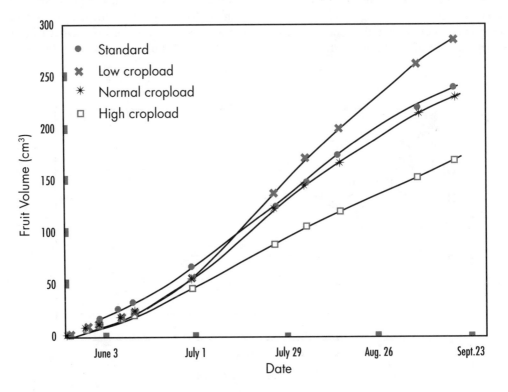

FIGURE 3. Apple fruit-growth curve as affected by thinning in mid-June.

Dehorning is clearly the way to save valuable trees. It is not the way to manage an orchard with good prospects for a crop the following year, particularly if water availability is in question. Dehorning worked well with peaches. There was a great deal of regrowth

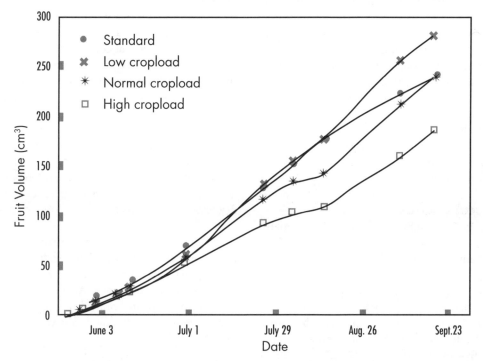

FIGURE 4. Apple fruit-growth curves from low, normal and high crop loads as affected by withholding water in June, July and early August, then restoring irrigation in mid-August.

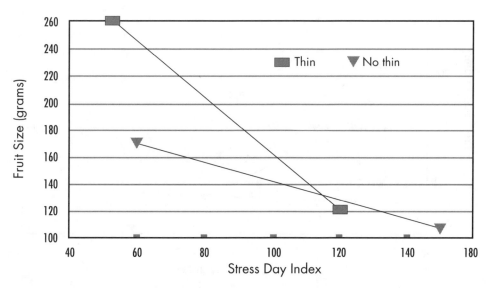

FIGURE 5. Effect of increasing Stress Day Index (drought) on apple fruit size at harvest, as influenced by thinning.

that fruited well the next year except where it was most dry and that area failed to bloom. The vigorous growth on the old trees researchers studied gave them the opportunity to rejuvenate the fruiting wood at the same time.

The pears were almost as good. They had fruit the following year but, of course, it was all from flowers borne on one-year-old wood. Basically, the pear trees were out of production both in the drought year and the following year.

Dehorned apple trees survived drought in excellent shape but were very difficult to bring back into bearing quality fruit even two years after the drought year.

Miscellaneous

The 1977 drought threat brought out many ingenious ideas for beating the drought. Many of them were for sale. We found nothing that was as effective as the two possibilities mentioned above. One legitimate group of products that will be suggested widely is the antitranspirants. Antitranpirants have horticultural value but probably not to prevent damage from severe drought. IAREC reseachers have found it very difficult to measure response to orchard-applied antitranspirants in our evaluations.

Nitrogen

Increased nitrogen likely will help trees survive the drought. IAREC experiments, however, did not support that concept. In the scientists' drought experiments nitrogen was applied in May, in response to a hypothetical drought. This was too late to have an effect that year.

On the other hand, they observed a major effect of nitrogen when applied in combination with dehorning apples *(Figure 6)*. The dehorning response itself was analogous to high nitrogen. Finally, non-irrigated trees in dry areas respond to nitrogen, doing better than trees not fertilized.

The evidence suggests that normal fertilization is safe and that probably extra nitrogen applied early in the year and watered in would help trees survive. A major risk in using nitrogen to ameliorate drought injury in apples would be inducing excessive vigor in the trees.

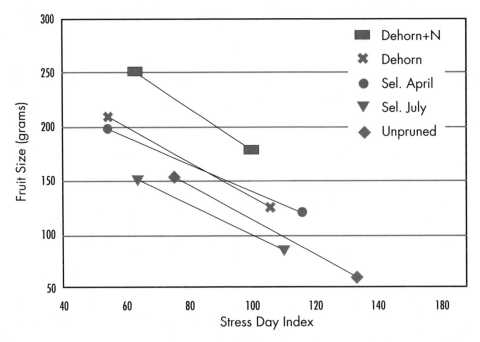

FIGURE 6. Effect of increasing Stress Day Index (drought) on apple fruit size at harvest, as influenced by pruning and nitrogen.

DROUGHT MANAGEMENT STRATEGIES

The most effective drought-management strategies will not be in the manipulation of the trees. Monitoring the trees, along with the soil and atmosphere, will provide valuable information to assist in operational decision-making on a week-to-week basis. Experience has been that our drought emergencies develop on a week-to-week basis, so decisions will be better if based on the best possible data on the water status of the orchard.

Find water

There is no substitute for water. Wells have been drilled. Water can be taken off low-value crops to save high-value crops or perennial plants. If water can be purchased from a neighbor at a fair price, buy it. Watch for developments in allowing inter-district transfers. A source of water and a tank truck won't keep many trees going. You will need large amounts of water. Look especially for opportunities to find water late in the season.

Save water

To have all irrigation systems working at top efficiency growers should follow the advice of the irrigation engineers. They should not water plants not absolutely needed and should save water by eliminating the cover crop. Applying water at a single point under each tree with trickle irrigation will save water. Soil, plant and atmosphere should be monitored to assess what is happening throughout the system. If water can be saved to apply during the latter stages of fruit growth, it should be saved. Water can be stored in the soil. When water is available, irrigation is desirable, but over-irrigation should be avoided. Applying water to soils at field capacity wastes water.

Establish priorities

If water is limited, growers should know which blocks have the highest value and protect them. Reducing water to lower value blocks is a way to save water.

Monitor soil, plant and atmosphere, and forecasts

It will be important to have as much information at hand as possible to make good decisions. The water situation changes throughout a drought year. Growers should be prepared to respond in the best possible way to changing conditions.

Modify the plant

If a grower learns early and with a great deal of certainty that no water will be available, there are some things that can be done to help save trees. The problem is, who does one believe and when?

Forecasting of water supply has improved but changes in weather can alter even a perfect forecast. It would take a high degree of certainty about water supplies early in the season to warrant doing anything as drastic as crop removal or severe pruning.

The treatments, however, become less effective farther into the growing season, which underlines the need to know early and accurately what water supplies will be.

Regardless of drought threats, the advantages that will favor orchard operators who understand and monitor the water status of their orchards are increasing.

Acknowledgements
The IAREC research discussed in this chapter was supported by the Washington Tree Fruit Research Commission, National Crop Insurance Services, and Washington State University.

Research collaborators include T.E. Middleton, Robert Evans, Tom Ley, Bob Stevens, Steve Drake and Robert Ebel.

Soil water monitoring and measurement

Thomas W. Ley, P.E.
Extension Irrigation Engineer
IAREC, Washington State University, Prosser, Washington

Efficient irrigation requires a systematic water management program. Such a program answers the questions of when to irrigate, how much water to apply during irrigation, and how best to apply the water (rate of application, method, etc.). A key component of good on-farm irrigation water management is the routine monitoring and measurement of soil water. Soil water must be maintained between desirable upper and lower limits of availability to the plant. This requires accounting for soil evaporation, crop water use, irrigation, drainage and rainfall. Accurate assessment of the soil water-holding characteristics along with periodic soil water monitoring and measurement are required.

Monitoring and measuring soil water under irrigated crops is part of an integrated management package and helps avoid: 1) the economically disastrous effects of both under-irrigation and overirrigation on crop yields and crop quality, and 2) the environmentally costly effects of overirrigation: wasted water and energy, the leaching of nutrients or agricultural chemicals into groundwater supplies, and degradation of surface water supplies by sediment-laden irrigation water runoff.

This chapter provides a review of several tools and techniques that can be used to monitor or directly measure soil water. Among the most common approaches are: 1) soil feel and appearance, 2) soil sampling, 3) tensiometers, 4) porous blocks, and 5) neutron scattering.

Newer methods that measure the dielectric constant of the soil water medium and then estimate soil water content have recently become commercially available. These methods include time domain reflectometry, frequency domain reflectometry and soil capacitance measurements.

Questions often arise about which technique is best, which is most accurate, how different methods compare under the same situation (irrigation practice, soil type, etc.), what are the relative costs are to purchase and operate the different methods, and so forth. Several tools and techniques available to growers for monitoring and measuring available soil water were evaluated with these questions in mind.

TOOLS AND TECHNIQUES

The goal of soil water monitoring or measurement should be to determine the soil water available for use by the crop. Typically this will require some calibration of the method or instrument used for the specific soil being sampled. Soil water measurement should be done routinely both in time and spatially to obtain the best results. Often the difference in soil water content from one sampling to the next—its relative change—provides more information about its absolute value. Soil water should be measured or monitored in at least two depths in the expected crop root zone. Additionally, several locations in a field (at least three for large uniform soil areas) should be measured to obtain a field average. Subareas within fields having different soil characteristics should also be measured.

Soil feel and appearance

Monitoring by soil feel and appearance is easy but requires some skill. The procedure involves the use of a soil auger or core sampler to obtain soil samples at various depths of the rooting zone to assess soil water status. Samples taken are compared to tables and charts that give the characteristics of different soil textures in terms of feel and appearance at different water contents. This requires some judgement but, with enough practice, estimates can usually be obtained within ±10-15

percent of the true soil water content. In many situations, this may be accurate enough.

Table 1 is one version of the type of chart used to describe soil feel and appearance characteristics versus soil water content. The Soil Conservation Service's State Irrigation Guides include similar tables and several excellent photographs of the feel and appearance method on three different soil textures.

A soil probe is recommended, rather than a shovel, so that samples can be drawn from deep in the profile without digging a big hole. Augers and core samplers that allow sampling down to four feet are available for less than $100. Core sampling on rocky or stoney soils can be frustrating, if not impossible.

Soil sampling

Soil sampling is the only direct method for measuring soil water content. When done carefully with enough samples it is one of the most accurate methods, and is often used for calibration of other techniques. This approach requires careful sample collection and handling to minimize water loss between the time

TABLE 1. Soil feel and appearance chart for estimating available soil water.

Available Moisture	Coarse (sand, loamy soil)	SOIL TEXTURE Moderately Coarse (sandy loam, fine sandy loam)	Medium (loam)	Fine (silt loam clay loam)
100% (field capacity)	Leaves wet outline on hand when squeezed. (0.0)	Appears very dark, leaves wet outline on hand; makes a short ribbon. (0.0)	Appears very dark, leaves wet outline on hand; will ribbon out about 1" (0.0)	Appears very dark, leaves slight moisture on hand when squeezed; will ribbon out about 2" (0.0)
70% - 80%	Appears moist; makes a weak ball. (0.2 - 0.3)	Dark; makes a hard ball. (0.3 - 0.4)	Quite dark; makes tight plastic ball; ribbons out 1/2" (0.4 - 0.6)	Quite dark; ribbons and slicks easily; makes plastic ball. (0.5 - 0.7)
60% - 65%	Appears slightly moist; forms weak brittle ball. (0.4)	Fairly dark, makes a good ball. (0.6)	Fairly dark, forms firm ball; barely ribbons (0.8)	Fairly dark, forms firm ball; ribbons 1/4"-1/2". (0.9)
50%	Appears dry; forms very weak ball or will not ball. ((0.5)	Slightly dark; forms weak ball. (0.8)	Fairly dark, will form ball; slightly crumbly. (1.0)	Balls easily; small clods flatten out rather than crumble; ribbons slightly. (1.1 - 1.2)
35% - 40%	Dry; will not ball. (0.6 - 0.7)	Light color; will not ball or forms brittle balls. (0.9 - 1.0)	Slightly dark; forms weak ball; crumbly. (1.2 - 1.3)	Slightly dark; forms weak balls; clods crumble. (1.4 - 1.5)
Less than 20%	Very dry; loose, flows through fingers. (0.8 - 1.0)	Dry; loose, flows through fingers. (1.3 - 1.6)	Light color; powdery, dry. (1.6 - 2.0)	Hard, baked, cracked light color. (1.8 - 2.3)

Note: Figures in parentheses at end of each entry represent approximate moisture deficit from field capacity when soil is uniform with depth. Ball is formed by squeezing soil hard in fist. Ribbon is formed by rolling soil between thumb and forefinger.

a sample is collected and processed. Replicated samples should be taken to reduce the inherent sampling variability that results from small volumes of soil. Equipment required includes a soil auger or a core sampler (with removable sleeve of known volume to obtain volumetric water content), sample collection cans or other containers, a balance accurate to within at least one gram and a drying oven.

Soil sampling involves taking soil samples from each of several desired depths in the root zone and temporarily storing them in water vapor-proof containers. The samples are then weighed and the opened containers oven-dried under specified time and temperature conditions (220°F or 104°C for 24 hours). The dry samples are then re-weighed. Percent soil water content on a dry mass or gravimetric basis, Pw, is determined with the following:

Equation 1:

$$Pw = [(\text{wet sample weight - dry sample weight}) / \text{dry sample weight}] \times 100$$

The difference in the wet and dry weights is the weight of water removed by drying. To convert from a gravimetric basis to water content on a volumetric basis, Pv, multiply the gravimetric soil water content by the soil bulk density, BD.

Soil bulk density is the weight of a unit volume of oven-dry soil and usually is determined in a manner similar to gravimetric sampling by using sample collection devices that will collect a known volume of soil.

Equation 2:

$$BD = \text{weight of oven dry soil} / \text{unit volume of dry soil}$$

Equation 3:

$$Pv = Pw \times BD$$

Soil water content on a volumetric percentage basis is a preferable unit for irrigation management. It is easily converted to a depth of soil water per depth of soil. For instance, a volume soil water content of 30 percent is easily converted to inches of water per foot of soil depth by multiplying by 12 inches/foot and then dividing by 100 to remove the percentage.

Example:

$$Pv = 30\% = 30 \times 12 / 100$$
$$= 3.6 \text{ inches per foot}$$

Comparison of the measured volumetric soil water content with field capacity and wilting point of the soil is used to determine the available soil water and the percent of total available soil water. Either of these figures can then be used to determine if irrigation is needed.

Example

If the above sample having 30 percent volumetric water content was obtained from a silt loam soil having a field capacity of 4.3 inches per foot and a wilting point of 1.9 inches per foot, then this soil has total available water of (4.3 minus 1.9) 2.4 inches per foot. At the current total water content of 3.6 inches per foot (30 percent by volume), the available water above wilting point (3.6 minus 1.9) equals 1.7 inches of water. Or, the soil currently has (1.7 divided by 2.4) times 100 equal to 71 percent of total available water remaining. If the management allowable depletion (MAD) for the crop being grown is 50 percent, then irrigation is not yet needed. However, if the MAD is 30 percent then irrigation should be scheduled soon, i.e., a MAD value of 30 percent means irrigation should be applied when the percent of total available water reaches (100 minus 30) or 70 percent.

Soil sampling for gravimetric analysis is time consuming and labor intensive. Results are generally not known for a minimum of 24 hours after sampling (unless a microwave oven is used for drying). A large number of samples must be taken each time sampling is done to remove the inherent variability of this approach. Samples cannot be taken from exactly the same point on subsequent sampling dates.

Several irrigation-scheduling consultants use this approach because of its accuracy and low equipment cost. One of the advantages of gravimetric soil sampling, like the feel and appearance method, is that soil sampling is done at several locations in a field and throughout the soil profile. Information on soil layering and compaction, changes in soil texture, etc., is often found while other methods may not yield this information.

Tensiometry

Soil water tension, soil water suction or soil water potential are all terms describing the energy status of soil water. Soil water potential is a measure of the amount of energy with which water is held in the soil. A soil water characteristic or water-release curve shows the relation between soil water content and soil water tension.

Tensiometers have been used for many years to measure soil water tension in the field. Tensiometers are water-filled tubes with hollow ceramic tips attached on one end and a vacuum gauge (or mercury manometer) and air-tight seal on the other end. The device is installed in the soil with the ceramic tip in

good contact with the soil at the desired depth. (See Figure 1 for an example of the typical recommended installation of tensiometers at two depths of the root zone.) The water in the tensiometer eventually comes to pressure equilibrium with the surrounding soil through the ceramic tip. Water is pulled out through the ceramic tip into the soil creating a tension in the closed tube. As the soil is rewetted, the tension gradient declines, causing water to flow into the ceramic tip. As the soil goes through wetting and drying cycles, tension readings can be taken.

Most commercially available tensiometers use a vacuum gauge to read the tension created and have a scale from 0 to 100 centibars (one bar or 100 centibars of pressure or tension is equal to 14.7 psi). The practical operating range is from 0 to 75 centibars. If the

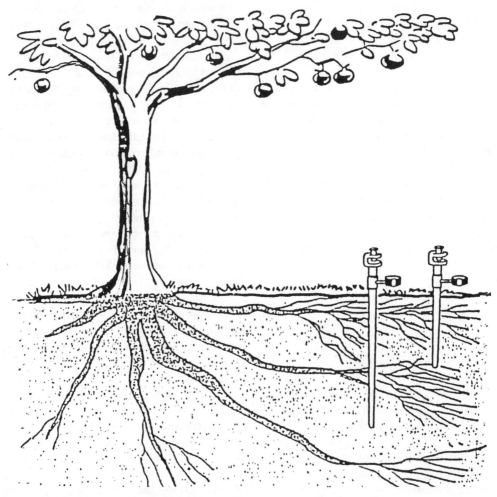

Figure 1. Typical tensiometer bank installation at two depths in the crop root zone.

water column is intact, a zero reading indicates saturated soil conditions. Readings of around 10 centibars (cb) correspond to field capacity for coarse-textured soils, while readings of around 30 cb can approximate field capacity for some finer-textured soils. The upper limit of 75 cb corresponds to as much as 90 percent depletion of total available water for the coarse-textured soils, but is only about 30 percent depletion for silt loam, clay loams and other fine-textured soils. This limits the practical use of tensiometers to coarse-textured soils or to high-frequency irrigation where soil water content is maintained high.

Tensiometer readings may be used as indicators of soil water and the need for irrigation. When instruments installed at shallower depths of the root zone reach a certain reading, they can be used to determine when to start irrigating, based on soil texture and crop type. Similarly, instruments deeper in the root zone may be used to indicate when adequate water has been applied. A soil water release curve is used to translate tensiometer readings into percent of available water, water depletion, etc. Examples of these curves for several soil textures are shown in Figure 2. These should be used with caution, however, as specific soils will deviate from the generalized relationships shown.

Careful installation and maintenance of tensiometers is required for reliable results. The ceramic tip must be in complete contact with the soil. This is done by augering a pilot hole out to the proper depth, making a soil-water slurry mix with the soil that has been removed and re-introducing this into the hole. Finally, the tensiometer tip is pushed into this slurry. Soil is banked up around the tube at the soil surface to prevent water from standing around the tube itself. A few hours to a few days are required for the tensiometer to come to equilibrium with the surrounding soil. The tensiometer should be pumped with a hand vacuum pump to remove air bubbles.

Routine maintenance includes refilling with water and hand pumping. Under extreme drying cycles enough water may be lost from the tensiometer that it breaks suction and gives only zero readings. Tensiometers also break suction when improperly installed, when there are air leaks, or there is too much air in the water used to fill the tube. Most tensiometer manufacturers provide maintenance kits that include a hand vacuum pump for checking for leaks, or drawing air bubbles out.

Banks or pairs of tensiometers at two lengths should be installed in at least three locations within a field. More may be needed depending upon soil variability. Installation sites should represent the field in terms of water application patterns, soil types, slopes and exposure.

Tensiometers come in lengths from six to 48 inches. Price depends on length, and varies from about $45 to $80. It is generally recommended that tensiometers be installed in pairs, one at one third and one at two thirds of the crop rooting depth. They should be installed out of the way of traffic and cultivation. In freezing climates, insulate or remove tensiometers during winter months. It takes only a small frost to knock the vacuum gauges out of calibration.

Porous blocks

Porous blocks are made of materials such as gypsum, ceramic, nylon and fiberglass. Similar to tensiometers, the blocks are buried in intimate contact with the soil at some desired depth and allowed to come to water-tension equilibrium with the surrounding soil. Once equilibrium is reached, different properties of the block that are affected by its water tension may be measured.

One of the more common types of porous blocks are electrical resistance blocks. Electrodes are buried in the block, which is usually made out of gypsum, and are used to measure the resistance to electrical current flow between them. The water content of the block, which is a function of the soil-water tension, affects resistance. Higher resistance readings mean lower block-water content and thus higher soil water tension. Lower resistance readings indicate higher block-water content and lower soil water tension. Individual electrical resistance blocks usually sell for between $5 and $20, depending on materials of construction. Some may last for only a season.

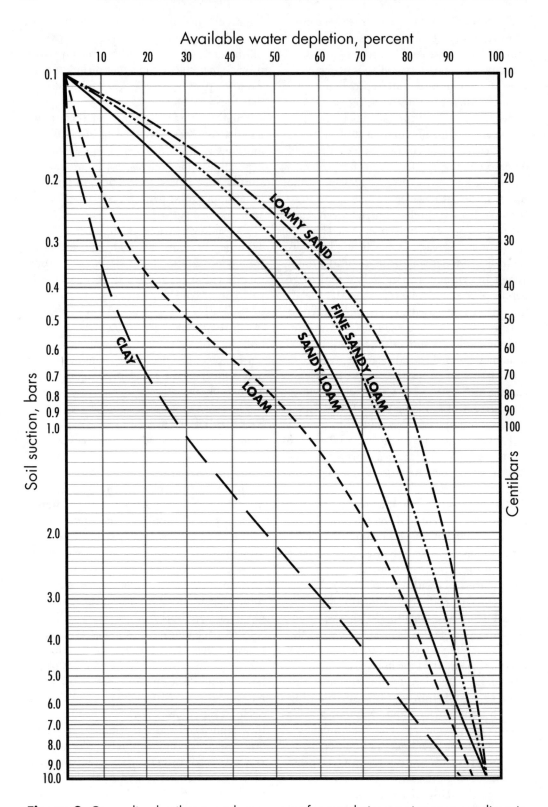

Figure 2. Generalized soil water release curves for translating tensiometers readings in centibars to soil water depletion.

Thermal dissipation blocks are porous ceramic blocks in which a small heater and temperature sensors are embedded. This arrangement allows measurement of the thermal dissipation of the block, or the rate at which heat is conducted away from the heater. This property is directly related to the water content of the block and thus soil water tension. Thermal dissipation blocks must be individually calibrated. They are considerably more expensive than electrical resistance blocks. Thermal dissipation blocks are sensitive to soil water content across a wide range.

Meters used to read porous blocks may range in price from $150 to $600. They are portable, may be used to read several blocks and will last for several seasons. Meter readings can be used directly or translated using the manufacturer's charts to soil water tension. Readings do not mean the same across all meters and for all types of blocks. Manufacturers make meters and blocks to be used together. As with a tensiometer, to obtain soil water content and available soil water, a calibration curve for each specific soil type of soil water content versus soil water tension must be used (see Figure 2 for examples).

Porous blocks require the same careful installation considerations as tensiometers but generally require less maintenance. Gypsum blocks can be prone to breakdown under alkaline soil conditions. High soil salinity (high electrical conductivity of the soil solution) can cause misleading readings.

Gypsum blocks

One type of electrical resistance block, the gypsum block, has been in use since the 1940s. Blocks are installed in the soil similar to the procedure for tensiometers, ensuring intimate contact with the surrounding soil, and are allowed to come to water-tension equilibrium with the surrounding soil. Soil is carefully tamped back into the hole and the wire leads brought to the surface. Readings are taken by attaching an electrical resistance meter to the wire leads. Some meters give readings between 0 and 100, with 0 meaning dry and 100 wet. Manufacturer's charts are required to translate these readings into soil water tension.

Gypsum blocks are best suited for finer-textured soils. They are generally not sensitive to changes in soil water tension less than 100 centibars. For most coarse-textured soils readings of 100 cb and above are well outside the available soil water range. Tensiometers and electrical resistance blocks are often used together to monitor soil water over a wider range of conditions than either can measure alone.

Gypsum blocks require little maintenance and can be left in the soil under freezing conditions. Being made of gypsum, the blocks will slowly dissolve, requiring replacement. The rate of dissolution depends upon soil pH and soil water conditions. High soil salinity affects the electrical resistivity of the soil solution, although the gypsum buffers this effect to a degree.

Watermark blocks

The Watermark block, a new style of electrical resistance block, is a gypsum block with a granular matrix material, which approximates fine sand, encased with it. A synthetic porous membrane and a PVC casing with holes drilled in it hold the block together. The granular matrix material next to the gypsum block enhances the movement of water to and from the surrounding soil, making the block more responsive to soil water tensions in the 0 to 100 cb range. Watermark blocks exhibit good sensitivity to soil water tension over a range from 0 to 200 cb. This makes them more adaptable to a wider range of soil textures and irrigation regimes than gypsum blocks.

Readings are taken by attaching a special electrical resistance meter to the wire leads and setting the estimated soil temperature. The Watermark meter gives readings in centibars of soil water tension similar to the tensiometer. Watermark blocks require little maintenance and can be left in the soil under freezing conditions. The blocks are much more stable and have a longer life than gypsum blocks. Soil salinity affects the electrical resistivity of the soil water solution and may cause erroneous readings. The gypsum in the Watermark blocks offers some buffering of this effect.

Neutron scattering

Neutron scattering is a time-tested technique for measuring total soil water content by volume. This method estimates the amount of water in a volume of soil by measuring the amount of hydrogen. A neutron probe consists of a source of fast or high-energy neutrons and a detector, housed in a unit,which is lowered into an access tube installed in the soil. The probe is connected by cable to a control unit that remains on the surface. Clips on the cable allow the probe to be set at preselected depths in the soil profile. Access tubes should be installed at least to the depth of the expected rooting zone. The control unit includes electronics for time control, a counter, memory and other electronics for processing readings *(Figure 3)*.

Fast neutrons emitted from the source and passing through the access tube into the surrounding soil gradually lose their energy though collisions with other atomic nuclei. Hydrogen molecules in the soil (mostly in soil water) are particularly effective in slowing the fast neutrons since they are both of near equal mass. The result is a cloud of slow or thermalized neutrons, some of which diffuse back to the detector. The size and density of the cloud depends mainly upon soil type and soil water content, is spherical in shape, and ranges in size from six to 16 inches. Thermalized neutrons that pass through the detector create a small electrical impulse. These electrical pulses are amplified and then counted. The number of slow neutrons counted in a specified interval of time is linearly related to the total volumetric soil water content. A higher count indicates higher soil water content, a lower count indicates lower soil water content.

A manufacturer's calibration curve relating the count to soil water content is supplied with the neutron probe. However, a calibration must be developed for the type of access tube used (PVC, aluminum and steel pipe are most common). Calibrations should be developed for soils high in organic matter and some ions such as boron. If it is desired to translate the total volumetric soil water content reading of the neutron probe into available soil water, then field capacity and wilting point of each soil must be known. Some probes are programmable so several different calibrations can be stored in memory. Also, the desired soil water content units can be changed with the push of a button (inches per foot, percent by volume, pounds per cubic foot, etc.).

The neutron probe allows relatively rapid and repeatable measurements of soil water content to be made at several depths and locations within a field. Being able to repeat measurements at the same location through the growing season minimizes the effects of soil variability on the measurements. Depending on the number of access tube installations per field and number of fields, the time required to take probe readings and analyze the data may become extensive. A minimum of three access tubes per field is recommended. Readings should be taking in six-inch increments to the bottom of the expected rooting depth.

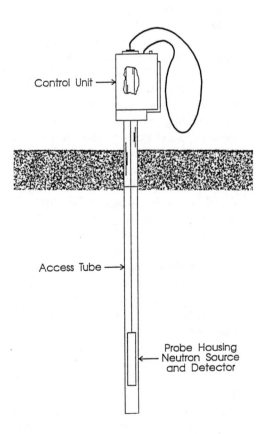

Control Unit

Access Tube

Probe Housing Neutron Source and Detector

FIGURE 3. Sketch of neutron probe and access tube.

Neutron probes are considered among the most accurate methods for measuring soil water content when properly calibrated. They are inaccurate, however, when used within the top six to eight inches of the soil surface, because of the escape of fast neutrons. Surface readings must be carefully calibrated or a different method used.

Because of their high cost, from $3,000 to $4,000 depending upon features, neutron probes are not extensively used by individual farmers. There is also a radiation safety hazard, which requires special licensing, operator training, handling, shipping and storage procedures. Many large corporate farms are using this method, as well as numerous irrigation-scheduling consultants.

Methods based on dielectric constant measurement

The dielectric constant of a material is a measure of the capacity (or electrical permittivity) of a non-conducting material to transmit high-frequency electromagnetic waves or pulses. The dielectric constant of dry soil varies between two and five, while the dielectric constant of water is 80 at frequencies between 30 MHz and one GHz. A large volume of research has shown the measurement of dielectric constant of the soil water media to a be a sensitive measurement of soil-water content. Relatively small changes in the quantity of free water in the soil have large effects on the electromagnetic properties of the soil-water media.

Two approaches developed for measuring the dielectric constant of the soil-water media and hence the volumetric water content are time-domain reflectometry and frequency domain reflectometry.

Time Domain Reflectometry (TDR)

Currently, TDR technology for soil water content measurement is based upon cable testers used by many utilities to test the integrity of buried cables, find breaks, couplings, etc. For soil water content measurement, the device propagates a high-frequency transverse electromagnetic wave along a cable attached to parallel conducting probes inserted into the soil. The signal is reflected from the end of the waveguide back to the cable tester where it is displayed on an oscilloscope, and where time between sending the pulse and receiving the reflected wave is accurately measured by the cable tester. By knowing the length of the transmission line and waveguide, the propagation velocity of the signal in the soil can be computed. The dielectric constant is inversely related to this propagation velocity, i.e., faster propagation velocity yields a lower dielectric constant and thus a lower soil water content. Or, as soil water content increases, propagation velocity decreases, and dielectric constant increases.

Waveguides inserted into the soil usually consist of a pair of parallel stainless steel rods spaced about two inches apart. They may be installed in the soil horizontally, vertically, or at a 45° angle, etc. A shielded, parallel transmission line connects the waveguide to the cable tester. The TDR soil water measurement system measures the average volumetric soil water percentage along the length of the waveguide. The volume of soil sampled approximates a cylinder surrounding the waveguide with a diameter about 1.5 times the spacing of the parallel rods.

The waveguides may be permanently installed with wire leads brought to the surface, but this requires care to minimize soil disruption. However, this is the only way to obtain TDR measurements at specific multiple soil depths. The installation generally requires the excavation of a pit in the soil, with waveguides inserted into the undisturbed face of one of the pit walls. Horizontal insertion yields a depth-specific measurement, while insertion at a 45° angle integrates a larger volume of soil both horizontally and vertically. An alternative to permanent installations are portable hand-push waveguide probes, which may be used to measure the top 18 to 24 inches of soil. For either approach, waveguides must be carefully installed in the soil with soil contact along their entire length. Annular air gaps around the rods will lower readings. The waveguide rods must remain parallel.

Once properly calibrated and installed, the TDR technique is highly accurate. Accurate measurements may be made near the surface, an important advantage compared to techniques like the neutron probe. Measurements are not affected by soil salinity. Research has shown the dielectric constant to be nearly independent of soil type and bulk density and relatively unaffected by soil salinity. Soil salinity or bulk electrical conductivity affects the degree of attenuation of the electromagnetic pulse in the soil. Researchers are studying this effect so that TDR may be used to measure both soil water content and bulk electrical conductivity.

Because of the high cost of the cable tester and associated electronics, TDR soil water-measurement system costs usually begin in the range of $6,000 to $7,000. Individual sets of waveguides cost between $20 and $80 depending on length. TDR instruments are commercially available, but, primary users are university researchers and irrigation consultants. Cable testers currently used for TDR contain many features not used or unnecessary for soil water content measurement. Research efforts have been undertaken to build considerably less expensive TDR units for soil water measurement containing the necessary electric-pulse generation and accurate timing electronics. Such devices will make TDR the instrument of the future.

Frequency-Domain Reflectometry

Frequency domain reflectometry approaches to measurement of soil water content are also known as radio-frequency (RF) capacitance techniques. This technique actually measures soil capacitance. A pair of electrodes is inserted into the soil. The soil acts as the dielectric completing a capacitance circuit, which is part of a feedback loop of a high-frequency transistor oscillator. As high-frequency radio waves (about 150 Mhz) are pulsed through the capacitance circuitry, a natural resonant frequency is established that is dependent on the soil capacitance. The soil capacitance is related to the dielectric constant by the geometry of the electric field established around the electrodes. There are currently two commercially available instruments using this technique: the Troxler Sentry 200-AP probe and the Aquaterr probe.

The Troxler Sentry 200-AP probe uses an access tube similar to the neutron probe approach for measuring volumetric soil water content with depth. The Sentry probe is lowered into the access tube and the natural resonant frequency or frequency shift between the emitted and received frequency is measured by the probe. The access tube used with the Sentry 200-AP must be two-inch Schedule-40 PVC. This size and wall thickness of pipe ensures very close fit of the Sentry probe inside the access tube, minimizing any annular air gaps which greatly affect the travel of the signal into the soil. Installation of the access tube requires extreme care to ensure a very tight fit in the augered hole. Annular air gaps or soil cracks around the outside of the tube result in erroneous low readings.

The manufacturer's calibration of the probe is for sand and yields generally very high volumetric soil water percentages on other soils. Calibration of the probe for soils other than sands is therefore required for use in an irrigation scheduling program. Bulk density differences in soils (i.e. with depth) will also require separate calibrations. The volume of soil measured is not dependent on soil type or water content and approximates a cylinder four inches tall with a diameter of about 10 inches, assuming there are no air gaps. Properly calibrated and with careful access-tube installation, the probe's accuracy can be good. Many of the advantages of the neutron probe system are available with this system including rapid, repeatable measurements at the same locations and depths. The disadvantages of the neutron probe (radiation hazard and licensing requirements) are eliminated, while near surface measurements are possible. The cost of the Sentry 200-AP is about $4,000-$4,500.

The Aquaterr probe is also an electric capacitance probe and generally works on a similar principle as described above. This probe is a highly portable hand-push probe and allows rapid, easy, but qualitative readings of soil water content. Probe use is difficult in drier soil and soils with rocks, stones or hard pans. In these cases, a separate auger is needed to make a pilot hole for the probe.

The probe comes with either an analog, color-coded (for three different soil types:

sand, loam and clay) dial gauge or a digital readout. Both give readings on a scale from 0 and 100. High readings reflect higher soil water content and vice versa. Probe readings near 100 percent (blue range) represent saturated conditions. Readings near 85 to 90 (dark green range) are near field capacity. Readings in the 50 to 70 (light green) range indicate adequate soil water. Readings in the 30 to 50 (orange range) represent onset of water stress and readings below 30 (red range) represent conditions approaching wilting point.

The probe operates on a replaceable 9-volt battery and requires very little maintenance. The volume of soil sampled is quite small and approximates a cylinder four inches tall and an inch in diameter. The probe must be calibrated in water (dial the gauge or digital readout to a reading of 100) before use. This should be done before each field monitored, although the manufacturer suggests it is necessary only once per day. The probe should be dried after water calibration and wiped clean between each insertion into the soil. The Aquaterr probe costs between $400 and $500, depending on length and other features.

FIELD EVALUATION AND COMPARISON OF TECHNIQUES

Methods and materials

During the summer of 1992 a field study was conducted to evaluate the performance of commercially available soil water monitoring and measurement tools in side-by-side comparisons on different soil types and under different irrigation regimes. *(See Table 2.)* Comparisons include the initial capital cost of the equipment, installation requirements, labor requirements, ease of interpretation of measurements, accuracy, operation and maintenance requirements, relative performance on different soils and other special requirements or precautions. The following methods or devices were evaluated.

1) neutron probe
2) time-domain reflectometry (TDR)
3) soil sampling
4) RF capacitance probes
   - Troxler Sentry 200-AP

   - Aquaterr probe
5) tensiometers
6) electrical resistance blocks
   - gypsum blocks
   - Watermark blocks

Soil water measurement installations were established in four irrigated locations in southcentral Washington with four different soil types and irrigation methods. Site details are provided in Table 2.

At each location, instruments were installed so that samples or readings could be taken at depths of 12 and 24 inches. For all methods, three replications of readings or samples were taken at the 12-inch depth. Neutron probe, TDR and Sentry probe readings were replicated three times at the 24-inch depth. The tensiometers and electrical-resistance blocks were replicated only once at the 24-inch depth at each site. Aquaterr probe readings were taken only in the top 12 inches of soil because of difficulty pushing the probe into the ground. Readings or samples were collected on a weekly basis from early June to late September 1992. Soil samples were collected for gravimetric analyses three times during this period.

Irrigation and/or rainfall was measured at each monitoring site using portable rain gauges. Irrigations were scheduled by the grower/operator at each location, except at WSU-IAREC, where several wetting and drying cycles were implemented to evaluate instrument response.

Results

Weekly measurements at each site were averaged and grouped according to instrument output. The neutron probe, TDR, Troxler Sentry probe and gravimetric sampling all ultimately yield volumetric soil water content. Tensiometers and Watermark blocks give readings of soil water tension in centibars. Readings of the gypsum blocks and the Aquaterr probe are on a scale from 0 to 100.

In general, methods that can be directly compared with each other compared fairly well, although the instrument response (sensitivity to wetting and drying) was more obvious for some instruments. The neutron probe and TDR compared well at all sites and both compared well with the gravimetric samples. The Troxler Sentry probe was calibrated using the gravimetric samples taken at all sites. The manufacturer's calibration (developed on sand) resulted in considerably higher soil water content values at all sites except the sandy soil at Paterson (*See Table 2*). Using the calibration developed in this study, the Troxler probe still generally yielded higher soil water content values than the neutron probe and TDR. It also showed less sensitivity to wetting and drying than the neutron probe or TDR. Some of the differences between these four methods can be attributed to volume of soil sampled in each measurement.

The tensiometer and Watermark blocks compared fairly well across all four sites, although the tensiometer readings showed considerably more movement at the 12-inch depth. The tensiometers at the 12-inch depth broke suction several times on the heavy silt loam soil at Walla Walla. At Granger and Paterson, where soil water content was maintained at even levels for most of the season, these two methods compared well, although the Watermark block readings tended to lag behind the tensiometer readings following wetting of the soil by irrigation. Watermark blocks required considerably less maintenance of the field installation than tensiometers.

Gypsum blocks showed very little sensitivity at both soil depths at Granger and Paterson, where higher soil water contents were maintained throughout most of the season. Considerably more sensitivity to the fluctuating soil water at the 12-inch depth at WSU-IAREC and on the heavy silt-loam soil at Walla Walla was evident. Upon excavation to remove the gypsum blocks at the end of the field study, approximately half of them were found to have dissolved to the point of being non-usable. This effect was more apparent at Granger and Paterson where the soil water contents were higher.

All readings made with the Aquaterr probe were limited to the top foot of soil. The

TABLE 2. Description of soil water measurement study sites.

Location	Site Characteristics
Prosser, Wash: (WSU-IAREC)	All instruments installed within a 15' x 15' area
	Soil type: Warden very fine sandy loam, uniform with depth, >5 ft deep
	Crop: turfgrass
	Irrigation: surface flooding
Granger, Wash:	Instruments installed within dripline on southwest corner of 3 different trees in same tree row. Instrumented trees were in same relative position within sprinkler pattern and about 300 ft apart.
	Soil type: Warden silt loam, hardpan at 18-24 inch depth, > 5 ft deep
	Crop: apples with cover crop
	Irrigation: solid set undertree impact sprinkler
Paterson, Wash: (USDA-ARS)	Instruments installed in plant row in 25 foot section of same crop row
	Soil type: Quincy loamy sand, some pebbles and stones, > 5 ft deep
	Crop: grain corn
	Irrigation: linear move sprinkler
Walla Walla:	Instruments installed within dripline on southwest corner of 3 different vines in same vine row. Instrumented vines were in same relative position within sprinkler pattern and about 300 ft apart.
	Soil type: Catherine/Onyx silt loam-silty clay loam, > 5 ft deep
	Crop: wine grapes
	Irrigation: solid-set overcrop impact sprinkler

Aquaterr probe was difficult to evaluate because of difficulty in pushing the probe into the soil to the same depth, particularly once the surface six inches had dried. No effort was made to auger a pilot hole as recommended by the manufacturer. At Granger, where the surface layer was relatively moist all season, the Aquaterr was much easier to use. Readings obtained at the Granger site remained fairly even through the season, similar to the trends seen with the other methods. Only sporadic readings could be obtained at the other sites but, in general, the readings tracked the wetting and drying of the soil. A more thorough and fair evaluation would require greater time and labor to auger pilot holes and ensure probe readings are obtained at the same depth at each sampling. As the interpretation of readings and ranges could not be accurately verified (i.e., correlated against volumetric soil water percentages) in these field tests, the probe readings are qualitative.

Table 3 is a qualitative comparison of the methods evaluated, based on the conditions under which this study was conducted. Factors included in the table were rated on a scale from one to 10, with one being least favorable and 10 most favorable. The composite ratings are simple sums with equal weight placed on each factor.

Field site setup requirements include factors such as time, labor and equipment for site preparation. In this study, the TDR was used with permanently buried waveguides, requiring excavation of a pit, which resulted in a lower score. Portable TDR push probes are available which would result in a much higher score. A routine reading considers the time and effort to obtain a single reading.

Methods giving readings that are readily interpreted in terms of soil water-holding capacity and depth of water to refill the root zone received high scores for ease of interpretation of readings. Methods that give readings of soil water tension received medium scores. Accuracy includes comparison against a standard procedure such as gravimetric sampling (once an acceptable calibration is developed), repeatability, and adaptability across a wide range of soil types.

Maintenance includes activities necessary for routine operation (battery charging or replacement, frequency of calibration, field installation maintenance, etc.). Special considerations refer to licensing and storage requirements, specialized training needs, instrument longevity, amount of ancillary equipment required (soil augers, ovens, scales), permanence of field installations, etc.

Soil sampling and gravimetric analyses received the highest rating. It was assumed that a balance for weighing samples and an oven for drying were available. If this were not the case, initial cost rating and the composite rating would be lower. The neutron probe and TDR were equally rated overall. The high cost

TABLE 3. Qualitative evaluation of soil water monitoring devices. A score of 1 is least favorable while a score of 10 is most favorable.

Device	NP	TDR	GS	AP	AQ	TM	GB	WB
Initial cost	3	1	8	2	7	8	8	8
Field site setup requirements	7	3	10	3	10	7	6	6
Obtaining a routine reading	8	8	1	8	4	10	8	8
Interpretation of readings	10	10	10	10	3	5	3	5
Accuracy	10	10	10	8	2	7	2	3
Maintenance	9	9	8	9	7	3	9	9
Special considerations	2	8	5	8	9	7	5	8
Composite reading	49	49	52	48	42	47	41	47

NP = Neutron Probe
AP = Troxler Sentry 200-AP
GB = Gypsum Block

TDR = Time Domain Reflectometry
AQ = Aquaterr Probe
WB = Watermark Block

GS = Gravimetric Sampling
TM = Tensiometer

of TDR offsets the regulatory requirements involved in owning and operating a neutron probe. The Sentry probe was ranked next. Accuracy improvements may be possible with this method as more calibration information is developed. Of the four methods most likely to be used by an individual grower, tensiometers and Watermark blocks offer the best overall capabilities.

SUMMARY AND CONCLUSIONS

Understanding soil water holding capacity and the factors affecting the plant available soil water is important for good irrigation management. Information is readily available from Cooperative Extension and the Soil Conservation Service to help growers assess the conditions specific to their own fields and crops.

Several different techniques are available that can be used to effectively monitor or directly measure soil water content. Some are extremely simple and are well worth the investment of time and labor. Many irrigation-scheduling consultants are using these different methods.

The cost of keeping track of soil water independently or by using a service can be paid back through the benefits of effective water management. Included among these benefits are energy savings, water savings, water-quality improvement and improved crop quality and yields.

Successful implementation of any of the methods evaluated requires careful attention to the installation, operation and maintenance

requirements discussed. Soil type and irrigation regime are important parameters affecting the choice of a method or technique that will yield the best results.

A routine sampling schedule should be implemented to obtain the most information from any of these methods. The difference in soil water content at a given location from one sampling time to the next often provides more information than random space and time measurements. Soil water should be measured or monitored in at least two depths in the expected crop root zone at several locations in a field to obtain a field average. Areas within fields having different soil textures or other characteristics should also be monitored.

Acknowledgements

The field evaluation of the various soil water monitoring and measurement tools was supported by a grant from the Washington State University Cooperative Extension Water Quality Competitive Grants Program. The donation of an Aquaterr Moisture Meter by Aquaterr Instruments and a Sentry 200-AP Moisture Monitor System by Troxler Electronic Laboratories for use in this study is gratefully acknowledged. The cooperation of Clayton Gould and Paul Stonemetz, Granger, Washington; the USDA-ARS, Prosser, Washington; and Scott Bylery, Walla Walla, Washington, in allowing the installation of equipment and weekly measurements in their fields is much appreciated. Tanya Underwood provided considerable assistance in obtaining the weekly field measurements.

Scheduling sprinkler irrigation of fruit orchards

Timothy J. Smith

Washington State University Cooperative Extension
Wenatchee, Washington

Rainfall is usually insignificant and unreliable during the growing season in most of the Pacific Northwest. This dry, relatively cool weather provides very good tree fruit growing conditions, with low disease pressure compared to summer rainfall regions. However, the warm, low-humidity conditions during the summer can cause a high amount of water to pass through the trees, and if the supply of water in the orchard soil is not maintained properly, tree growth and fruit quality can be seriously affected.

The soil in the tree's root zone will swing slowly from wet to dry in the cool months. The surface soil will dry rapidly, the grass and weeds may appear water stressed, but the second and third foot of soil often remains adequately moist for several more days. In the spring, weeds and grasses root in the top six to 12 inches of soil and should not be used as a visual sign of dry soil. The tree's roots are cool and moist in the spring, and the leaves are under very low water demand from the air around them. Stress is unlikely, even when the soil is allowed to dry out more than during the summer. Most growers irrigate too frequently during these cool months of April, May, early June, late September and October.

During hot weather in late June, July,

August, and early September, daily water use may be four times greater than in the early season, and trees experience daily water stress, even when well watered. As the soil becomes increasingly dry between irrigations, the degree of daily water stress increases. While growers cannot prevent water stress in the orchard, they must irrigate in a pattern that replaces the soil water before the stress adversely affects the crop. Fruit that has suffered excessive stress during the hot months never recovers to its potential size and shape.

Since the weather and trees change each month of the growing season, growers cannot have a predetermined, constant irrigation schedule. They must either vary the number of hours they irrigate each set, or must vary the number of days between sets. There are many ways to irrigate to replace accurately the water used by trees. This chapter will outline only three of these methods.

There is no truly simple way to schedule irrigation, so it may be tempting to just "wing it," and irrigate by experience and the appearance of the trees and soil. Some growers with large, deep-rooted trees growing on good quality soils are successful using intuition. Most growers, however, have young trees, variable soil quality, and a mixture of irrigation systems. In this case, the effort to schedule may pay off with better fruit and increased economic returns, as well as water and power savings.

Sometimes the simple things, such as irrigation, are the limiting factors in an orchard. If water supply is limiting the performance of an orchard, fruit size, shape, and keeping quality will be reduced. In many instances, simply improving irrigation scheduling has solved long-term fruit size and shape problems.

Proper scheduling must be done in relation to the orchard soil, the trees, the irrigation system and the weather. There is some unavoidable effort involved in setting up basic assumptions about orchard conditions.

After a grower has chosen a scheduling method, estimated the orchard's conditions, and set up an irrigation schedule, the process is not complete. Soils must be monitored and estimations adjusted during the first growing season. After adjustments are made, proper scheduling requires a few minutes a day to calculate seasonal adjustments relative to weather.

Below are the basic steps necessary to schedule irrigation in your orchard:

STEP 1. Estimate usable water storage capacity of the soil

Soil texture, depth, compaction, layering and percentage of stones can vary considerably within an orchard irrigation unit. Soil texture and depth can be used as a rough guideline of moisture-holding capacity, but this estimated value must be reduced for areas with a significant percentage of rocks or compaction of the tree's root zone. Soils that have layers of fine-textured soil over coarser-textured soils tend to hold slightly more water than their texture would indicate. Observation of the moisture condition of soil just prior to irrigation can help guide the adjustment of the estimation of the soil's "usable" water-holding capacity during the growing season.

Tables 1 and 2 provide approximate water-holding capacity of various textured soils. The amount listed is the usable water, or the amount of water that may be removed by the tree prior to excessive stress. On older trees with vigorous rootstocks planted on high quality soils, it is safe to use 50 percent of the water in the top three feet of soil, especially in the cooler months. However, on sandier soils, it would be better to use 40 percent between irrigations.

Older, larger trees have the bulk of their active roots in the top three feet of soil (if the orchard has that much). Younger or dwarfing rootstocks root mostly in the surface two feet. The lowest usable water value should be chosen that matches the soil depth and texture of large zones in the orchard.

If the soil is rocky, reduce the estimate of usable water, by whatever percentage of volume the rocks take. If the soil volume is about 30 percent rocks, use the texture and depth value on the table, then multiply the usable water by 0.70.

STEP 2. Determine net application rate for system

Measure the gallon per minute (GPM) output from several sprinkler heads in the block. The simplest and most accurate way to measure output is to catch the water in a five gallon white plastic bucket for a minute. The bucket should be calibrated with one quart increments. A piece of garden hose about eight feet long, and a tall, sturdy ladder may be useful. If there is more than five percent variation in gallons per minute per sprinkler head, the system may need repair. One should check for mismatched nozzle sizes or excessive wear. (Note: A five percent variation means more than a pint difference out of 2 1/2 gallons per minute.)

The number of feet between sprinkler heads along the lateral pipe should be measured, then the distance between laterals, measuring on the square, not the diamond. This determines the average square feet irrigated by each sprinkler in the block.

The average gallons per minute, times 96.3, divided by the square feet per head, equals the gross acre inches of water applied per hour. (See Example equation 1.)

All the water that comes out of a sprinkler is not available to the trees. Some evaporates, some may run off, but the most important inefficiency is uneven application. Trees can't be counted on to use water that was unevenly applied, as some of the orchard surface will have an over-application, and much of that water will move to below the tree's root zone. Widely spaced, over-tree systems running on hot summer days may have efficiencies as low as 50 percent. Well designed, closely spaced microsprinklers operating at proper pressures may have efficiencies as high as 85 percent. Most orchard systems probably fall between those extremes. Most well-designed, under-tree solid-set sprinkler systems in orchards have about 70 percent efficiency.

Multiply the system's gross hourly application rate by the decimal equivalent of the estimated system efficiency. This gives a value for the system's hourly net-acre inches applied. *(See Example equation 2.)*

The net inches per hour must then be multiplied by the number of hours the irrigation set is run. This will give the net application of water per set. *(See Example equation 3.)*

STEP 3. Match usable water storage to net application per set

The net application per set should not be more than slightly over the usable water"value you determined in Step 1. If net application is more than five percent over the amount of water the trees should be using between sets, the hours irrigated per set, or the application

rate must be reduced. An irrigation supplier or advisor should be consulted on proper nozzle sizes or other system design changes.

If the net application per set is less than the usable water value, water will be applied water before the orchard soil reaches the lower limit of safe field capacity. There is nothing dangerous about this approach, unless the usable water storage of the soil is more than double the net application per set. If the net per set is less than the usable water storage, this net application rate should be used rather than the soils' usable water value to determine the amount of water that the trees may use between sets. If the soil becomes too dry between irrigations, it will not be fully recharged by the set length used.

STEP 4. Compare system capacity against peak water use

Some irrigation systems cannot apply water fast enough to keep up with the trees' water use during July. Using information determined in steps 1 and 2, the grower can determine if the system has the capacity to keep up with peak water demand.

Which is the lowest amount, the soil's usable water or the net application? This is the amount of water available to the trees between sets. The smallest of the two numbers must

Example equation 1:
$$\frac{2.96 \text{ gpm} \times 96.3}{40 \text{ feet} \times 40 \text{ feet}} = 0.178 \text{ acre inches per hour (gross)}$$

Example equation 2:
$$0.178 \text{ acre inches gross} \times 0.7 \text{ efficiency} = 0.125 \text{ inches per hour net}$$

Example equation 3:
$$0.125 \text{ inches per hour} \times 12 \text{ hour set} = 1.5 \text{ net acre-inches per set}$$

Example equation 4:
$$0.165 \text{ inches net per hour} \times 12 \text{ hour sets} = 1.98 \text{ inches per set}$$
(Three feet of fine sand; usable water storage is 1.80 acre-inches; can irrigate no more frequently than every seven days.)

$$\frac{1.80 \text{ (usable water-the lesser value)}}{7 \text{ (days between sets)}} = 0.257 \text{ net inches per day}$$
(This system is unable to keep up with peak use.)

be divided by the minimum number of days that it takes to irrigate the block if the entire orchard was watered 24 hours per day, seven days a week. The resulting number is the maximum acre-inches per day one could apply if one irrigated as much as possible. Peak use periods in eastern Washington often average more than 0.35 inches of daily water use. Cooler, higher-elevation orchard areas average about 0.30 inches per day in July, with a few days that may approach 0.35 inches use. *(See Example equation 4.)*

If the irrigation system cannot apply an average daily net water equal to these peak-use periods, the system is under-designed. Being able to apply water at a rate equal to peak water demand does not allow for inevitable break-downs during hot weather, and the need to catch up if one gets behind in irrigation. If the system is underdesigned, redesign it to avoid fruit damage during hot weather. Increasing application efficiency often improves the situation, providing more usable water and the ability to reduce set intervals.

STEP 5. Determine the appropriate times to irrigate

Three methods of determining the interval between sets or the length of sets are described below. One of them may be more practical than the others for a particular situation. The variable between growers involves water delivery. Some growers have any rate of water available whenever they want it. Most have some restrictions on the amount per day and time of delivery.

Growers must have some variation built into their irrigation program, as there is a great variation in the rate that orchards use water during the season. Orchard water use averages about five inches in May, and between nine and 11 inches in July. It is relatively easy to keep adequate water in the trees' root zone when use is low. It takes careful scheduling in April, May, September and October to avoid the common problem of over-irrigation. Scheduling to avoid over-stressing trees and fruit during mid-June through August is even more complicated and important.

SCHEDULING METHOD 1: Estimated days between sets

After determining the usable water value, it is possible to estimate the approximate time it will take for trees to use that amount of water, based on historic water use during any given time of the season. This is the simplist scheduling procedure that puts water back into the soil at approximately the rate that it is being used. The approximate use rate can be determined, then the estimation relative to actual weather may be adjusted. The interval should lengthen about 10 percent during cooler than normal weather, and shortened by 10 percent during a hot, dry period.

The approximate number of days between sets was determined using average evaporation over a 30 year period in Wenatchee, Washington. This use rate assumes reasonable weed control under the trees.

Table 3 outlines the approximate number of days between sets, by month, relative to the amount of usable water in the trees' root zone. *(Table 3.)*

In this example, the usable water is 2.0 inches. The first set was be in very early May (unless irrigation was used for frost control.) The orchard was then irrigated about every 13 days in May, every eight days in June, every sixth day in July, every eighth day in August, every two weeks in September, and one more time in October, (if water was still available.) During a hot, dry period in July, the irrigation interval was reduced to 5.5 days. During a cool, wet period during June, the days between sets were increased to 9 days.

SCHEDULING METHOD 2: Actual tree use replacement-variable interval

A safe usable water value for the orchard block should be selected. *(See Steps 1, 2, and 3 in this chapter.)*

At each irrigation the year's pan evaporation total, or the year's calculated orchard water use value available through the WSU Public Agriculture Weather Service (P.A.W.S.) or Agrimet should be recorded.

If the P.A.W.S. or Agrimet calculated orchard water use, then the usable water value for the orchard unit must be added to the year's total. When the year's total orchard water use equals that value, watering should begin again. *(See Example equation 5.)*

If a pan evaporation total is used to schedule irrigation, the pan values must be adjusted to actual tree use. This adds one more simple step to the procedure described in example equation 5. The usable water value must be divided by 0.38 in April, .68 in May, 0.92 in June, 1.0 in July and August, 0.96 in September, and 0.75 in October. *(An example is outlined in example equation 6.)*

SCHEDULING METHOD 3:
Actual tree use replacement, regular interval

There may be circumstances that force irrigation with a fixed number of days between sets. If a limited amount of water is available each day, it may not be possible to catch up if the soil is allowed to dry to 50 percent of field capacity between irrigations. If application is on a fixed interval, the set length must be reduced during the early- and late-growing season to avoid over irrigation.

If this is the case, the number of hours to run each set to replace only the water that the trees have used since the last irrigation must be determined .

It is important to go over Step 4 of this chapter to check that the system is designed to irrigate properly during peak use periods, especially during July. If one can keep up with the water demand during the hot weather, irrigating the same way is unacceptable during the spring and fall.

It is often difficult to irrigate odd set hours. Most growers prefer to apply water for about 12 or 24 hours, because the time of day that water is changed is more convenient. If water demand is low, it may be possible to run water only during the day, which would allow for shorter than usual sets, with no water changing at odd times during the evening or night. When water must run both day and night to keep up, the short set will cause inconvenience. This is the fault of the system design.

Many growers compensate for poor system design by over irrigating at certain times of the season. With reduced water supplies certain to come to the region, a redesign of the system should be considered. Meanwhile, the set length should be adjusted as well as possible with the following procedure:

First, the actual tree use between irrigations should be determined.

The grower should record either the pan evaporation total reported for the area, or the calculated orchard use reported on the P.A.W.S. system or on Agrimet.

The difference between the yearly total for the day last irrigated and the day irrigating to be started should be determined. *(See Example equation 7.)*

If calculated orchard use values are used, this number indicates how much water the trees have used between sets.

If pan evaporation is used, the grower must multiply the difference by a monthly

---

Example equation 5:

Orchard was irrigated today:
Today's orchard water use to date: 18.66 acre-inches
Usable water value for the orchard: +2.2 acre-inches
TOTAL: 20.86

(Next irrigation begins when orchard water use to date is 20.86)

Example equation 6:

Orchard was irrigated today:
Today's pan evaporation total: 16.24 acre-inches
Usable water of 2.2 inches divided
by June factor of 0.92 equals: +2.39 acre-inches
TOTAL: 18.63

(Next irrigation should be when pan evaporation totals 18.63.)

adjustment number to calculate the tree water use. For April use 0.38; May, 0.68; June, 0.92; July and August, 1.0; September, 0.96; and October, 0.75. *(See Example equation 8.)*

Next, the hours needed to run the sets should be determined. Water used should be divided by the net inches per hour the irrigation system applies. (See Step 2 for net application rate and apply it to *Example equation 9.*)

In the example, each should be run about seven hours until the irrigation cycle has been completed. Recalculate set length each time irrigating starts.

Observe the soil

All of the scheduling systems described above approximate tree water use. Some estimations of soil water-holding capacity and tree root depth was also made when the usable water value was estimated. The net water application rate of the system has been estimated, but it is unlikely that all of the factors that determine the orchard irrigation schedule have been accurately estimated. The soil must be observed prior to irrigation.

It is likely that the soil will be wetter than expected on the day that the estimations indicate that irrigation is due. If this is the case, the calculated set interval must be increased by five to 10 percent. For instance, if the calculated interval is 6.5 days, the figure should be rounded to seven days. The soil prior to irrigation should be observed each time until one is confident that the estimations are correct.

Once the grower has made all adjustments, the scheduling assumptions will be set, and determining an accurate irrigation schedule will be relatively simple. The hard work and adjustments made while working out the orchard scheduling method will pay off in long-term labor, power, and water savings. More importantly, water stress will not cause reduced tree growth and poor fruit quality.

Example equation 7:

Total year evaporation today :	26.82 inches
Total for year on last irrigation start:	25.15 inches
DIFFERENCE:	1.67 inches

(If calculated orchard-use values are used, this number indicates how much water the trees have used between sets.)

Example equation 8:

Using the 1.67 inches from equation 7, and the adjustment number for June:

1.67 inches X 0.92 = 1.54 inches actual tree water use.

Example equation 9:

$$\frac{1.54 \text{ inches used since last irrigation}}{0.22 \text{ net inches applied per hour}} = 7.0 \text{ hours}$$

Using PAWS and AgriMet for irrigation scheduling

Thomas W. Ley, P.E.
Extension Irrigation Engineer
Irrigated Agriculture Research and Extension Center, Washington State University, Prosser

A number of tools are available to assist growers with irrigation management decisions. These include the various approaches to monitoring plant and soil water status discussed in earlier chapters, as well as the soil water balance approach to irrigation scheduling discussed in the previous chapter.

The routine use of the soil-water balance based on soil water-holding properties, engineering data about the irrigation system, and model estimates of crop water use is termed scientific irrigation scheduling. Scientific irrigation scheduling is an important tool growers can use to improve irrigation water management. It is practically the only approach which provides answers to the questions of when to irrigate, how much water to apply, and how to apply water, in order to satisfy crop water requirements and avoid plant water stress. A true scientific irrigation scheduling program also provides forecasts of future irrigation dates and amounts so that other farm operations can be planned around irrigation events.

When carefully used, irrigation scheduling has been documented around the world to save water, energy, labor and fertilizer, and in many cases improve crop yields and crop quality. In a situation when water supplies are very tight and deliveries are made at much reduced rates from normal, irrigation scheduling can help to stretch the available water to be of the greatest benefit to the crops being irrigated.

There are many approaches available for trying to answer the questions of when to irrigate and how much water to apply. Some are based on plant observations and measurements and some are based on soil measurements or monitoring. Plant measurements such as plant temperatures, leaf water potentials and so forth provide good information about the plant's water status and thus can give good answers to when irrigation is needed. However, how much water to apply is not readily apparent. On the other hand, soil water measurement can be used to provide good information on when soil water levels are depleted and how much water is needed to irrigate the soil up to field capacity. There are many arguments concerning how well this correlates with plant water status, however.

In order to adequately answer when, how much and how to apply water, an approach which takes into account the plant, the soil and the irrigation system is necessary. Scientific and engineering data about crops, soils and irrigation systems are available and can be systematically integrated for scheduling irrigations. One of the more difficult pieces of information to obtain is a reliable and accurate estimate of crop water use. One objective of this chapter is to discuss approaches which have been used over the years to estimate crop water use. Important tools such as pan evaporation and weather-based methods for calculating evapotranspiration will be discussed. Automated weather station networks have been developed in the Pacific Northwest for the express purpose of providing crop water use data for irrigation scheduling. The Washington State University Public Agriculture Weather System (PAWS) and the U.S. Bureau of Reclamation AgriMet network will be discussed in this context.

A second objective is to present an overview of irrigation scheduling computer software developed by WSU to make the whole job of irrigation management easier. This software is entitled the Washington Irrigation Forecaster (WIF).

Evapotranspiration (ET): What is it, how to use it

A large number of factors affect crop water use, or evapotranspiration, including crop type, crop density, amount of vegetative cover or leaf area, crop health, available soil water, stage of growth, and climatic and environmental factors. Crop water use for all crops typically begins at very low rates in the spring because there is little or no demand, i.e., perennials have not leafed out yet, annuals are very young or just planted, climatic conditions are cool with little atmospheric demand for water. As the crops develop and climatic conditions progress toward those of summer, the demand for water increases, rapidly reaching a peak as the summer weather conditions peak. Water use typically falls off as the weather cools down in late summer, or as the crop reaches maturity and is harvested.

ET defined

Evapotranspiration, or ET, is traditionally defined as the combined loss of water from the soil surface by evaporation and from plant tissue by transpiration. Evapotranspiration and consumptive use of water are often used interchangeably. However, consumptive use of water by plants includes transpiration, plus water which is used in other plant processes such as tissue-building and growth. The difference is usually less than one to two percent.

The process of evaporation involves a change of state of water from a liquid to a gas or vapor. The rate of evaporation depends chiefly on the total supply of energy available from radiation (direct solar and radiation which is reflected and/or re-radiated), and advective or horizontal air flow (wind), which carries the water vapor away.

Transpiration is the process of water flow to plant tissue surfaces, primarily those within plant stomata, where it is subsequently converted to a vapor and lost through evaporation. Plant factors such as leaf structure (size, shape, orientation) and degree of stomatal opening control the rate of transpiration. This gives plants a mechanism for reducing water loss to rates less than evaporation rates from free water surfaces.

How is ET used

Evapotranspiration is of considerable interest (or should be) to anyone involved with irrigation. Some applications are:

1) Peak ET rates during the growing season are used in the design of irrigation systems, i.e., required pump capacity, mainline sizing, etc,. to ensure that enough water can be applied to meet crop needs.

2) Daily and/or weekly estimates of ET rates during the growing season are used to determine irrigation schedules (when to irrigate and how much to apply).

3) Long-term average ET and rainfall amounts totalled over a growing season are used to determine net crop irrigation requirements. Total irrigation requirements are determined by adding in the leaching requirement for maintaining a favorable salt balance, and the losses of water caused by inefficiencies and nonuniformities of the irrigation application system.

4) Aggregate totals of the total irrigation requirement for individual fields or farms over a basin or region are used in irrigation delivery system operation and management, and water supply allocations.

Having reliable ET information and using it properly in each of the above situations contributes considerably to the success of individual farming operations, irrigation delivery operations and the long-term sustainability of irrigated agriculture. Irrigated crops are provided with the correct amount of water at the right time, improving yields. Water, energy and labor are often saved, and water quality maintained as a result.

Approaches to measuring ET

Evapotranspiration is determined through direct measurement or is calculated using climate and environment data. Direct measurement of actual crop ET is based upon measuring all water entering, leaving and being stored in some defined system. This is called a water balance. The most accurate technique for doing this is with a device called a lysimeter.

Lysimeters are buried, soil-filled tanks with the crop of interest being grown in and around the tank. Instrumentation is carefully set up in and around the lysimeter to measure all water inputs (irrigation and rainfall), drainage or outflow, and changes in soil water storage. The water balance results in a measurement of ET. Because of their expense and the careful instrumentation and monitoring required, lysimeters are most often used only in research settings.

Field soil water balances can be carried out to measure ET, but are less accurate than lysimeters because of the difficulty of measuring some factors, such as deep percolation or subsoil water movement into and out of the study area. These factors are eliminated or are more easily measured in a lysimeter. Soil variation and nonuniform irrigations also cause problems with this approach.

Weather-based ET estimates

Several meteorological and climatological methods have been developed for indirect estimation of ET. These range from empirical models based on a single meteorological parameter such as temperature, to more physically-based, theoretical methods requiring considerably more weather data. All of the climatological methods for calculating ET for a given crop involve first determining potential ET or reference crop ET. The actual ET of a given crop is then related to the potential or reference ET using a crop coefficient. Potential ET represents the maximum rate of water use under conditions when water is not a limiting factor, the crop is healthy and actively growing, and usually at full canopy cover development. In this context, estimates of crop water use are going to be conservative in nature, i.e., they represent an upper estimate of what the crop *potentially* could use if all conditions were ideal. For all practical purposes, with very careful water management, high quality crops and yields can be produced with less water.

Reference crop ET is the potential ET for a specific crop under certain growth and environmental conditions. Two reference crops which have received the most study are alfalfa and grass:

Alfalfa ETr is the daily reference crop evapotranspiration of a well-watered (i.e., soil water does not limit ET), actively growing, erect standing alfalfa crop with at least eight inches of top growth and occupying an extensive area.

Grass ETo is the daily reference crop evapotranspiration from an extensive surface of three to six inches tall, green grass cover of uniform height, which is actively growing, completely shading the ground and not short of water.

Empirical models for estimating evapotranspiration which have been used extensively in Washington State include the Blaney-Criddle temperature-based model; the Jensen-Haise model, which is based on solar radiation and temperature; and pan evaporation. These models tend to be less accurate over shorter time intervals than the physically-based methods. There is often a recommended minimum time interval with which these models should be used.

The **Blaney-Criddle model** is one of the more popular methods worldwide because of the minimal data requirements: mean monthly temperatures. Only monthly estimates of potential ET should be derived with this method. A modification called the FAO (Food and Agriculture Organization) Blaney-Criddle model considerably improved the accuracy of the estimates by allowing for some simple local calibration, usually with weather data and/or observations which are not difficult to obtain. This model yields monthly grass reference ET_o.

The FAO Blaney-Criddle model served as the basis for the development of WSU Extension Bulletin EB 1513: *Irrigation Requirements for Washington—Estimates and Methodology*. This model was chosen after rigorous evaluation of 17 different models showed this one to have the best combination of precision and accuracy for predicting seasonal irrigation requirements for conditions at Prosser, Washington. It also was used to develop Appendix B of the *State of Washington Irrigation Guide*. This appendix gives monthly and season total net irrigation water requirements for up to 40 different crops at 90 locations around the state. Net irrigation water requirement of a crop is the amount of water needed, over and above effective precipitation, which must be provided either by stored soil water, irrigation, lateral and/or upward movement of shallow groundwater, or a combination of all of these to meet potential crop water demand.

The **Jensen-Haise model** is based on the energy balance of incoming solar radiation and an empirical relationship of actual ET measurements with local temperature and elevation. An alfalfa reference ET_r is estimated with the model. The minimum recommended time interval for use is five days. This method is used in the Washington Irrigation Forecaster (WIF) computer model to be discussed later.

Pan evaporation is a method for measuring potential ET which has been and continues to be used extensively in Washington State. A number of different types of pans have been researched and utilized, but the most common (and the one used in Washington) is the U.S. Weather Bureau Class A pan. This is a four-foot diameter pan, 12 inches deep. Daily measurements of the amount of water evaporating from the pan, corrected for rainfall, provide an estimate of potential ET.

It is recommended that pan evaporation readings not be used on time intervals of less than a week to 10 days. In other words, a week or 10 day's worth of readings should be added up and the average for that interval found. This daily average then becomes an indicator of crop water use. Individual daily pan evaporation readings may be as high as 0.50 to 0.60 inches of water on hot, sunny, windy, dry days. In this case, the pan reading is not a reliable indicator for crop use. Many plants have a mechanism for "shutting off" or reducing water loss under these conditions.

When the evaporation pan is set up and maintained under a set of standard conditions, such as at the WSU Research Units at Prosser and Othello (surrounded by green, well-watered, clipped grass in a large irrigated environment and without influence of buildings, trees or large paved areas nearby), then grass reference crop ETo is estimated as:

Equation 1:
$$\text{grass } ET_o = 0.8 \times E_{pan}$$

WSU Extension Bulletin EB 1304 provides details on how to use pan evaporation readings to schedule irrigations. Evaporation pan crop factors for several crops for conditions when the crops are in full cover are included.

Daily and even hourly estimates of potential ET can be derived from meteorological models which are based on the physics of the evaporation process. Approaches include aerodynamic transport models, energy balance methods, or a combination of the two.

The most popular combination method is called **the Penman method**. Considerable research has been accomplished with this model. Both alfalfa reference ET_r and grass reference ET_o estimates can be obtained. To utilize the Penman model, measurements of temperature, relative humidity, solar radiation and wind speed are required.

These measurements must usually be taken on an hourly basis to obtain daily maximums, minimums, and/or totals for these parameters. Weather measurements for use with the Penman model are most often being obtained throughout the U.S. with remote automated weather stations equipped with the proper sensors. Weather stations must be carefully sited to represent the irrigated area in which they are located, particularly with respect to irrigated, green fetch in the immediate vicinity of the weather station and for several hundred feet in the prevailing wind direction.

One of the purposes of the Washington Public Agriculture Weather System is to provide the data necessary for calculation of Penman-based daily reference crop ET values. Both alfalfa and grass reference ET estimates are calculated each day for each of the PAWS stations. These daily data and daily crop coefficient data are used to construct crop water use charts which give the crop ET for the last several days and estimates for the coming several days.

Crop coefficients

Crop coefficients (K_c) relate the actual rate of crop water use, ET_c to potential ET (ET_r or ET_o above).

Equation 2:
$$ET_c = K_c \times \text{potential ET}$$

Values of K_c are determined experimentally and reflect the physiology of the crop, the degree of crop cover, the location where data were collected and the reference crop used to determine potential ET. Thus, different crop coefficients exist for the same crop, but are applicable for use either with alfalfa ET_r or grass ET_o. They generally are not directly interchangeable. The appropriate crop coefficients must be applied to estimate actual crop ET. Research has shown, however, that in general alfalfa reference ET_r is approximately 120 percent of grass reference ET_o. This would indicate that crop coefficients for use with alfalfa reference ET_r may be estimated as 0.83 times grass reference ET_o crop coefficients.

Monthly average evaporation pan crop coefficients were published in Appendix B of the *State of Washington Irrigation Guide*. These factors are actually grass-reference crop coefficients multiplied by the pan factor, 0.80, so that they can be used directly with evaporation pan readings. The evaporation pan crop coefficients given in the *Washington Irrigation Guide*, divided by 0.80, yield monthly crop coefficients which can be used with grass reference crop ET_o. Further information on these crop coefficients and how they were developed is given in WSU EB 1513 *Irrigation Requirements for Washington—Estimates and Methodology*.

Monthly average crop coefficients for use with alfalfa ET_r, grass ET_o, and Epan for tree fruit crops with and without a cover crop are listed in Table 1. These values are based on grass reference ET_o crop coefficient data taken from EB 1513. An evaporation pan factor of 0.80 is assumed in deriving the evaporation pan crop coefficients. Crop coefficients for alfalfa reference ET_r are taken as 0.83 times the value of the grass reference ETo crop coefficients. Note that some differences exist between the pome and stone fruits, as well as between the cover crop and no cover crop situations.

The crop coefficients listed in Table 1 are for mature orchards having canopy size which shades at least 65 to 70 percent of the orchard floor. Crop water use by young orchards can be estimated by accounting for canopy size as a percentage of the orchard floor area (percent ground shading) and the amount of cover crop surface, also as a percent of the total orchard floor area. Studies of drip-irrigated deciduous orchard in California have estimated the percentage of mature orchard water use by young trees is dependent upon the percent ground shading of the young orchard (Snyder et al., 1989). The relationship given is:

Equation 3:
$$\%M = 3.05 + 2.558 \times (\%GS) - 0.016 \times (\%GS)^2$$

where %M is the percent of mature orchard water use by the young orchard which has a percent ground shading (%GS). This relationship gives the percentage of mature orchard water use, %M, equal to 100 percent at percent ground shading, %GS, of 60 to 65 percent, which coincides with the statement in the previous paragraph.

A procedure for estimating crop coefficients for young orchards with a cover crop is as follows:

1. estimate the cover crop area (%CC) as percent of total orchard floor area,
2. estimate percent of ground area shaded by tree canopy (%GS),
3. find mature orchard ET percentage (%M) using %GS in the relationship given above,
4. multiply %CC (expressed as a decimal) from Step 1 by the crop coefficient for grass, which is 1.0, to obtain a base coefficient for the cover crop, K_c base,
5. compute the crop coefficient for young orchard with a cover crop as follows:

Equation 4:
$$K_c = K_{c \text{ base}} + \%M \times (\text{mature } K_c - K_c \text{ base})$$

This process applies to the period May to October. For November to April use mature orchard with cover K_c values. For a young orchard without cover, the procedure is similar, except there is no need to use a base coefficient. The crop coefficient for young orchard without a cover crop is computed as:

Equation 5:
$$K_c = \%M \times \text{mature } K_c$$

TABLE 1. Monthly average crop coefficients for orchard crops with and without a cover crop.

Month	Pome fruits with cover			Stone fruits with cover		
	K_c-ET_o	K_c-ET_r	K_c-PAN	K_c-ET_o	K_c-ET_r	K_c-PAN
January-March	0.45	0.38	0.36	0.45	0.38	0.36
April	0.45	0.38	0.36	0.45	0.38	0.36
May	0.85	0.71	0.68	0.80	0.67	0.64
June	1.15	0.96	0.92	1.05	0.88	0.84
July	1.25	1.04	1.00	1.15	0.96	0.92
August	1.25	1.04	1.00	1.15	0.96	0.92
September	1.20	1.00	0.96	1.00	0.83	0.80
October	0.95	0.79	0.76	0.85	0.71	0.68
November-December	0.45	0.38	0.36	0.45	0.38	0.36

Month	Pome fruits without cover			Stone fruits without cover		
	K_c-ET_o	K_c-ET_r	K_c-PAN	K_c-ET_o	K_c-ET_r	K_c-PAN
January-March	0.40	0.33	0.32	0.40	0.33	0.32
April	0.40	0.33	0.32	0.40	0.33	0.32
May	0.60	0.50	0.48	0.55	0.46	0.44
June	0.85	0.71	0.68	0.75	0.63	0.60
July	1.00	0.83	0.80	0.90	0.75	0.72
August	1.00	0.83	0.80	0.90	0.75	0.72
September	0.95	0.79	0.76	0.70	0.58	0.56
October	0.70	0.58	0.56	0.65	0.54	0.52
November-December	0.40	0.33	0.32	0.40	0.33	0.32

Crop coefficients for young orchards without a cover crop should be constrained to a minimum value of 0.40. This process applies to the period May to October. For November to April use mature orchard without cover K_c values.

Table 2 gives an example of grass reference ET_0 crop coefficients for young orchards at various stages of canopy development (percent ground shading, %GS, from 10 to 60%). The young orchard is on a 7 feet by 14 feet planting with a four-foot weed-free strip. This gives a percent cover crop area, %CC =(10/14) x 100 = 71.43%. Thus, since K_c for grass cover is 1.00, then $K_{c\ base}$ equals 0.71.

PAWS and AgriMet systems

During 1988, Washington State University in cooperation with the National Weather Service (NWS), the Washington State Energy Office, the U.S. Bureau of Reclamation (USBR), and several private organizations, installed a remote, automated, real-time weather data acquisition and reporting network to serve Washington agriculture. This network has become known as the Washington Public Agriculture Weather System (PAWS).

Washington State University's intent in developing the PAWS system is to provide growers with a tool, and the educational support for the effective use of that tool, to help improve efficiency in crop production. The real-time weather data collected and reported by the PAWS network are being used in a variety of crop production and management practices, including scientific irrigation scheduling, frost warning and protection, and integrated pest management.

Funding of the initial capital expenditures and the first three years of operation and maintenance of PAWS was provided through a 1987 grant from the Washington State Energy Office (from oil overcharge monies) and from WSU Cooperative Extension. Funds were budgeted to provide for acquisition and installation of 14 remote weather stations, a radio frequency (RF) data telemetry system, and two RF computer base stations located primarily in the Yakima Valley and Columbia Basin. Estimated annual operating and maintenance expenses were set aside, as well as funds to support education and demonstration programs. Since its inception, PAWS has attracted private support for 26 additional remote weather stations in the southcentral part of the state.

In addition to the WSU stations, the U.S. Bureau of Reclamation operates 10 remote weather stations in Washington and northern

TABLE 2. Crop coefficients for grass reference ET_0 for young orchards at various stages of canopy development, %GS, from 10% to 60%.

			Stage of canopy development, %GS					
			%GS=10 %M=27	%GS=20 %M=47.8	%GS=30 %M=65.4	%GS=40 %M=80	%GS=50 %M=91	%GS=60 %M=99
Month	Mature K_c	$K_{c\ base}$	K_c	K_c	K_c	K_c	K_c	K_c
Jan-Mar	0.45	-	0.45	0.45	0.45	0.45	0.45	0.45
April	0.45	-	0.45	0.45	0.45	0.45	0.45	0.45
May	0.85	0.71	0.75	0.78	0.80	0.82	0.84	0.85
June	1.15	0.71	0.83	0.92	1.00	1.06	1.11	1.15
July	1.25	0.71	0.86	0.97	1.06	1.14	1.20	1.24
August	1.25	0.71	0.86	0.97	1.06	1.14	1.20	1.24
September	1.20	0.71	0.85	0.95	1.03	1.10	1.16	1.19
October	0.95	0.71	0.78	0.83	0.87	0.90	0.93	0.95
Nov.-Dec.	0.45	-	0.45	0.45	0.45	0.45	0.45	0.45

Oregon. These are part of a system known as AgriMet, a network covering the Pacific Northwest. Daily data collected at these 10 stations are available on PAWS. AgriMet was initiated in 1983 and consists of over 40 remote stations in Washington, Idaho, Oregon, northern California, western Montana and western Wyoming, all linked by satellite to a central computer in Boise, Idaho (USBR, 1990).

In fall 1991, another weather station and computer base station were established at WSU Mt. Vernon. In fall 1993, expansion of the system into northcentral Washington began with the installation of two weather stations in the Wenatchee area and a computer base station at WSU Wenatchee

During the spring of 1994, two additional PAWS weather stations will be installed in the Naches and Gleed areas near Yakima, five new weather stations and a computer base station will be installed in Okanogan County, and a new AgriMet weather station, installed by the Lake Chelan Reclamation District, will be brought on-line. PAWS will then consist of a network of 61 automated agro-meteorological stations located primarily in irrigated lands of central Washington and northern Oregon (see Figure 1). Data will be accessible from five computer base stations and two National Weather Service offices.

PAWS has been fully operational in south central Washington since the spring of 1989. Weather data have been used operationally by individual growers, crop consultants, and in demonstration projects which illustrate data applications. These include:

1) Reporting of hourly temperatures, dewpoints and wind during the spring frost season by the National Weather Service over the NOAA Weather Radio as part of the fruit frost warning program.

2) Reporting of daily maximum and minimum air temperatures, precipitation, soil temperature, blossom degree-days and evapotranspiration by the NWS over the NOAA Weather Radio.

3) Pest management updates and warnings for fruit growers compiled by WSU Cooperative Extension in Yakima County and reported over the NOAA Weather Radio. Information on such pest problems as apple scab, codling moth and fireblight was provided.

4) Scientific irrigation scheduling using PAWS weather data or evapotranspiration estimates and the Washington Irrigation Forecaster computer model. More information on the Washington Irrigation Forecaster is given later in this chapter.

Weather data are available by personal computer and telephone modem access to PAWS base stations at WSU-Prosser, WSU-Mt. Vernon, WSU-Wenatchee, Oroville-Tonasket Irrigation District and Lake Chelan Reclamation District. Weather-driven computer models currently available on-line include pest management models for tracking and predicting pest problems. These are codling moth, fireblight, cherry fruit fly and apple scab, and a base five degree Celsius soil temperature degree-day model. Crop growth models include growing degree-day models with base temperatures of 40, 43, 45, 50, 55 and 60 degrees Fahrenheit.

Reference crop evapotranspiration for alfalfa and grass reference crops is calculated daily and made available by another model. Crop water use charts are developed daily for each weather station location using the reference ET values and crop coefficient data. These charts show the water use by crop for the past several days, expected water use for the coming few days and total water use for the season to date. Estimated air stability and inversion conditions for weather stations having air temperature measurements at both five feet (1.5 m) and 33 feet (10 m) above the ground surface are also available. Additional models will be added as they become available.

Touchtone telephone access to PAWS weather data is possible at WSU-Prosser and is planned for the Okanogan base station to be located at the Oroville-Tonasket Irrigation District.

Washington Irrigation Forecaster

The soil water balance or checkbook approach to irrigation scheduling is not difficult to implement once the appropriate data have been assembled. The checkbook method requires that one knows the net amount of water applied at each irrigation, the total available and usable soil water in the crop root zone, and the rate at which the crop extracts water from the soil. These three factors are balanced against each other to ensure the

plant available soil water is maintained at readily available levels. These data are also used in projecting when plant available soil water content in the root zone should be replenished.

In simplest form, the problem of managing plant available soil water in the root zone is similar to tracking cash flow and can be

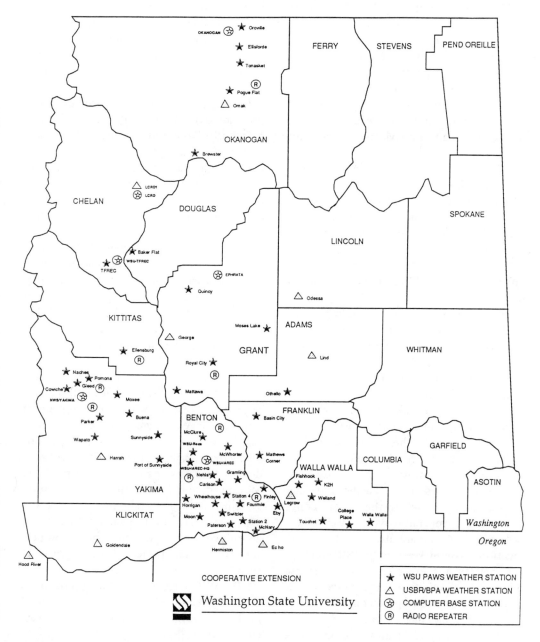

FIGURE 1. Map of Eastern Washington showing the Washington State University PAWS automated weather station network.

done by hand with pencil and ledger. Depending on the numbers of fields, crops, soil types and climatic zones an irrigation manager must deal with, however, the process may become cumbersome. For this reason, computer software packages have been developed by both the university community and private industry to assist irrigation management record-keeping and decision-making.

The Washington Irrigation Forecaster (WIF) is one such software package for the IBM PC, PS/2 and PC-compatible computers, which provides the user with computer-assisted checkbook irrigation management information. WIF was originally developed by Ken Best as part of his Master of Science degree thesis in Agricultural Engineering, and then enhanced with a menu-style user interface for data entry.

The WIF software package includes models of crop growth, crop water use, irrigation systems, and supporting data files specific to Washington State, which may be used to provide irrigation management information for 39 different crops.

Data files included with WIF contain information on field capacity, permanent wilting point and basic infiltration rate for seven general soil textures ranging from sandy to clay loam. Six different types of irrigation systems are modeled including center pivots, set-move sprinklers (wheel-lines and hand-lines), solid set sprinklers, furrow and border systems, and drip/trickle.

Washington was divided into 10 climatic regions having similar characteristics. Long-term weather data for these 10 regions included with WIF are the mean monthly temperatures and mean monthly solar radiation. These data are used to calibrate the crop water use estimating models to the region. Long-term average temperature data, as well as latitude and elevation, are also included for 41 locations around Washington State. These data help to further calibrate the water use model to local conditions and are used in estimating the expected crop water use.

Crop data files include information on 18 perennial crops and 21 annual crops. Data included are default maximum rooting depths, management allowable soil water

depletion and crop coefficients based upon stage of growth for estimating crop water use. A root growth model is used for annual crops to predict the root zone for the crop between emergence and maximum expected rooting. The average dates for the beginning of crop water use in each of the 10 climatic zones for each of the 39 crops is also given. These dates were estimated by using the long-term average weather data in each region and at each location in different types of growing degree-day or heat unit accumulation models.

The WIF software package really consists of two programs: one to help build a data file for each field to be scheduled, and one to provide irrigation scheduling information. The program to build a field data file must be used before scheduling can commence. Input data required include the crop (and emergence date if an annual), the location, soil type and depth (if depth is limiting to full root zone development), field soil water status and the date of measurement, and irrigation system type and application rate.

Default values are provided for rooting depths, field capacity and permanent wilting point, and irrigation application efficiency. These can be used, but site-specific data for a field and system are strongly recommended in order to obtain more accurate results. These data are saved in a file, which can be updated or revised as needed.

Figure 2 is a sample printout of the information stored in a field data file. In this example, the crop is apples with a cover crop grown near Prosser, Washington. The soil has a field capacity of 0.21 inches per inch (or by multiplying by 12, 2.52 inches per foot of root zone depth). The soil water was at field capacity on May 30 (date of last update). The irrigation system is solid set sprinklers with a gross application rate of 0.14 inches per hour, and an estimate application efficiency of 80 percent (0.80). The preferred set length is 24 hours.

The WIF irrigation scheduling program is used to update the current soil water content in the root zone of the crop and to forecast crop water use.

The soil water update portion of the program provides several means to accomplish this. One option is to enter a direct measurement of the soil water content. Other options accomplish the update by calculating a soil water balance in the root zone. This means that since the last time the soil water was known, an estimate of crop water use (removal of water from the root zone) and measurements of irrigation and rainfall (additions of water to the root zone) must be entered. Crop water use is estimated by entering pan evaporation data for the interval; by entering daily maximum temperature, minimum temperature and solar radiation data for the interval; or by using the built-in historical weather files. The maximum/minimum temperatures and solar radiation data may be obtained from PAWS. Irrigation and rainfall data are the responsibility of the user and are measured or estimated for each individual field.

Once the current root zone soil water content is known, the model provides a forecast of crop water needs and irrigation management recommendations up to 28 days into the future. This forecast is unique in that the first week of the four-week forecast is based upon standard weather forecast information given in newspapers, or on radio and TV. These forecasts include the 48-hour forecast and the three-to five-day extended forecast. The information needed is the expected high and low temperatures and the expected cloud cover conditions.

The second through fourth weeks of the forecast are based upon long-term average weather data files for each of the 41 different locations in Washington State. The long-term average weather data were found to provide more accurate estimates of the expected crop water use as compared to the longer range weather forecasts of 10 days or more.

Figure 3 is a sample printout of an irrigation forecast for the field given in Figure 2. The field data file *(Figure 2)* shows the soil water was at field capacity, 0.21 inches per inch or 2.52 inches per foot, on May 30. In this example, the program is being run on June 1 and a forecast for the first four weeks of June is generated. Each week of the forecast provides an estimate of the root zone soil water at the beginning of the week and the estimated daily average crop water use for the week. If irrigation information for any given week is left blank, then the program has determined no irrigation is needed.

In the first row of the forecast in Figure 3, June 1 to June 7, the initial soil water is estimated to be 0.20 inches per inch or 2.40 inches per foot. This figure results from the checkbook balance procedure by subtracting the water use for May 30 and 31 from the last known soil water level on May 30. Water use for May 30 and 31 were obtained from either of PAWS weather station data or pan evaporation reports.

WIF field data file example

Filename: sample.l01   Emergence date: none

Crop: Apples w/cover crop   Location: Prosser
Climatic zone: Central Col Basin   Field elev: 903 feet
Latitude: 46 deg 15 min   Last update: 5/30
                Average temp of warmest month > Max: 92.5 F Min: 57.5 F
                Soil Moisture   Max root depth: 4.0 feet
Field capacity: 0.210 in/in   Irrig system: solid set
Wilting point: 0.090 in/in   Application rate: 0.1400 in/hr
Minimum level: 0.132 in/in   Preferred set length: 24 hours
Current level: 0.210 in/in   System efficiency: 0.80

FIGURE 2. Example of a WIF field data file for an apple orchard with a cover crop located near Prosser, Washington.

Example 1:
soil water on May 30 = (48 inch root
zone) x 0.21 in/in water content)
= 10.08 inches water

May 30-31 = 0.48 inches
soil water on June 1 = 9.60 inches
= 0.20 inches in 48 inch root zone

WIF projects the soil water level on the first day of the second week is 0.175 inches per inch or 2.10 inches per foot. Again, this is determined using the checkbook balance procedure:

Example 2:
soil water on June 1 = (48 inch root zone)
x (0.20 in/in water content) = 9.60 inches

water use for June 1-7 = 0.19 in/day
x 7 days = 1.33 inches

soil water on June 8 = 9.60 - 1.33
= 8.27 inches = 0.175 in/in
(for 48-inch root zone)

For this example, the WIF program is estimating the next irrigation should occur at the earliest on June 13. From June 8 through June 12, five days of water use occurs at a rate of 0.20 inches per day or 1.00 inches. Adding this to the 0.48 inches of water use of May 30 and 31, and the 1.33 inches used during June 1-7, a total of 2.81 inches is depleted from the root zone. This is the equivalent of the net depth applied by the sprinkler system in a 24-hour set. Thus, a 24-hour set would refill the root zone to field capacity.

The return irrigation date given in the last column of Figure 3, July 1, is the latest date for the next irrigation assuming the June 13 irrigation is applied. This is the date when the soil water content is projected to reach the management allowable depletion level. Irrigation should be applied before that date to avoid crop water stress. The next recommended irrigation is actually June 26. This is the earliest date of return for that irrigation set so that a 24-hour set will not result in over-irrigation. The WIF program allows flexibility in making your irrigation decisions, and generally will provide information to help minimize overirrigation as well as avoid crop water stress.

It is recommended to run the WIF program routinely through the season and not rely completely on the long-range forecast of irrigation needs simply because we never seem to have an average year as far as weather is concerned. It is also recommended that soil

FORECAST IRRIGATION SCHEDULE
FOR SOLID SET SYSTEMS

DATA FILE: sample.l01   CROP: Apples w/cover crop
IRRIGATION RECOMMENDATIONS
soil water moisture refill of 100%

PERIOD	EST. ROOT ZONE (in)	INITIAL SOIL WATER (in/in)	AVG WATER USE (in/day)	EST IRRIG DATE	APPLY GROSS DEPTH (in)	OPT SET LGTH (hr)	NET DEPTH APPL (in)	RET IRRIG DATE
6/1-6/7	48.0	0.20	0.19					
6/8-6/14	48.0	0.175	0.20	6/13	3.46	24.7	2.77	7/1
6/15-6/21	48.0	0.21	0.22					
6/22-6/28	48.0	0.174	0.22	6/26	3.35	23.9	2.68	7/11

FIGURE 3. Example WIF irrigation forecast for the orchard field data given in Figure 2.

water content be routinely measured through the season to keep the estimating procedures used on track, and that flow measurements be used (i.e., flow meters, etc.) to check that the desired depths of application actually are applied.

Summary

The process of performing a soil water balance, or scientific irrigation scheduling, will result in the maintenance of appropriate soil water content in the crop's root zone. The term appropriate in this context means not being too dry as well as avoiding being too wet. This process will help to save and stretch water, especially in situations where there previously has been no attempt to use the scientific information available in a systematic record-keeping procedure.

The number of approaches and methods for estimating crop water use in addition to trying to interpret crop coefficients can be very confusing. This chapter has provided information on how reference or potential evapotranspiration is calculated. Crop coefficients for translating reference ET into crop ET for the crop of interest were discussed.

Washington State University and the U.S. Bureau of Reclamation operate the PAWS and AgriMet weather station networks, respectively, for the purpose of collecting the necessary detailed weather data to compute reference evapotranspiration for a large number of agricultural locations. Both systems make crop water use estimates available for each location for a variety of crops using published crop coefficient data. These crop water use estimates reduce the number of steps an irrigation manager must go through to perform a daily soil water balance.

WSU has developed the Washington Irrigation Forecaster (WIF), a computer software package with much of the required basic soils, crop and irrigation system information pre-programmed into the package, to assist growers with irrigation scheduling.

PART THREE

Water quality and quality considerations

Assuring future water supply and delivery

Paul R. Cross, P.E.
District Manager, Lake Chelan Reclamation District
Manson, Washington

Approximately eighty percent of the freshwater supplies in the western United States are used by irrigated agriculture. In the state of Washington there are more than two million irrigated acres with over one million acres of irrigated lands within irrigation districts. These lands produce crops with values exceeding two billion dollars annually. Despite these economic benefits, irrigated agriculture is being mandated to become more efficient in both crop production and water use. Irrigation districts must become more responsive to on-farm needs. This will mean changes in both administrative policies and structural components. In many cases the structural changes are both costly and difficult to do. This chapter will discuss some of those difficulties as they relate to typical irrigation distribution systems.

HISTORICAL PERSPECTIVE

Irrigation distribution design

Irrigation system design revolves around four basic components; the total acres served and how each acre will be served from a rate, duration and frequency or schedule basis. Early designs in Washington State assumed that water users needed water delivered at a constant rate for the entire irrigation season. Most designs recognized a typical water use total for the season that was needed to successfully grow a crop. In some of the early irrigation projects, the irrigation distribution system was designed to provide one cubic foot per second of water (approximately 450 gallons per minute) per 160 acres. Over the course of a 200-day season the system would provide just over 2.6 acre-feet per acre. (An acre-foot is the volume of water that would provide 12 inches of water over an entire acre of land). These early systems did not account for soil differences nor for varying crop demands from season to season.

By the 1920s in Washington State, system designs began recognizing soil type and varying crop needs caused by temperature and growth stage. The systems were still based upon rill irrigation with water delivered continuously for the entire irrigation season. Water was typically allotted between three and five acre-feet per acre based upon the water-holding capacity of the soil.

System conveyance

System conveyance systems were designed to carry the cumulative flows of individual farm turnouts. Labor was typically less expensive than materials and most systems were predominantly open channel systems. In areas of high permeability, pipelines were used. Most typically the water was delivered out of the pipeline to an open point of delivery for gravity distribution. This kind of system is termed either semi-closed or semi-open. A few systems had hydraulic ram-type pumps or high-elevation water sources where a totally enclosed pressurized delivery could be made through a valve. Until the advent of sprinkler irrigation there was little advantage in a pressurized delivery.

System control

In open conveyance systems, the predominant method of control is downstream control. Control structures were built to fill the conveyance channels up to a high level with an objective of maintaining them at a relatively constant water level unconditional of the actual rate of flow passing the structure. Laterals and individual deliveries off the main canals would be gated off and could deliver a constant discharge when the water surface elevation in the main canal remained constant.

In Washington State, many of these early control structures were adjusted manually, oftentimes with stop logs in channeled slots. The lower the rate of flow passing the structure the more stop logs were needed to maintain the water surface elevation. If a change of rate passed the structure without a corresponding change in stop logs, the water surface elevation in the open channel could change significantly. If the water surface lowered significantly, some laterals or turnouts would be left high and dry. These 'top draw' turnouts are common as they avoid diverting the sediments in the bottom of the channel and typically serve higher adjacent lands. If the water surface is raised significantly, there is a danger of overtopping the canal prism or increasing the discharge of the lateral canals causing problems on that system.

System control is constrained to constant rates and arranged, fixed schedules so that manual control can be used to move water through the system. A certain overflow is also needed at key locations within a system to make up for unaccounted supply or demand.

IMPACTS OF MODERN PRACTICES ON OLDER SYSTEMS

On-farm practices and better knowledge of crop needs have changed irrigation delivery from continuous season-long flow to intermittent deliveries using higher instantaneous rates and shorter durations. Some crops like tree fruit have gone predominantly into sprinkler application. Other needs in the treefruit industry have included using water for frost control, fertigation and evaporative cooling. Labor has become expensive, and more flexibility generally translates into lower labor costs. Bringing modern irrigation practices to older systems is an expensive challenge that may require large retooling efforts on the irrigation distribution system.

Measurement and control

Understanding the limitations of the older systems makes it easier to understand how modern practices have significant impacts on water measurement and control. Today's on-farm systems require significantly greater flexibility in rate and duration. From a water-delivery perspective, flexibility in rate and duration leads to problems keeping a uniform water-surface elevation. As was illustrated earlier, nonuniform water surface elevations lead to inconsistent discharge on laterals and higher levels of waste. Rate changes most typically must be arranged and done on the district's schedule rather than on the water user's schedule.

Extreme peaking rates that are experienced on older open channel systems and even closed systems can be extremely disruptive. An example of peaking rates is the use of irrigation systems for frost control. Water users would like to pump water for only the time they need it. In frost conditions, critical temperatures may last anywhere from one hour to all night. The flow rates required to do an entire acreage are large. Many canals and laterals cannot respond to the increase in demand without taking water away from others. In this case, the "tailenders" lose most or all of their water during the peak draw and get flooded out when the frost conditions subside.

Districts have historically responded to these situations by keeping operational wasteways as full of water as practical. The waste-way can be dried up when demand increases and flooded when demand subsides.

On-farm needs

Irrigation districts recognize the needs of today's water users and are developing ways to meet those demands. Water users require flexibility. In an ideal situation, a water user could turn on as much water as wanted, keep it on as long as they wanted and turn it off when done. This kind of unpredictability creates havoc on older systems. It is also very expensive to size facilities based upon "want" instead of need. Water users must get a better understanding of what actual crop needs are and take responsibility for improving the application efficiency of their on-farm system.

Other impacts

Water use efficiency and polluted runoff are key themes of the 1990's. Irrigation districts and individual water users will be scrutinized in their beneficial use of water. The operational wasteways that give irrigation districts some additional flexibility in delivery will be closed down or shut off completely. Supply and crop demand must come closer together. Use in excess of crop requirements will be defined as misuse.

Washington State is also going through one of the most severe droughts in this century. From an irrigation district perspective, distribution systems were not designed to run below minimum thresholds. Top-draw laterals and turnouts go high and dry during periods of low rate. The district's charge remains to distribute the supplies equitably among users. Many districts are also set up financially to recoup operating expenses through the sale of excess water. In drought years there is no excess to sell. Several dry years in a row can have significant financial impacts on districts.

MODERNIZING SYSTEMS

Distribution system design

Distribution system design must be done in consideration of crop irrigation requirements plus a reasonable transportation loss between the point of diversion and the actual crop.

Allowances need to be made for reducing labor costs of applying the water but only to the extent that water-use efficiency is not compromised. It is not practical to have the central authority arranging every delivery. The system must have some capabilities to respond to user and crop demands.

System conveyance

Open-channel distribution is still important in modern irrigation district systems. It is cost prohibitive to pipe irrigation distribution systems when there is not adequate elevation change to keep up the velocity of flow. Open channels do need to be armored or lined with a good drainage system behind the lining to survive drastic water-elevation changes. Control structures should be spaced closely together to respond to both low and high rates of flow. Semi-open systems combine open-channel distribution with piped-distribution systems. The piped portions have a greater capacity to provide on-demand delivery than the open-channel portions.

Closed systems are totally piped systems that oftentimes provide pressurized water at the turnout. The turnout or delivery is often metered to record total use but does not record instantaneous demand. Typical irrigation demand in Washington State for fruit trees ranges from three to five cubic feet per second per 160 acres. Typical closed systems have difficulty meeting these demand levels during peak use. Most districts do not allow or at least do not recognize the use of district water for frost control or evaporative cooling. These high demand functions make distribution system operations unstable and can cause system shutdown.

System control

Modernized system control for open-channel and semi-open systems rely upon automated control structures to maintain water-surface elevations. Regulating reservoirs are added at key points in the system to collect and store supply in excess of demand and to add supply to the system when demand exceeds supply. Control of the automated structures and reservoirs can be done locally or through central supervisory control and data acquisition systems. These type of telemetry systems are called SCADA systems. Communication between remote sites and the central system is commonly done via telephone or radio.

The use of programmable logic in the SCADA software allows sophisticated modeling and control strategies that can be customized for each individual system. The nearly instantaneous monitoring of demand allows system supply to respond more quickly.

Environmental Concerns

The regulations and resource demands of the future will begin tying water quantity with water quality concerns. Demands for clean water and the preservation of endangered species will have big impacts on irrigated agriculture and irrigation districts in the near term. Society has rediscovered the importance of water and as begun examining the highest and best use of water among competing demands. Eight years of drought have magnified the issue in some areas where the water resource is over-allocated. Now is the time for water users and water purveyors to improve their water use efficiency.

In the Lake Chelan Reclamation District agriculture has been identified as contributing nearly 50 percent of the man-induced phosphorus and over 50 percent of the man-induced nitrogen that returns to Lake Chelan.

The district has begun an irrigation water management program with water users to match more closely water application to crop requirements. The objectives of the program are twofold. First, proper irrigation applications will result in less runoff and deep percolation past the root zone. This will mean less runoff returning to Lake Chelan. The second objective is that proper irrigation applications will lead to healthier trees and better fruit size and quality. If both objectives can be met, a win-win situation will develop that addresses both water-use efficiency and water quality in a forum that is cost effective to the water user.

CONCLUSION

Water supply issues from an irrigation district perspective are changing. On-farm needs and growing concerns about water-use efficiency mean that older systems must modernize their facilities. The needed changes are not easy or cheap. Water users must evaluate realistically how much flexibility in rate and duration they can afford. Water conservation must occur both on farm and on the distribution system. Water quantity and water quality are interrelated. Irrigated agriculture must take a lead in finding means of change that are affordable. Water will be the key issue in Washington State for the remainder of the 1990s. Start planning for that change now.

Water quality concerns in irrigated agriculture

Michael A. Hepp

Hydrogeologist, Water Quality Program
Olympia, Washington

This chapter presents an overview of recent literature concerning the occurrence of pesticides and nutrients in the waters of Washington State. The principle sources of this data are studies by Washington Department of Ecology's Environmental Investigations and Laboratory Services (EILS) Program. The original references for this chapter are recommended for detailed data, such as analytical methods or complete analytical results.

The data compiled in this chapter do not commonly reach deciduous treefruit growers because they focus not on responsibility for contamination but on ways pesticide contamination occurs. That is unfortunate. Action by a group is the key in preventing water contamination from that group's activities. Knowledge of the presence and sources of contamination is the first step in acting to avoid additional contamination.

History

The Washington State Department of Ecology has collected fish tissue to obtain information on metals and synthetic organic compounds since 1978 (Hopkins et al, 1985).

Pesticides, especially dichlorodiphenyl trichlorethane (DDT) and its breakdown products, dichlorodiphenyl dicloroethylene (DDE) and dichlorodiphenyl dichloroethane (DDD), were found at sites primarily in eastern Washington State.

Eleven micrograms per liter (11 µg/l) of ethylene dibromide (EDB) was found in western Washington State in late 1983 along the upper Skagit River flood plain in a sampling of a private well by a citizen who had just bought property next to a strawberry farm (Department of Social and Health Services, 1985). The Department of Social and Health Services followed up the Harris discovery with a use-records recall and sampling of 96 sites (wells) in western Washington between June and October 1984. Fourteen sites returned EDB levels above the health advisory limit of 0.02 µg/L.

The EDB discoveries resulted in the 1987 Washington State Legislature directing the Department of Ecology to ascertain the extent of pesticides in ground water in Washington. This project was known as the Washington State Agricultural Chemicals Pilot Study. The Washington State Pesticide Monitoring Program was started in 1991 and included both ground and surface waters plus associated biota and sediments (Davis, 1993).

National studies of pesticides and nutrients in water

Pesticides and nutrients have been included in many of the numerous water-quality monitoring programs in the United States dating back to the National Pesticide Monitoring Program of early 1970s (Spencer, 1974).

Monitoring data is found in varied formats from the U.S. Geological Survey's National Water Information Systems (NWIS) database which contains comprehensive and detailed water-quality data from surface and ground water to the 305 (B) Waterbody Systems database which contains evaluations of water-quality impairments for specific surface waterbodies, but does not include site-specific data.

The Pesticides in Ground Water Database (PGWDB) (USEPA, 1991) was created by the U.S. Environmental Protection Agency (USEPA) to provide a more complete picture of groundwater monitoring in the United States. The PGWDB database contains data from over 48,000 wells from 1979 to 1990. Ninety-eight pesticides and pesticide metabolites or degradates (breakdown products) were found.

This database is derived from isolated studies and is difficult to interpret on a national basis because of variations in sampling density and analytical methods. The PGWDB database does not include more general data from STORET and WATSTOR databases (see references) or the extensively reported National Survey of Pesticides in Water Wells (NPS) database.

The National Survey of Pesticides in Water Wells (NPS) (EPA, 1992) was the first national study of pesticides, pesticide degradates, and nitrates in drinking water wells. More that 1300 wells were sampled for 127 analytes. Based on the NPS results, the EPA estimates that nitrate-N is present at or above the analytical minimum reporting limit (0.15µg N/l) in about 57 percent of rural wells nationwide. The survey detected pesticides and pesticide degradates much less frequently.

Twelve pesticide or pesticide degradates were found with DCPA acid metabolites (dacthal or dacthal degradates) and atrazine, the most common. The EPA estimates that 10.4 percent of community wells and 4.2 percent of rural wells nationwide contain pesticides or pesticide degradates.

Spalding and Exner (1993) summarized the results of more than 200,000 nitrate data points from published data. They found that nitrate contamination of ground water depended on climate, soils and agricultural practices and not just fertilizer application rates.

High temperatures, abundant rainfall and relatively high organic-carbon content of soils promoted denitrification and reduced nitrate loading to ground water in the Piedmont and Coastal Plain of the southeastern United States. Interception of nitrate-enriched water by field tile drains in eastern portions of the United States cornbelt resulted in increased nitrate in surface water, but lower nitrate in ground water. Ground water was found to be most seriously impacted by nitrate in areas of irrigated row crops on well-drained soils.

OCCURRENCES OF PESTICIDES AND NUTRIENTS IN WATER

Surface water

One of the earlist pesticide studies in Washington was a study of runoff at Padilla Bay in Skagit county (Mayer and Elkins, 1990) in 1987 and 1988. Analysis of 14 pesticides commonly applied to farmlands in the Padilla Bay area returned widespread dicamba (all 15 bay and slough water samples) and 2,4-D (one bay and nine slough water samples) after a heavy (1.14 cm) rain. No pesticides were detected at other times in the two-year sampling program.

The widespread nature of the pesticide occurrence and the coincidence of the rain suggest that a storm was the cause of the 1987 dicamba and 2,4-D occurrence. Dicamba and 2,4-D are both herbicides used to control vegetation along roads.

Surface-water samples were taken as reconnaissance sampling of surface waters at 11 sites in May and June, 1992, to help refine final methods and identify sampling sites for the Washington State Pesticide Monitoring Program (Davis, 1993). Samples were analyzed for 162 pesticides and pesticide degradates.

Sample collection was timed to coordinate with peak application and high probability of storm-water runoff.

Eleven sample sites were chosen to represent the major pesticide use types (urban, forest practices, and agriculture east and west of the Cascades) and areas of known pesticide contamination. Target pesticides were selected based on use patterns and analytical cost and difficulty considerations.

A total of 23 target pesticides were detected in the water samples. Nine nontarget pesticides were also identified and quantified with the atomic emission detector. DCPA's (dacthal or dacthal degradates) were found at nine sites, 2,4-D at seven sites, glyphosate at six sites, and both simazine and atrazine at four sites. Dacthal was found at the highest concentration of 12.1 µg/l in the Walla Walla River.

The Davis (1993) data contains interesting results. Sampling at Thorton Creek (in north Seattle) and Sullivan Slough (in the Skagit Delta) found more pesticides (nine versus eight) and greater concentrations (0.066 versus 0.017 µg/l DCPA's, and 0.23 versus 0.039 µg/l 2,4-D) at Thorton Creek than at Sullivan Slough. Similar results can be seen by comparing Mercer Creek (near Bellevue) and Moxee Drain (near Yakima). Mercer Creek 2,4-D (0.19 versus 0.15 µg/l) and glyphosate (1.07 versus 0.65 µg/l) values were higher than those of the agricultural Moxee Drain. Diazinon and dichlobenil (heavily used in urban areas) were detected only at Mercer and Thornton Creeks

The agricultural community should not look at the relative abundance of pesticides in water in urban areas as a reason to become complacent. Storm water is too common a transport mechanism for pesticides at all locations. Atrazine and simazine (used primarily in agriculture) were detected only at six agricultural sites. Water from Mission Creek (near Cashmere) showed detectable amounts of azinphos-methyl (0.033 µg/l), glyphosate (1.13 µg/l) and simazine (0.041 µg/l), chemicals all commonly used in the apple industry, plus the wood preservative pentachlorophenol (0.002 µg/l).

Ground water

Washington State agricultural chemicals pilot study

Ground water sampling, as part of the Washington State Agricultural Chemicals Pilot Study, was started in 1988 (with followup in 1989) at locations in Whatcom, Franklin and Yakima counties (Erickson and Norton, 1990). The pilot study had the objectives of providing information on the presence and concentration of pesticide residues in ground water plus evaluating indicator parameters to identify wells for further testing. Test areas were chosen because of their expected vulnerability to pesticide contamination.

Of the 81 wells sampled, 23 wells contained at least one pesticide. All but three occurrences were verified in the second sampling. Pesticides detected include: 1,2 dichloropropane, dibromochloropropane, ethylene dibromide, carbofuran, prometon, DCPA's (dacthal or degradate), bromacil, and atrazine. Nitrate/nitrite exceed the primary drinking water standard Maximum Contaminant Level (MCL) of 10 mg N/L in 18 wells. The study recommended that sampling be done in the Quincy and Gleed areas and that future sampling emphasize areas with detected nitrate contamination, known pesticide use and high vulnerability.

Gleed study

Sampling in the Gleed area began in June 1990, with confirmation sampling in February 1992. The Gleed area was picked because of its orchards (an untested type of agriculture) and vulnerable shallow ground water.

Of the 27 wells tested, xylene was detected in five wells (0.2 to 0.9 µg/l) and DCPA's (0.88 µg/l, dacthal and metabolites) in one well (Erickson, 1992). The five wells occurred in a 0.15 square mile area. Xylene and DCPA's were not found in the confirmation sampling. This could be caused by reporting limits for xylene in the confirmation sampling being higher (2 µg/l) than the reported levels in the first sampling, or only three wells being for resampled or the timing of the second sampling. Arsenic (max. 5.4 µg/l), copper (max. 129 µg/l), and lead (max. 2.8 µg/l) were detected in 13, 23 and 11 wells respectively. Pesticide use is only one the possible sources for these elements.

Nitrate/nitrite was detected at a mean level of 2.9 mg N/l. The relative low nitrate values combined with the low incidence of pesticides agrees with previous findings that nitrate concentration is a good guide for the presence of pesticides in ground water.

The source of xylene is more difficult to determine since xylene is present in many compounds including gasoline and is used for weed control in canals and ponds. The lack of xylene in the confirmation sampling and the size of contaminated area indicates a one-time exposure such as a surface spill or local use as an herbicide and not a long term point release such as a leaking tank. The presence of xylene in ground water at Gleed is a warning for users that use of xylene in leaking irrigation ditches is a potential source of ground water contamination.

Quincy, Washington, study

In May 1991, twenty-seven wells and two field drains near Quincy were tested for 76 agricultural pesticides. One or more pesticides were detected in all sites except for one well (Larson and Erickson, 1993). Pesticides detected include ethylene dibromide (18 detections—max. 0.26 µg/l), DCPA's (16 detections—max 8.30 µg/l), 1,2 dichloropropane (19 detections—max. 0.72 µg/l), (trans) 1,3 dichloropropene (3 detections—max. 0.11 µg/l), and atrazine (1 detection—0.28 µg/l). Arsenic was detected in each of six wells tested with a range of values from 1.7 µg/l to 7.9 µg/l. Nitrate/nitrite was found in all samples with an average value of 6.1 mg N/l.

Verification sampling was done in February 1992. Ethylene dibromide was detected in 10 sites, DCPAs at two sites, and 1,2-dichloropropane at 15 sites. Statistical analysis was performed on the pesticide and indicator parameter data. A correlation was found between total organic carbon and DCPAs and between nitrate/nitrite and 1,2 - dichloropropane. The correlation coefficients are too low to reliably predict the presence of these pesticides at specific sites.

The presence of ethylene dibromide and 1,2-dichloropropane in ground water at Quincy is believed to be the result of historic applications since they were so widespread and are no longer used. The decrease in DCPAs and atrazine sites between the initial and verification sampling is likely the result of a seasonal effect related to dilution and degradation between pesticide use and sampling time.

Ahtnaum and Moxee aquifers

Twenty-seven wells were sampled for 123 agricultural pesticides and nitrate/nitrite (N) in the Ahtanum and Moxee aquifers near Yakima in September and October, 1992 (Larson, 1993). This area was sampled to evaluate an area where agriculture and residential development overlap. Pesticide detections were verified by a second round of sampling in February, 1993.

Four pesticides were detected in the initial sampling: dacthal (DCPAs) (2 wells—max. 0.55 µg/l), atrazine (4 wells—max. 0.05 µg/l), simazine (3 wells—max. 0.023 µg/l), and ethylene dibromide (2 wells—max. 0.050 µg/l). Only atrazine and simazine were detected in the verification sampling. One well with dacthal could not be resampled, however. The decrease in detections between the initial and verification sampling is likely the result of a seasonal effect, as at Quincy.

Nitrate/nitrite averaged 3.61 mg N/l in the Moxee aquifer and 2.03 mg N/l in the Ahtanum aquifer. These values are higher than would be expected from natural background.

Expectations and discoveries

"If you look for it, you will find it"

As sampling for pesticides has increased, more pesticides have been found, and will likely continue to be found, in the waters of Washington State. This is a result of increased sampling, as well as improvements in analytical methods and sampling skill.

Improvements in analytical methods have resulted in approximately one order of magnitude decrease in detection limit for organic toxicants every decade (Seiber, 1982). Rinella et al.(1993) report DDT analysis data from the Yakima River with no samples at or above the

Laboratory Reporting Level of 0.01 µg/l total DDT from 1973 to 1985, but a number of samples with detectable total DDT after 1985 when the Laboratory Reporting Level was lowered to 0.001 µg/l.

Increases in sampling skill are more difficult to quantify. The 1992 Washington State Pesticide Monitoring Program detected a total of 23 target pesticides, but 1993 sampling detected over 40 pesticides (Davis, 1994). This could be attributed to the 1993 samples being taken during four, rather than one, sampling events and more total samples being taken, but individual 1993 sampling events also had more pesticide detections than found at the same site in 1992. As knowledge of pesticide fate and transport increases, the samplers' ability to "catch" pesticides also increases.

Leaching and adsorption

The study of leaching and transport of pesticides involves many contaminant-based mathematical models for determining the potential for specific pesticides to leach to ground water. Soil characteristics and pesticide chemistry are the principle factors evaluated in these models.

Cheng (1990) and Geraghty & Miller (1990) describe pesticide-leaching models and their development in great detail. The two main limitations to calculating leaching models are: 1) the large number of input data requirements (e.g., 23 for the SWAG model) and 2) variation in individual input parameters (carbaryl Koc [soil sorption coefficient] values of 298, 104 and 121).

California study

Seiber (1992) reported work in California where five of 25 pesticides found in ground water were not predicted to leach based on a Koc, hydrolysis half-life, aerobic-metabolism rate and water-solubility factor prediction model. The same survey found ten of 27 contaminants predicted to occur in ground water were not found using the same model.

The reasons for these differences include the variation in input parameters mentioned above, use and non-use patterns and analytical detection limits. It is likely that with greater dependence on fewer registered pesti-

cides and development of lower detection limits pesticides will be detected more often in ground water.

Irrigation water and pesticides

There appears to be a greater chance of agricultural pesticides and nutrients to reach ground water where irrigated crops are grown than areas with similar crops grown without irrigation. Spalding and Exner (1993) reported that ground water in the United States was seriously affected by nitrate in areas of irrigated row crops on well drained soils, but rarely in areas like the southeastern United States. The southeast corn crops used high amounts of fertilizer, but high soil organic carbon permitted denitrification.

Domagalski and Dubrovsky (1991) showed similar results for pesticides in the San Joaquin Valley where leaching to ground water was enhanced by flood irrigation methods and areas of coarse-grained, low-carbon soils on the eastern side of the San Joaquin Valley. Shallow ground water was present in the western portion of the valley, but few pesticides were found in the water because of the fine-grained nature of the soil.

Spalding and Exner (1993) reported low nitrate in ground water in corn areas in Ohio where field tile drains are common. The tile drains intercepted nitrates before they reached ground water, resulting in high nitrate levels in streams. Pesticides also reach surface water bodies by transport through tile drains.

Contamination of surface water by agricultural pesticides and nutrients as a consequence of transport in return flows from irrigated areas is also a problem. Return flows account for as much as 80 percent of the mainstem flow in the lower Yakima Valley during the irrigation season (Rinella, 1993). The DDT in sediment in the Yakima River is a result of runoff and return flow carrying eroded soil contaminated with DDT.

Leaching of pesticides after normal use is not the only way pesticides contaminate ground water. Direct contamination, such as down wells and through spills, are also possible. This is a likely method for contamination by pesticides that are not predicted to leach. As many as 50 percent of the occurrences of pesticides in ground water have been attributed to direct contamination.

Spills and leaks at storage and mixing sites and backflow into wells during chemigation or tank mixing have been too common. Improper disposal of waste pesticides has been a problem. Less common is the contamination of deep aquifers as a result of poor well construction by shallow ground water contaminated through normal use. An additional contamination transport method, which is not allowed in Washington, is the use of tailwater disposal wells. Improperly abandoned wells in agricultural areas can have the same effect.

The future

The number of pesticides available for use is decreasing. Most of the pesticides with criteria listed in the state ground and surface water quality standards (Chapter 173-200 and 173-201A Washington Administrative Code) are no longer registered for use. This fall, the Environmental Protection Agency is expected to require states to develop State Management Plans for five or six pesticides with high leaching potential if the state wishes to be able to continue to use these pesticides, rather than have complete cancellation.

Sampling of water for pesticides will increase. Sampling of public water systems for volatile organic compounds and pesticides is required under the Safe Drinking Water Act Phase 2/5 rule. There are approximately 2600 public water-supply systems in Washington. Only those systems that can demonstrate low risk of contamination because of local ground water and well conditions or nonuse of pesticides in the vicinity are expected to be granted waivers. The detection of a compound will result in additional sampling at a cost of $720 per quarter for pesticides alone. This cost will be high on a user basis for the smaller systems.

The effects of pesticide use and irrigation on fish have been severe in some places. The Chelan County Conservation District (1994) reports that spray drift from a pesticide application virtually eliminated the population of salmon and steelhead smolts in Brender Creek in spring 1993. They also report that there are times of year when Mission Creek is completely drained from irrigation and other times when excessive silt loads are caused by storms and the spilling of irrigation water into the creek. The negative effects on fish are obvious. These and other activities that negatively impact salmon and steelhead are the subject of increasing public scrutiny.

Projects such as the Mission Creek Restoration Project of the Chelan County Conservation District give hope for the future. A committee of concerned citizens, local government, schools, orchardists, state and federal agencies and environmental groups is serving as a vehicle to inventory problems and develop a plan of action for the cleanup and prevention of future water quality problems.

REFERENCES

Chelan County Conservation District. 1994. Mission Creek Restoration Project, Work Program for Clean Water Act Federal FY94 & 319 Grants. 9 p.p.

Cheng, H.H. (ed.). 1990. "Pesticides in the soil environment: Processes, impacts, modeling." *Soil Science Society of America Book No. 2,* 530 p.p.

Davis, D.A. 1993. "Washington State Pesticide Monitoring Program - Reconnaissance Sampling of Surface Waters (1992)." Washington State Department of Ecology, 38 p.p.

———, 1994, Personal Communication, Lacey, Washington, February 1, 1994

Department of Social and Health Services. 1985. "Results and Implications of the Investigation of Ethylene Dibromide in Ground Water in Western Washington," 32 p.p.

Domagalski, J.L. and D.M. Dubrovsky. 1991. "Regional Assessment of Nonpoint-Source Pesticide Residues in Ground Water, San Joaquin Valley, California," *U.S. Geol. Survey Water-Resources Investigations Report 91-4027,* 64 p.p.

Erickson, D. 1992. "Gleed Agricultural Chemicals Ground Water Assessment," Washington State Dept. of Ecology, Environmental Investigations and Laboratory Services Program, Olympia, Washington, 16 p.p.

Erickson, D. and D. Norton. 1990. "Washington State Agricultural Chemicals Pilot Study - Final Report," Washington State Dept. of Ecology, Environmental Investigations and Laboratory Services Program, Olympia, Washington, 76 p.p.

Geraghty & Miller, Inc. and ICF, Inc. 1990. A Review of Methods for Assessing the Sensitivity of Aquifers to Pesticide Contamination, prepared for U.S. EPA, 55 p.p.

Hopkins, B.S., D.K. Clark, M. Schlender, and M. Stinson. 1985. Basic Water Monitoring Program - Fish Tissue and Sediment Sampling for 1984, Washington State Department of Ecology Pub. No. 85-7, 43 p.p.

Larson, A.G. 1993. Pesticide Residues in the Moxee and Ahtanum Surficial Aquifers, Washington State Dept. of Ecology, Environmental Investigations and Laboratory Services Program, Olympia, Washington, 14 p.p.

Larson, A.G. and D.R. Erickson. 1993. Quincy Agricultural Chemicals Ground Water Quality Assessment, Washington State Dept. of Ecology, Environmental Investigations and Laboratory Services Program, Olympia, Washington, 14 p.p.

Mayer, J.R. and N.R. Elkins. 1990. Potential for Agricultural Pesticide Runoff to a Puget Sound Estuary: Padilla Bay, Washington, Bull. Environ. Contam. Toxicol., No. 45, p.p. 215-222.

Rinella, J.G., P.A. Hamilton, and S.W. McKenzie. 1993. Persistence of the DDT Pesticide in the Yakima River Basin, Washington, U.S. Geological Survey Circular 1090, 24 p.p.

Seiber, J.N. 1982. 1982 Analysis of Toxicants in Agricultural Environments, Genetic Toxicology, R.A. Fleck and A. Hollaender ed., Plenum, N.Y., p.p. 219-234.

Seiber, J.N. 1992. Overview of the Problem of Pesticides in Ground Water, Factors which Influence Fate Processes, in Senior Pesticide Officials Program, Ground-Water Protection, April 5-11, 1992 University of California, Davis.

Spalding, R.F., and M.E. Exner, Occurrence of Nitrate in Groundwater - A Review, J., Environ. Qual., Vol. 22. p.p. 392-402.

Spencer, D.A. 1974. The National Pesticide Monitoring Program, U.S. Environmental Protection Agency, published by The National Chemicals Association.

USEPA. 1991. Pesticides in Ground Water Database, U.S. Environmental Protection Agency, Office of Pesticides and Toxic Substances, 15 p.p.

USEPA, STORET (Database), U.S. Environmental Protection Agency, Office of Information Resources Management, Washington D.C., User Assistance: (800) 424-9067.

USGS, NWIS (Database), U.S. Geological Survey, 1201 Pacific Avenue, Suite 600, Tacoma, Washington, (206) 593-6510.

USGS, WATSTOR (Database), U.S. Geological Survey, National Water Data Exchange, Restor, VA, Further Information: (703) 648-5671.

BMPs for surface and ground water quality protection

Ronald E. Hermanson, Ph.D., P.E.
Extension Agricultural Engineer, Water Quality
Washington State University Cooperative Extension

Landmark legislation with long-term effects for quality water became reality when the U.S. Congress passed the Federal Water Pollution Control Act Amendments of 1972 (PL 92-500) on October 18. The act was the most comprehensive plan ever to clean up the nation's water. If mandated, a sweeping federal-state campaign would begin to prevent, reduce and eliminate water pollution. Agriculture was specifically included, whereas, it was not in the existing 1965 Water Pollution Control Act.

The 1972 act instituted the National Pollutant Discharge Elimination System discharge permits, which set out a detailed system defining the discharge permit requirements for confinement animal feeding operations, and the continuing, but more rigorous discharge permits for municipalities and industries. The federal intent was for the states to adopt and administer the act. The Department of Ecology administers PL 92-500 for Washington State.

Animal agriculture was regulated by federal law for the first time, but crop production was not regulated by the permit system. Confined animal-feeding operations were defined as point sources of pollution because discharges could be through pipes or water-courses. Crop production is not a point source of pollution, but was defined as a nonpoint source because sources of contamination are diffuse and widespread. These sources could be called surface runoff because that is the means of transporting the contaminants. Section 208 of the 1972 act required state plans for nonpoint sources including agriculture, forestry and urban sources.

Agricultural nonpoint source program

In 1979, the governor of Washington State sent nonpoint source plans to the federal government's Environmental Protection Agency (EPA) for dairy, dryland and irrigated agriculture. EPA approved these the same year. The state defined dairies as nonpoint sources of pollution, but kept other livestock and poultry as confined animal-feeding operations.

This legal background explains how all of irrigated agriculture has been, and continues to be, regulated as a nonpoint source of pollution since 1979, as have dairy and dryland agriculture. The programs are voluntary, driven by complaints of water quality violations made to the local conservation district. If an alleged violation is found factual, the producer is given a period of time to correct the problem. Ultimately, the Department of Ecology will investigate and cite violations if the producer refuses to cooperate. This section 208 program of voluntary compliance operates jointly by partnership of conservation districts, the Conservation Commission, and the state Department of Ecology (Ecology). The major agricultural industries of Washington are fortunate to have this system of voluntary compliance operated locally, rather than by regulation and permits.

New management manual for irrigated agriculture

The 208 plan and its manual of practice, Management Practices for Irrigated Agriculture, is designed for surface water quality protection. Very correctly, Ecology and the U.S. Environmental Protection Agency (EPA) decided that ground water can be contaminated or polluted by sometimes unfortunate combinations of practices, systems and management. Clearly, a best management practices (BMP) manual was needed for irrigated agriculture to protect ground water quality.

Discussions with Ecology staff produced a grant contract and funds from the new Section 319 nonpoint source program to evaluate the effects on ground water quality of the 1979 BMPs which were designed to protect surface water quality. A manual of practices to protect ground water also was planned as the most important product of the project. Funds were passed from EPA to Ecology. Ecology granted the funds to WSU-Cooperative Extension by a contract that detailed the project conditions.

Early in the course of the project Extension saw that separating surface water and ground water was illogical because:

1. Surface water and ground water are connected and make one water resource.
2. Although the contract would be fulfilled by producing the two documents previously described, we would do the user a disservice by not combining surface water and ground water.

Therefore, the evaluation now completed and explained in an unpublished report was made by studying the effects of surface water on ground water and vise versa, to make the comparisons complete. Further, the irrigation practices manual combined surface water and ground water practices into one manual.

Uses and sources of water

Good quality water is essential to man's existence. The highest use of clean water is for drinking. However, many industrial processes also require extremely clean water. Other beneficial uses of water include irrigation, livestock, fish habitat (spawning, rearing, migration, and harvest), wildlife habitat, recreation (swimming and boating), and navigation.

Water may come from surface waterbodies such as rivers and lakes. Or, it may come from ground water. Ground water is surface water that has percolated (moved through ground) to a usable aquifer. An aquifer is an underground geologic formation, composed of either fractured rock or porous soil, that provides water storage. A usable aquifer will allow sufficient water, of sufficient quality, for the desired purpose to flow to a well for extraction.

Regardless of whether the source is ground water or surface water, water is supplied by precipitation as in rain, sleet, hail, or snow. The ultimate source of all water is the ocean. Water moves from the ocean to the atmosphere, to land, and back to the ocean in the continuous water cycle.

Ground water in Washington State is extremely important. Approximately two-thirds of the population of Washington drink ground water. Virtually all the rural population (about 20 percent of the total population) drink ground water. Seepage from ground water to streams and lakes can contribute substantially to those water bodies. The process reverses when the water table is lower than the level in streams and lakes. Thus, while ground water is most important for supplying drinking water, it can also affect fish and wildlife, and human recreation.

Water quality assessment

Ecology now gathers all available information concerning water quality in the state and reports this information every two years. Only 14 percent of total stream miles in Washington

State have been assessed. However, 46 percent of the assessed mileage was found not to support designated uses. Another six percent was threatened. In decreasing order, the major contaminants impairing the use of rivers and streams were fecal coliform, high temperature, toxic metals and low dissolved oxygen. Major sources in decreasing order were agriculture, point sources, hydromodification and natural conditions.

Thirty-seven percent of the total area designated as estuary was assessed and 54 percent of that area did not support beneficial uses. Another 13 percent was categorized as threatened. In decreasing order, the major contaminants impairing the use of estuaries were low dissolved oxygen, fecal coliform and high temperature. Only 13 percent of the total lake area was assessed and 27 percent of that area did not support beneficial uses. Another 5 percent was categorized as threatened. The major causes impairing the use and the sources of contaminants in lakes, in decreasing order, were nutrients, pesticides, sediment and low dissolved oxygen.

Assessment of ground water quality

Assessment of ground water quality is difficult as Washington State does not have a comprehensive monitoring program. However, what information is available indicates that pollution of ground water, either real or potential, is a serious concern.

For example, a pilot testing program in the late 1980s in Yakima, Franklin, and Whatcom counties tested 27 wells in each county for 46 pesticides and nitrate contamination. Of the 81 wells tested, 23 were positive for at least one of the pesticides and seven were above drinking water standards. Sixty-one of the wells tested positive for nitrate and 18 were above drinking-water standards.

Results from a study of ground water quality near Gleed (located about 5 miles northwest of Yakima in an orchard area) were released by Ecology in December 1992. Twenty-seven wells were sampled and analyzed for 74 compounds. Xylene was detected in five of the wells, arsenic in 13, copper in 23, and lead in 11. However, none of the chemical

levels exceeded drinking-water standards. Also, sources of the chemicals could not be identified.

The results of a study of ground water in the Quincy area were released by Ecology in March 1993. Twenty-seven wells and two field drains were sampled in May 1991. Pesticides were detected in 26 of the wells and both drains. Ethylene dibromide was found at 62 percent of the sites and concentrations exceeded drinking water standards in nine wells and one drain. Concentrations of nitrate plus nitrite-nitrogen exceeded drinking water standards in two wells.

Not all ground water tests are reported here, but clearly blanket statements concerning ground water quality in all Washington aquifers cannot be made from limited testing. However, contamination of ground water in some locations can be taken as a warning.

Overall strategy for reduction of nonpoint source pollution

Water quality standards (WAC 173-201) protect the beneficial uses of surface waterbodies. The standards are intended to protect water quality, not to react to water pollution. The standards incorporate a portion of existing state law termed the anti-degradation policy (WAC 173-201-035[a]). This policy forbids degradation of water that would preclude its beneficial uses for drinking water, irrigation, and wildlife habitat, but it is not a policy of no degradation.

The overall strategy for protecting waterbodies is technology based. If land-use activities are the primary causes of nonpoint source pollution, modification of the activities should reduce the pollution. Thus, the strategy depends on the implementation of practices that will minimize contaminating activities. Such practices generally have been termed "Best Management Practices." In the manual (described elsewhere in this book by Peter Canessa) these practices are referred to as "Implementation Practices."

Other parts of the strategy include technical assistance, educational programs, and enforcement of state and local regulations. Enforcement and regulatory tools include the following:

1. State Water Pollution Control Act - this is chapter 90.48 of the Revised Code of Washington. This act authorizes the administration of programs mandated by the Federal Clean Water Act and also establishes the anti-degradation policy.

2. Water Quality Standards - Chapter 173-201 of the Washington Administrative Code sets numerical criteria for the several classes of surface water. They were established to protect current and potential uses of water. If testing shows that the waterbody is threatened or impaired, action must be taken.

3. State Environmental Policy Act - This act requires consideration of impacts on the environment by significant activities. These activities may be construction projects or implementation of policies, plans, ordinances, or regulations.

4. Shoreline Management Act - This is Chapter 90.58 of the Revised Code of Washington. It establishes a policy of "protecting against adverse effects to the public health, the land and its vegetation and wildlife, and the waters of the state or their aquatic life." Shorelines where the mean annual flow is less than 20 cubic feet per second are exempt from regulation under this act.

5. Coastal Zone Act Reauthorization Amendments - Amendments were enacted in 1990 by congress to the Coastal Zone Act of 1972. The amendments specifically charge the states and territories to address nonpoint source pollution in their water quality programs. Section 6217(b) of the Amendments states that the state programs "...provide for the implementation, at a minimum, of management measures in conformity with the guidance published under subsection (g) to protect coastal waters generally."

6. Water Quality Standards for Ground Waters of the State of Washington - In December 1990, the state adopted a set of ground water standards to prevent ground water pollution (Chapter 173-200 of the Washington Administrative Code). The public and private agencies, groups, and people who developed and reviewed the standards intend them to protect ground water quality rather than react to ground water pollution.

The standards incorporate an existing part of state water quality law: the anti-degradation policy. This policy strictly forbids degradation which would harm existing or future beneficial uses of ground water. Beneficial uses of ground water include drinking water, irrigation, and support of wildlife habitat.

Numerical values which must not be exceeded to protect the beneficial use of drinking water were established and called criteria. For example, the criterion for nitrate-nitrogen is 10 milligrams per liter. The established criteria are generally derived from health-based drinking-water standards.

7. Agrichemicals - Examples of specific state regulations are WAC 16-200-742, which governs application of fertilizers through irrigation systems and WAC 16-228-232 which governs applications of pesticides through irrigation systems.

State agencies that have regulatory authority and responsibility or develop water quality management programs include the following: the Departments of Ecology, Agriculture, Fisheries and Wildlife, Natural Resources, Health, Transportation; the Parks and Recreation Commission; Cooperative Extension; and the Conservation Commission.

Local conservation districts educate and help growers to develop management plans to protect water quality.

Major federal agencies involved in educational, financial, and technical assistance include the Soil Conservation Service, the Agricultural Stabilization and Conservation Service, the Forest Service, the Bureau of Reclamation, the Bureau of Land Management; and the Environmental Protection Agency.

Strategy for protecting ground water quality

The Assessment and Management Program document addressed nonpoint source pollution of ground water and surface waterbodies from all activities. A subsequent joint effort between several state and federal agencies and the agricultural community culminated with the publishing of "Protecting Ground Water: A Strategy for Managing Agricultural Pesticides and Nutrients" (referred to as the Strategy document) in 1992. The document lays out the strategy developed by the group for protecting ground water from pollution by agricultural activities.

Agencies participating were the Washington State Departments of Ecology, Agriculture, Natural Resources, and Health; Washington State University Cooperative Extension; Washington State Conservation Commission; Washington State Water Research Center; U.S. Department of Agriculture; and the Environmental Protection Agency. Also involved were independent scientists, businessmen, agriculturists, environmentalists, and lay people.

Two priorities established were:

1. Support for statewide technical assistance programs; and
2. Support for expanded programs in areas with highly vulnerable ground waters.

Regulatory enforcement was also recognized as part of the strategy. However, it was felt that the need for enforcement is minimized by involving local agricultural communities and providing the information necessary for voluntary compliance in the anti-degradation activities. The strategy seeks a partnership between regulatory agencies and the agricultural community.

An example of this aspect of the strategy would be WAC 16-228-232, which governs fertigation. This regulation was promulgated with input from agriculturists. It clearly defines the approved hardware for applying fertilizers through irrigation systems. Growers know that by following the regulation they are abiding by the law while protecting water quality.

The objectives of the strategy are:

1. Coordination among agencies in overall planning and carrying out activities of the strategy;

2. Development of tools needed by agencies for effective management of information and for evaluation of programs;
3. Identification and evaluation of agricultural best management practices and other measures to protect ground water from degradation by agricultural activities;
4. Effective and appropriate enforcement to ensure that voluntary efforts to protect ground water quality are not undermined; and
5. Generation of adequate funding to carry out activities.

Objectives 3 and 4 of the strategy are addressed by the manual being developed under contract with Ecology. This manual identifies overall management objectives for irrigated agriculture that, if achieved, can reduce potential ground water and surface water pollution. Implementation practices that can help achieve overall management objectives are also presented.

Dissemination of this information is one means of encouraging growers to adopt those practices deemed applicable to their situation.

The management manual

The manual is detailed in the next chapter by Peter Canessa. Four pertinent topics are:

1. Water pollution
2. Irrigation science
3. Overall management objectives
4. Implementation practices

The overall management objectives and implementation practices are the working elements of the manual. We chose not to continue the use of the "best" management practice terminology for several reasons, especially because what is best cannot be well determined. Rather, the term, "implementation practice," means that the practices are to be put to use.

Education

Growers are more likely to participate in a program to protect surface water and ground water quality if they understand the reason for the program and fully understand the variety of implementation practices they can use. A plan for their irrigated cropland can then be developed with assistance from conservation district, Soil Conservation Service and Cooperative Extension personnel.

WSU Cooperative Extension is planning training materials to be used by the conservation districts and Cooperative Extension as a part of an ongoing educational program on irrigation and clean water.

Education is the key to the success of this voluntary nonpoint source pollution control program. The people of Washington expect clean water. Agriculture can play a big and important part by practicing good stewardship. Despite little evidence that treefruit production pollutes ground water or surface water, increased water testing of the unknown can implicate the industry. The wise course is to begin planning and using the combination of implementation practices that make an effective strategy.

Acknowledgment

This chapter is based on a project, "Evaluate Ground Water Best Management Practices for Eastern Washington Irrigated Agriculture." It is part of the state Nonpoint-Source Pollution-Control Program, supported by the Washington Department of Ecology, Kahle Jennings, Project Officer.

Controlling and reducing nonpoint source pollution

Peter Canessa, P.E.

Agricultural water and energy management consultant
San Luis Obispo, California

G ood quality water is essential to man's existence. Clean water for drinking is vital. However, many industrial processes also require clean water. Other beneficial uses of water include irrigation, livestock, fish habitat (spawning, rearing, migration, and harvest), wildlife habitat, recreation (swimming and boating), and navigation.

Degradation of water quality has an economic impact. If the degraded quality of a water body prevents a beneficial use, the economic value of that use is lost. For example, if stream or lake quality is impaired to such a degree that fisheries are not supported, the economic value of fishing as both recreation and a food supply is lost. Although the values of lost beneficial uses are difficult to estimate accurately, they must be considered when setting policy or determining required actions.

The cost of degradation of domestic or industrial water supplies is more easily identified, especially if that supply is ground water. The minimum cost of individual household nitrate removal systems is in the $300 range. New domestic wells that might be required to reach a cleaner aquifer currently cost from $20-30 a foot to drill. Note also that areas with contaminated ground water are not as attractive to new businesses that might want to relocate.

And, in the worst case, home and land values may be reduced if located in an area with known water quality problems.

Controlling nonpoint source water pollution

There are two sources of water pollution, point and nonpoint. Point-source pollution occurs when the source of the pollution is identifiable. Examples of point-source pollution are a discharge pipe from a factory or the outlet from a city's sewage treatment plant.

Nonpoint-source pollution, as defined by the Federal Environmental Protection Agency, is " ... pollution ... caused by diffuse sources that are not regulated as point sources ... ." Further, the Washington State Legislature has defined nonpoint-source pollution as "pollution that enters the waters of the state from any dispersed water-based or land-use activities, including, but not limited to, atmospheric deposition: surface-water runoff from agricultural lands, urban areas, and forest lands, subsurface or underground sources; and discharges from boats or other marine vessels."

nonpoint-source pollution is cumulative in nature. While any source of nonpoint-source contamination may be insignificant, the cumulative effect of many such sources is measurable and leads to significant pollution of ground or surface waters.

Nonpoint-source pollution is usually the result of land-use activities. (dairies, irrigated and dryland agriculture, logging, rangeland management, food processing.) However, other sources of nonpoint pollution include:

1. Urban and suburban use of pesticides and nutrients.

2. Runoff from highways and paved areas.
3. Maintenance of highway and railroad rights of way.
4. Mosquito abatement activities.
5. Noxious weed control.
6. Naturally occurring contamination. Arsenic-bearing bedrock in Snohomish County would be an example of naturally occurring pollution.

TABLE 1. Sources for Best Management Practice Lists (Table 3-1 in Nonpoint Source Pollution Assessment and Management Program, published by Department of Ecology, October, 1989)

Source Category	Agency[1]	Origin
AGRICULTURE		
Dairy waste	CDs/Ecology	Clean Water Act
Dryland	CDs/Ecology	
Irrigated	CDs/Ecology	
Noncommercial	Ecology	
FOREST PRACTICES	Forest Practices Board/Ecology	
RANGELAND	CDs/CC	Informal Guidance
STORMWATER	Ecology	Development in progress
CONSTRUCTION		
Land development	Ecology	Guidelines
Highway runoff	WDOT	Highway Water Quality Manual
RESOURCE EXTRACTION	DNR	Surface Mining Act (Chapter 78.44 RCW)
LAND DISPOSAL		
On-site sewage treatment	State Board of Health/DOH	On-site System Rules (Chapter 248.96 WAC) Recycling Program
Landfills	Ecology	State Solid Waste Management Act (Chapter 70.95 RCW)
Land treatment	Ecology	Guidelines
HYDROLOGIC MODIFICATION	WDF	Hydraulics Code (Chapter 75.20 RCW)
OTHER		
Boats and marinas	Parks	Development in progress
Storage tanks	DL & I	Uniform Fire Code (Chapter 19.27 RCW)

T = agency abbreviations
Ecology = Washington State Department of Ecology
WDOT = Washington State Department of Transportation
DOH = Washington State Department of Health
Parks = Washington State Park Service

CDs = conservation districts
CC = Washington State Conservation Commission
DNR = Washington State Department of Natural Resources
WDF = Washington State Department of Forestry
DL & I = Department of Labor and Industries

Nonpoint-source pollution is difficult to control, both because of its diffuse nature and because of the many types of potentially polluting activities that can occur in an area. Thus, fairly assigning costs of pollution cleanup, or levels of effort to prevent pollution is difficult.

The overall strategy for protecting water bodies is based on technology and voluntary action. If land-use activities are the primary causes of nonpoint-source pollution, then modification of these activities should reduce the pollution. Therefore, the strategy depends on the implementation of practices that will minimize contaminating activities. These practices have generally been termed "best management practices." Other parts of the strategy include technical assistance, education programs, and enforcement of state and local regulations.

Practices to protect ground water and surface water quality

"Irrigation Management Practices to Protect Ground Water and Surface Water Quality - State of Washington" (IMP Manual) is in development now by Washington State University Cooperative Extension. It will address nonpoint-source pollution from agricultural activities. It will provide:

1. Education as to the nature and sources of nonpoint-source pollution.
2. Identification of overall objectives and specific practices that can be used to prevent or control nonpoint-source pollution.

The IMP Manual is part of a voluntary, technology-based effort to prevent or control nonpoint-source pollution resulting from irrigated agriculture.

The term "BMP," which stands for "best management practices" will continue to be used in literature and the field as a shorthand method of identifying the technology-based approach to controlling and reducing nonpoint-source pollution. However, the term "best management practice" itself leads to misunderstandings, especially for those not familiar with the unique circumstances and limitations of modern irrigated agriculture.

There are many specific types of management or hardware that are currently termed "best management practices." However, any one of these BMPs should not be considered a "best" combination of management/hardware to be used in controlling/reducing nonpoint-source pollution in every situation. (For example, all growers should not be using trickle irrigation.) "Best" can only be evaluated in light of the specific situation. What will be effective on one farm or field may not be as effective, or have no impact at all, on another.

Thus, the terms "overall management objective" (OMO) and "implementation practice" (IP) are used in the forthcoming IMP Manual. Overall Management Objective is an end result that, if achieved, should control or reduce nonpoint-source pollution. Implementation Practice is a specific type of management, hardware, or combination of management and hardware that will help in achieving the OMO. Depending on the situation, different IPs, or combinations of IPs, may be used to achieve the same OMO.

Complete understanding and effective use of the IPs in achieving the objectives requires an integrated knowledge of water quality issues and the contamination process. To that end the IMP Manual will provide the following:

1. A summary discussion of water-quality issues in Washington State.
2. A summary discussion of how water pollution occurs.
3. A summary discussion of irrigation science.
4. A presentation of OMOs to reduce the potential for water pollution, and IPs that will help achieve the objectives.
5. A listing of government and private resources available to growers to help achieve the objectives.

It is important to realize that science is not static. The objectives and practices listed in the IMP Manual are generally recognized to be effective in reducing the potential for point- and nonpoint-source pollution. However, there may be other practices not presented in the IMP Manual that are also effective. And, science and practical experience will develop new practices in the future. The IMP Manual is a living document. There will be periodic revisions to update objectives and practices.

AKART and the IMP Manual

Washington law states that "all known, available, and reasonable methods of prevention, control, and treatment" (AKART) will be implemented for those activities with the potential to pollute water. AKART must be used no matter what the quality of the receiving water. Further, if existing AKART are not sufficient to protect water quality, additional controls must be used.

Previous efforts leading to the current definition of AKART for agricultural land use included the "208 Irrigated Agriculture Water Quality Management Plan." This was a two-year planning effort mandated by Section 208 of the 1972 Federal Clean Water Act. As a part of this plan, *Management Practices for Irrigated Agriculture* was published by the Washington State Department of Ecology (Ecology) in 1979 (DOE Publication #79-5B-1). This was a listing of best management practices for irrigated agriculture which would help in protecting surface water quality.

Listings of best management practices for other sources of nonpoint-source pollution are identified in Table 1.

The OMOs and IPs presented in the IMP Manual may be considered additional AKART for irrigated agriculture. The IMP Manual is a response to Section 319 of the Federal Clean Water Act which mandates development of programs for control and reduction of nonpoint-source pollution of both surface and ground water.

Surface and ground waters are interrelated. Ground water is surface water that has percolated into and through the ground to an aquifer. Ground water may move back into surface water bodies through seeps, springs, or base flow into a river or lake depending on the geology of an area. Contaminated ground water can move into uncontaminated aquifers or return to surface water, depending on the geology. The IMP Manual addresses the interrelationship of ground and surface water and the concurrent impact of irrigated agriculture on them. The IMP Manual recognizes that protecting surface water must not adversely affect ground water and vice versa.

It is important to note that although the OMOs and IPs presented in the IMP Manual may be considered AKART, they may not be sufficient to absolutely protect ground or surface water quality, depending on the situation. Measures beyond the implementation of the practices presented in the IMP Manual may be necessary to protect water quality.

The process of pollution

Understanding how pollution occurs leads to a more effective choice of IPs to achieve an OMO. Pollution is the result of a series of processes. They can be generally categorized as availability, detachment, and transport.

1. *Availability* - Availability means that there is a potentially polluting substance in some amount and in some place. The potential pollutant could be sediment (from a highly erosive soil), nutrient (excess fertilizer in or on the soil, or from mineralization of crop residues), pesticide, bacteria, or some other harmful matter

2. *Detachment* - Detachment means that the potential pollutant or its environment is modified so that the substance can be moved from where it is supposed to be to where it should not be. For example, a pesticide is sprayed on a field. The residue adsorbs to soil particles. Because of excess irrigation or rainfall, or just a highly erosive soil in a high wind, the soil particles separate from the rest of the field. That is detachment. A substance dissolving into water is also a form of detachment since in many cases the substance will move readily with percolation. This type of detachment may or may not result in significant pollution depending on the substance. For example, the ammonium form of dissolved nitrogen (NH_4) does not move readily with water while the nitrate (NO_3) form is highly leachable. Hereafter, when the term "detachment" is used, it implies either:

   a. *a physical separation of soil particles (with or without adsorbed chemicals or nutrients) or,*

b. the dissolving of a chemical that allows it to move readily with surface runoff or deep percolation. The surface runoff or deep percolation could be the result of natural rainfall or irrigations.

3. *Transport* - Transport means that the pollutant is moved to where it may be harmful. For example, the soil particle carrying pesticide residues is carried off the field with surface runoff from irrigations or rainfall, or high winds. The runoff carrying the sediment then enters a river or lake. Another example is nitrate (NO_3) fertilizer being leached into ground water through excessive irrigation (intentional or not).

To summarize, pollution occurs through availability, detachment, and transport. There is a potentially polluting substance in some amount in some place (available). The substance can be separated from where it is supposed to be (detachment). And finally, the substance moves to where it becomes harmful to man or the environment (transport).

Thus, the main factors in reducing potential pollution are:

1. Minimizing availability of the potential pollutant in the environment
2. Minimizing detachment of the substance
3. Minimizing transport of the substance

The OMOs and IPs presented in the IMP Manual are all aimed at either availability, detachment, or transport.

The IMP Manual includes discussions of specific physical processes, such as the nitrogen and phosphorous cycles, detailing the important variables governing pollution from nitrogen and phosphorous. The IMP Manual also includes discussions of the factors involved in determining the susceptibility of any one chemical to become a pollutant. There is a section on basic soil-water-plant relationships and discussions of each of the major irrigation system types. The background science presented in the IMP Manual will help growers make more effective decisions as to what practices to use.

Overall Management Objectives

The following six Overall Management Objectives are presented in the Manual:

1. Minimize water losses in the on-farm distribution system. The distribution system is the combination of pipes and ditches that move water from the primary source (a canal gate, river, stream, or reservoir) to individual fields. Deep percolation, or excessive spill, can move contaminants to ground water reservoirs or natural surface waters.

2. Improve irrigation system performance and management in order to minimize deep percolation and surface runoff. Surface runoff or deep percolation from poorly timed or excessive irrigations are prime transport mechanisms for contaminants. Irrigation systems, no matter how sophisticated the hardware, are only as efficient as their management.

3. Manage fertilizer program so as to minimize excess nutrients available for movement. This OMO addresses both the availability and detachment processes. Excessive or inappropriate (either nonuniform or wrong formulations) fertilizer applications increase the possibility of detachment and transport.

4. Manage crop protection program so as to minimize chemical residues available for transport. This OMO is similar to the previous one but is intended to address herbicide, pesticide, or fungicide applications.

5. Reduce contamination of surface water from sedimentation. Certain irrigation methods will result in surface runoff. An unexpected rain will also produce runoff. There are certain practices that can reduce runoff's erosive action (a detachment process). There are also practices that can be used to treat runoff so as to prevent further transport of sediments and nutrients, or adsorbed chemicals.

6. Prevent direct aquifer contamination via wells. Water wells are a direct link between surface activities and ground water. This OMO addresses those practices associated with chemigation and protection of the well head.

Improving irrigation performance

The IMP Manual is aimed at irrigated agriculture. Thus, the achievement of OMO 2.00, "Improve Irrigation System Performance and Management in Order to Minimize Deep Percolation and Surface Runoff," is a primary goal of the IMP Manual.

A common question is: "How do I know if I am improving irrigation performance?"

There are two measurements: distribution uniformity and irrigation efficiency.

1. Distribution uniformity - how evenly water soaks into the ground. If eight inches soaks in at one side of the field and four inches at the other, that is poor uniformity. Four inches all over the field would be the ideal but is practically and economically impossible.

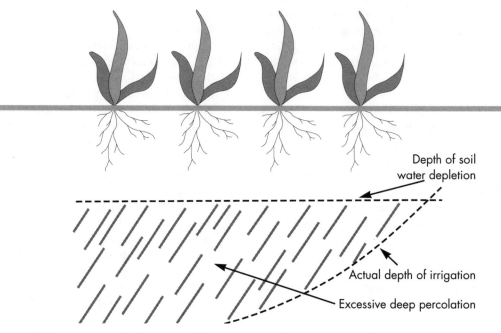

FIGURE 1. Depiction of irrigation resulting in poor distribution uniformity and excessive.

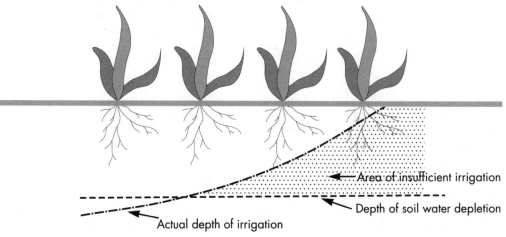

FIGURE 2. Depiction of irrigation resulting in poor distribution uniformity and insufficient irrigation in parts of the field.

2. Irrigation efficiency - how much of the applied water is used beneficially. Beneficial uses include crop water use (evapotranspiration), leaching for salt control, frost control, crop cooling, and other cultural purposes.

Distribution uniformity is a fairly straightforward concept and there are many methods employed to measure it. The Soil Conservation Service (SCS) employs standardized evaluation processes. Check with a local SCS or Conservation District office for information on evaluating distribution uniformity.

Irrigation efficiency can be somewhat harder to evaluate. One problem is the question of "beneficial uses" versus "beneficially used." That is, some leaching for salt control is needed to maintain agronomic viability. The question is how much. Another problem is accounting for surface runoff and deep percolation that returns to useable sources. They may or may not be counted against efficiency depending if the measure is for a specific field, for a specific farm, for a specific irrigation district, or a specific project or basin.

It is important to note that regardless of accounting for surface runoff and deep percolation for irrigation efficiency measurements, reducing runoff and percolation is almost always an objective for control and reduction of nonpoint-source pollution.

In discussing OMOs and their potential effects on water quantity and quality it is necessary to understand two important relationships between distribution uniformity and irrigation efficiency. They are graphically described in Figures 1 through 4.

Figures 1 through 4 are generalized depictions of a furrow profile with the top of the furrow, which will generally soak in the most water, at the left of the graphic. The horizontal, dashed line in the figures depicts the depth of the actual soil-water deficit at irrigation. This is the amount of water that the grower would be trying to soak into the soil to satisfy crop water-use requirements. The dotted-dashed line depicts the actual depth of water infiltrated during the irrigation.

Deep percolation is indicated whenever the depth of irrigation (the dotted-dashed line) is below the soil water deficit line (the horizontal, dashed line). Conversely, under-irrigation is indicated whenever the depth of irrigation line is above the soil-water deficit line. The depths multiplied by the area of a field indicate the volumes of water applied, stored, etc.

The first relationship is that there must be good distribution uniformity before there can be good irrigation efficiency, *if the crop is to be sufficiently watered.* This is demonstrated by Figures 1 and 2.

In Figure 1, the farmer has irrigated to sufficiently water the entire field. The poor distribution uniformity has resulted in excessive deep percolation. That is, the deep percolation was much more than would be needed to maintain a salt balance.

In Figure 2, the farmer has acted to prevent excessive deep percolation. Now part of the field remains under-irrigated. Under-irrigation usually results in a high irrigation irrigation efficiency as most water applied is stored in the root zone, available for plant use. But it may not be an effective way of growing as the resulting water stress on the crop in some parts of the field will usually decrease yields. Also, there is the need for some deep percolation for leaching to maintain a salt balance. Note that the leaching must be uniform over a number of years to prevent areas of excessive salt accumulation.

The second relationship is that good distribution uniformity is no guarantee of good irrigation efficiency. Figures 3 and 4 show that a good distribution uniformity allows a good irrigation efficiency, but the total amount of water applied must still be controlled.

Figure 3 depicts a good irrigation. There was high distribution uniformity as indicated by the flatter infiltrated depth line (the dotted-dashed line). About the right amount of water was applied. There is little deep percolation (enough for salt control) and the entire field is wetted sufficiently. It is assumed that surface runoff was minimal or reused.

Figure 4 depicts an irrigation with the same high distribution uniformity (same flat infiltrated water). However, twice as much water as needed was applied, resulting in a low irrigation efficiency. A practical example of this situation is the farmer who is using a well-designed and maintained micro-irrigation system. The hardware provides good distribution uniformity and the potential for high irrigation efficiency. But if the farmer runs the system twice as long as necessary, that potential is not realized.

Summary

Figures 1 through 4 demonstrate that:

1. Improved irrigation system hardware may result in higher distribution uniformity and also make it easier to achieve higher irrigation efficiency

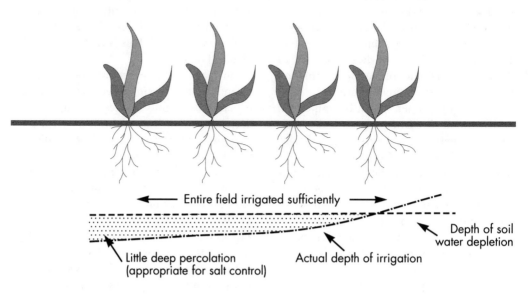

FIGURE 3. Depiction of an irrigation sufficiently watering the entire field with good distribution uniformity and application efficiency.

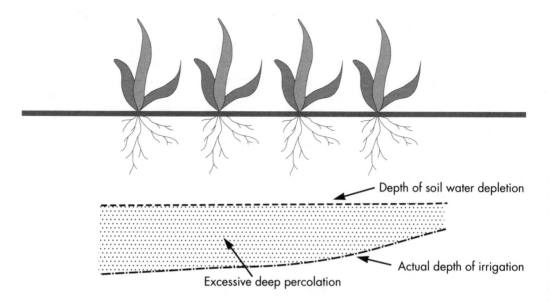

FIGURE 4. Depiction of irrigation resulting in good distribution uniformity but poor irrigation efficiency

2. Achieving high irrigation efficiency ultimately depends on the management of the system.

Remember, hardware is only as good as the management. An appropriate, well designed, and well maintained irrigation system is the basis for good distribution uniformity. However, the best designed, maintained and uniform trickle-irrigation system will only be 50 percent efficient if run twice as long as required.

Following are the basic factors in modern irrigation management, regardless of irrigation system type:

1. Know *when* to irrigate. This is an agronomic decision based on how the crop is developing. Sometimes, the choice of *when* to irrigate can increase the efficiency of irrigation, especially if water deliveries are on a set 12- or 24-hour basis. Some type and level of irrigation scheduling should be practiced by every grower. (Note that this does not mean everyone should be using a computer with a detailed water budget equation and a neutron probe for back-up soil moisture measurements.)

2. Know *how much* to irrigate. Have a purpose for each irrigation, the placement of a certain amount of water into a certain amount of soil. Again, some sort of irrigation scheduling, or, just feeling the soil (note the SCS pamphlet "Estimating Soil Moisture by Feel and Appearance"), is helpful.

3. Know *how* to irrigate. Know how to achieve high uniformity with control of the total application. Each irrigation system has certain operational characteristics to understand. These characteristics guide management in achieving uniform irrigations while controlling the total amount of water soaking into the soil.

4. PLAN each irrigation. There are certain techniques that can be used to plan an irrigation. They depend on knowing HOW MUCH to irrigate and HOW to react during an irrigation.

5. Follow the legal and practical requirements for chemigation.

Addressing the above factors, using one or more of the suggested Implementation Practices presented in the IMP Manual, will help to achieve the Overall Management Objective 2.00: "Improve overall irrigation performance so as to minimize deep percolation and surface runoff."

In conjunction with achieving the other OMOs, this will help to reduce and control nonpoint-source pollution from irrigated agriculture."

Water quality and treatment considerations

Robert G. Stevens
Extension Soil Scientist
Irrigated Agriculture Research and Extension Center, Washington State University, Prosser

A s society has become more aware of environmental quality and its effect on their lifestyles, water quality has surfaced as a major issue. People are concerned about what is in the water they drink and use for many other activities. The public is acutely aware that agricultural practices can affect their water quality. However, the general public does not seem to be aware that water quality has a major impact on agricultural producers. Producers also drink water, generally from ground water under their farms, and in the case of irrigated agriculture, they rely on irrigation to produce their crops. The quality of water supplied to the producer is vital to the producer's farming practices.

This chapter will address the chemical properties of water important to irrigation and cooling and how these properties can be altered. The effect of water quality on both soil properties and fruit quality will be covered. It will not address the effect of management practices on the quality of water leaving the farm through either leaching or runoff.

The quality of water delivered to the producer can vary widely across the Pacific Northwest. Quality of water supplied directly from rivers will depend upon the geology of the source area and any pollution prior to diversion. The quality of canal water will depend upon both the quality of the original river water and the quantity of return flow that has been added back to the canal before producers receive their allocations. Water quality from wells can vary widely depending upon the chemistry of geologic material from which the water is being extracted.

Because of the variability possible, the first step in evaluating any irrigation or cooling project should be to have the water analyzed. Because stream flows and return flows may vary during the year, it is advisable to sample more than once during the growing season. During low-flow years, water quality may be significantly poorer because of low volumes and a greater percentage of return flows. During years of potential low flow, management practices should be adjusted to compensate for potential degradation of water quality.

WATER ANALYSIS

The first step is to select a laboratory to do the analysis. Most soil-testing laboratories can perform water analysis for irrigation management. The laboratory should be contacted to determine if it can perform the analysis needed. The laboratory will also provide information on how to take the sample.

The following water quality parameters should be determined on all waters that are to be used for irrigation or cooling:

pH

The pH of a water sample is probably the most valuable indicator of other potential problems. The pH of the water is simply a measurement of the hydrogen (H^+) ion concentration or the relative acidity of the water. Over time, high or low pH waters can slowly change the soil pH, but this is generally not a management problem except at very high pH levels. Water pH values above 7.8 generally indicate potential problems with carbonate (CO_3^{2-}) or bicarbonate (HCO_3^-).

An important agronomic concern with water pH is its effect on pesticide activity. Pesticide labels should be consulted to determine the optimum pH range for a chemical.

Electrical conductivity

The electrical conductivity (EC) is a measure of the total salt content of the sample and it is reported in millimhos per centimeter (mmhos/cm) or decisiemens per meter (dS/m) which are equivalent numerically. A higher EC corresponds to a higher salt content.

The EC of an irrigation water can be used to estimate the potential for soil salinity problems. Soil salinity is commonly reported in terms of the EC of an extract from a saturated soil paste. Soils have been classified as saline (excessively salty) when EC is greater than four mmhos/cm. It is important to remember that more salt-sensitive crops such as small trees may be damaged by soil EC values of two mmhos/cm or below, depending upon management practices.

Because of evaporation from the soil surface and plant transpiration, much of the applied water is lost from the soil, leaving most of the soluble salts behind. Therefore, even waters with less than three mmhos/cm can lead to potentially high salt problems. Leaching with excess water is required to maintain the productivity of most irrigated soils in arid and semi-arid regions; however, leaching of salts from the root zone should be scheduled in the cropping sequence when residual soil nitrate levels are at a minimum.

Dissolved salts

Many salts are dissolved in typical irrigation waters and a complete analysis will provide concentrations of the individual ions. Concentration of specific ions will generally be reported in both milligrams per liter (mg/l) and, based on ionic charge, as milliequivalents per liter (meq/l).

The units of milligrams per liter may also be reported as parts per million (ppm). Calculation of several important water quality parameters will require the conversion (see Table 1) of ppm to meq/l so that ions can be compared based on electrical charge.

Calcium and magnesium

Calcium (Ca) and magnesium (Mg) are the principal divalent cations (ions having a charge of +2) in both irrigation water and the soil solution. The concentration of Ca^{2+} and Mg^{2+} will greatly influence the effect of water on soil structure and infiltration. Calcium concentration will also play a critical role in determining precipitate formation in water applied by over-tree sprinklers.

Sodium

The main effect of sodium (Na) in the orchard system is its negative effect on soil structure. Sodium may also have a direct

TABLE 1. Factors for converting meq/liter to mg/liter (ppm).

Ion	Multiplier	Ion	Multiplier
Ca^{2+}	20.0	HCO_3^-	61.0
Mg^{2+}	12.1	CO_3^{2-}	30.0
Na^+	23.0	SO_4^{2-}	48.0
K^+	39.1	NO_3^-	14.0

effect on plants when uptake is excessive. Progressive leaf-tip and marginal burn become evident at leaf sodium levels above about 0.2 percent. Foliar analyses can reveal if excess levels of Na^+ are accumulating prior to burn in environments where sodium problems are suspected.

Potassium

High levels of potassium (K) in Pacific Northwest irrigation waters are not common. In some areas when very pure water (very low salt levels) is used, monovalent K^+ may act like Na^+ and cause a breakdown in structure, leading to soil sealing.

Sulfur and nitrogen

Water is analyzed for sulfur (S) as sulfate (SO_4^{2-}). Sulfate is the form of sulfur utilized by plants. Irrigation water can supply a significant amount of the plant's requirement for SO_4^{2-}. However, some Washington State river waters are very low in SO_4^{2-} and fertilizer SO_4^{2-} will need to be increased in these areas if native soil levels are low.

Water samples are typically analyzed for nitrate (NO_3^-) nitrogen because high levels of NO_3^- can contribute significantly to plant-available nitrogen supplies. Some Northwest wells are high enough in NO_3^- that this supply should be factored into nitrogen recommendation to avoid excess nitrogen applications.

Carbonate and bicarbonate

Both carbonate (CO_3^{2-}) and bicarbonate (HCO_3^-) have a significant effect on water and soil pH, as well as calcium and sodium relationships. Canal waters that have a large portion of return flow and deep wells can have high HCO_3^- levels. The proportion of carbon in the water as CO_3^{2-} and HCO_3^- is controlled by water pH. At a pH of 10.5, approximately equal amounts of CO_3^{2-} and HCO_3^- will be found in water samples. As pH decreases, the portion of HCO_3^- increases to where all the carbon is HCO_3^- at approximately pH 8.5. High bicarbonate waters may cause soil pH to increase over time through the precipitation of $CaCO_3$. This higher pH may lead to micronutrient deficiencies, especially iron.

Boron and chloride

In many irrigated areas high concentrations of boron and chloride may represent a specific ion hazard; however, in Washington State this is generally not the case.

General guidelines for interpretation of water quality for irrigation can be seen in Table 2 (Vomocil and Hart, 1990).

IRRIGATION CONCERNS

Irrigation water quality affects water management by affecting the plant's ability to extract water from the soil and by altering infiltration and hydraulic conductivity rates. High pH waters also can affect soil pH and sodium accumulation, and thus nutrient availability as indicated above.

High soil salinity causes moisture stress in plants. As indicated above, soil EC values above 2.0 should be of concern in orchards. High salinity can be reduced by establishing drainage and leaching salts from the root zone. Leaching fractions needed will depend upon water quality and can be calculated from data in Handbook No. 60 (U.S. Salinity Laboratory Staff, 1954) or provided in Halvorson and Dow (1975).

Water infiltration into and hydraulic conductivity through soil can be reduced by the breakdown of soil structure on the soil surface. As soil structure breaks down, clay and silt particles settle into adjacent pores, plugging the pores and reducing the infiltration rate. Structure breakdown can be caused by the impact of water on the soil surface. It is accelerated by high quantities of Na^+ in low-salt irrigation water. High Na^+ levels in irrigation water leads to high exchangeable Na^+ levels on the exchange sites. High exchangeable Na^+ leads to dispersion of soil particles and loss of soil structure. A surface sodic (high Na^+) layer leads to decreased infiltration and poor aeration conditions. This is caused by the formation of platy structure at the soil surface. Sodic soils are normally defined as having an exchangeable sodium percentage (ESP) greater that 15 percent. In order to estimate the ESP of soil irrigated with a given water, a water parameter called the sodium adsorption ration (SAR) is calculated. The SAR is defined in Equation 1:

Equation 1

$$SAR = \frac{Na}{\sqrt{\dfrac{Ca+Mg}{2}}}$$

where all concentrations are in meq/l. The SAR of a soil extract is approximately equal to the equilibrium ESP of the associated soil, to ESP or SAR values of 30 to 40. However, the SAR of an irrigation water is usually 1.5- to 2-fold less than the equilibrium ESP of soil to be irrigated with that water, because of the increase in the soil's salt concentration as water is transpired by the crop.

Irrigation waters of SAR above four or five can be potentially hazardous for tree fruits on many of the silt-loam soils of eastern Washington and Oregon, and southcentral Idaho (McNeal, 1982). As can be seen in Table 2, the immediate potential for a negative effect of high SAR on soil infiltration is reduced by high salinity in the water. High salt levels encourage flocculation of soil particles. However, extended use of any waters with high SAR values will lead to soil degradation and management problems. Therefore, corrective action should be taken as soon as high SAR waters are used for irrigation.

Many deep ground waters in eastern Washington have very high levels of HCO_3^-. These high levels of HCO_3^- can lead to increased Na^+ hazard for soils irrigated with the water. The increased Na^+ hazard for the SAR is caused by the HCO_3^- reacting with Ca^{2+} in the irrigation water or in the soil solution to precipitate calcium carbonate (lime) by the following reaction:

Equation 2:

$$Ca^{2+} + 2HCO_3^- \rightarrow CaCO_3\downarrow + H_2O + CO_2\uparrow$$

This reaction lowers the soil solution Ca^{2+} levels and thus will produce a corresponding increase in SAR, since soluble Na^+ levels remain unchanged.

The tendency for lime precipitation can be determined from a water analysis by calculating an <u>adjusted</u> SAR value *(Table 3)*. This is an estimate of the SAR which will result after excess calcium carbonate ($CaCO_3$) has precip-

itated from the water. The adjusted SAR is calculated from the pH_c, a theoretical pH for the water after equilibration with precipitated calcium carbonate at atmospheric carbon dioxide levels. Either or both of these terms may appear on a water analysis report.

There are two general approaches to handling high HCO_3^- waters with a Na^+ risk. The first is to treat the water to remove the HCO_3^- prior to irrigation. Alternatives for this approach will be covered in detail in the orchard cooling portion of this chapter. The second approach is to treat the soil to remove the Na^+ from the exchange sites. This must be a two-step process: 1) establishment of drainage so that Na^+ can be leached from the root zone, and 2) providing Ca^{2+} ions to replace the Na^+ from the exchange sites.

The latter can be accomplished through the addition of gypsum ($CaSO_4 \cdot H_2O$) to maintain high soluble ca levels. On calcareous soils (soils containing calcium carbonate), sulfur (S) can be added. The elemental S is microbially oxidized to sulfuric acid (H_2SO_4) producing acidity that dissolves the calcium carbonate, thus supplying Ca^{2+} to the soil solution.

COOLING CONCERNS

The acceptance of cooling as a practice to improve color and quality of fruit has brought with it significant management and environmental concerns. The most immediate concern is the formation of precipitates on the surface of the apples. These residues are very difficult to remove during the washing process and can lead to down grading. Very small amounts of these residues left on the surface of fruit may possibly be seen by the consumer as pesticide residue. The second and more long-term concern is the effect of cooling waters on the soil environment.

The primary precipitate concern is the formation of calcium carbonate (lime) on the fruit surface. The potential for cooling water to form lime is referred to as the lime-deposition potential (Halvorson and Dow, 1975), which is defined as the maximum quantity of lime that can be precipitated from a water. The formation of lime is controlled by Equation 2. Therefore, the lime-deposition potential is equal to the smaller of the two quantities; Ca^{2+} or $(CO_3^{2-} + HCO_3^-)$ concentration in meq/l.

The lime deposition potential is expressed as milliequivalent of lime ($CaCO_3$) per liter. Under conditions where the water is being evaporated from a surface, the lime formation reaction proceeds to the right causing the maximum amount of lime to be deposited. The concentration of HCO_3^- and CO_3^{2-} must be added together because both will react with

Ca^{2+} to form $CaCO_3$. An example of the lime deposition potential for a water source is given in Table 4.

The lime deposition potential as a precipitate on the fruit surface is determined not only by the water quality, but also by environmental factors.

If we look closely at the objective of fruit cooling, it is to lower the temperature of the fruit itself. The most effective way to accom-

TABLE 2. General guidelines for interpretation of water quality for irrigation as adopted from Vomocil & Hart (1990).

GUIDELINES FOR INTERPRETATION OF WATER QUALITY FOR IRRIGATION[1]

Potential irrigation problem	Units	None	Degree of restriction on uses Slight to moderate	Severe
Salinity, water availability influence[2]				
ECW	dS/m or millimhos/cm	< 0.7	0.7 - 3.0	> 3.0
TDS	mg/L or ppm	< 450	450 - 2000	> 2000
Salinity, infiltration influence				
If = 0-3 and =		> 0.7	0.7 - 0.2	< 0.2
SAR[3] EC_W				
= 3-6 =		> 1.2	1.2 - 0.3	< 0.3
= 6-12 =		> 1.9	1.9 - 0.5	< 0.5
= 12-20 =		> 2.9	2.9 - 1.3	< 1.3
= 20-40 =		> 5.0	5.0 - 2.9	< 2.9
Specific ion toxicity *(affects sensitive crops)*				
Sodium (NA)[4]				
surface irrigation	SAR	< 3	3 - 9	> 9
sprinkler irrigation	meq/L	< 3	> 3	
Chloride (Cl)[4]				
surface irrigation	meq/L	< 4	4 - 10	> 10
sprinkler irrigation	meq/L[5]	< 3	> 3	
Boron (B)	mg/L or ppm	< 0.7	< 0.7 - 2.0	> 3.0
Miscellaneous effects *(affects susceptible crops)*				
Nitrogen (NO_3^- N)[6]	meq/L	<5	5 - 30	> 30
Bicarbonate (HCO^{3-})	meq/L	< 1.5	1.5 - 7.5	> 7.5
pH[7]			Normal range 6.5 - 8.4	

1   From Vomocil & Hart (1990) as adapted from Ayers and Westcott, 1985. These parameters may be overly restrictive for Northwest climatic conditions.
2   EC_W = electrical conductivity, a measure of the water salinity, reported in decisiemens per meter at 25°C (dS/m) or equivalent units, millimhos per centimeter (mmho/cm). TDS (total dissolved solids, reported in milligrams per liter (mg/L).
3   SAR = sodium adsorption ratio (sometimes reported as RNa). Applicable only in arid and semi-arid zones. Standard SAR only, not adjusted. The relationship between EC, SAR, and infiltration usually does not apply if soil pH is below 7. At a given SAR, infiltration rate increases as water salinity increases. Evaluate the potential infiltration problem by SAR as modified by EC_W. Adapted from Rhoades 1977, and Oster and Schroer 1979.
4   Most tree crops and woody plants are sensitive to Na and Cl; for surface irrigation use the SAR values shown. Most annual crops are not sensitive; for surface irrigation use the salinity tolerance tables from Ayers and Westcott, 1985, p31. With overhead sprinkler irrigation and low humidity (< 30%), Na and Cl may be absorbed through the leaves of sensitive crops.
5   To convert ppm to meq, divide meq by the following values for each component: Na - 23, Cl - 35, HCO_3^- - 61, and B - 11.
6   NO3-N means nitrate nitrogen reported in terms of elemental N. NH4-N and organic -N should be included when wastewater is being tested.
7   Fertilizer applications can change water and soil pH and have an effect on the potential toxicity of ions in the irrigation water

plish this goal is to evaporate water directly from the surface of the fruit. This process then creates the ideal conditions for the formation of a lime precipitate on the fruit surface. Therefore, when a water is completely evaporated on fruit or leaf surfaces, the complete lime deposition potential is expressed.

Halvorson and Dow (1975) first established the use of the lime deposition potential as a tool in developing management practices for overtree irrigation. Their guidelines as seen in Table 5 were established to prevent lime precipitation. It is important to remember that these management recommendations

TABLE 3. Calculation of the adjusted SAR of irrigation water (Stroehlein & Tisdale, 1975).

$$\text{adj. SAR} = \frac{Na}{\sqrt{\dfrac{Ca+Mg}{2}}}[1 + (8.4 - pHc)]$$

$pHc = (pK'_2 - pK'c) + p(Ca+Mg) + pAlk.$

pK'_2 is the second dissociation constant for H_2SO_3 and pHc is the solubility constant for $CaCO_2$, both corrected for ionic strength.

$p(Ca+Mg)$ is the negative logarithm of the molar concentration of calcium plus magnesium.

$pAlk$ is the negative logarithm of the molar concentration of the total bases ($CO_3^{2-} + HCO_3^-$).

pHc is a theoretical, calculated pH of irrigation water in contact with lime and in equilibrium with soil CO_2^-.

Obtained from water analysis $\left\{\begin{array}{l} (pK'_2-pK'C) \text{ is obtained from using the sum of Ca+Mg+Na in meq/l} \\ p\,(Ca+Mg) \text{ is obtained from using the sum of Ca+Mg in meq/l} \\ p\,(Alk) \text{ is obtained from using the sum of } CO_3+HCO_3 \text{ in meq/1l} \end{array}\right.$

Sum of Concentration (meq/l)	pK'2-pK'c	p(Ca+Mg)	p(Alk)	Sum of Concentration (meq/l)	pK'2-pK'c	p(Ca+Mg)	p(Alk)
.05	2.0	4.6	4.3	2.5	2.2	2.9	2.6
.10	2.0	4.3	4.0	3.0	2.2	2.8	2.5
.15	2.0	4.1	3.8	4.0	2.2	2.7	2.4
.20	2.0	4.0	3.7	5.0	2.2	2.6	2.3
.25	2.0	3.9	3.6	6.0	2.2	2.5	2.2
.30	2.0	3.8	3.5	8.0	2.3	2.4	2.1
.40	2.0	3.7	3.4	10.0	2.3	2.3	2.0
.50	2.1	3.6	3.3	12.5	2.3	2.2	1.9
.50	2.1	3.6	3.3	15.0	2.3	2.1	1.8
.75	2.1	3.4	3.1	20.0	2.4	2.0	1.7
1.00	2.1	3.3	3.0	30.0	2.4	1.8	1.5
1.25	2.1	3.2	2.9	50.0	2.5	1.6	1.3
1.5	2.1	3.1	2.8	80.0	2.5	1.4	1.1
2.0	2.2	3.0	2.7				

An example of calculating pHc:

A water sample contains:

Ca = 1.82 meq/l

Mg = 0.75 meq/l

Na = 6.70 meq/l

Ca + Mg + Na = 9.27 meq/l

Ca + Mg = 2.57 meq/l

$CO_3^{2-} + HCO_3^- = 0.35$ meq/l

$CO_3^{2-} = 0.05$ meq/l

$HCO_3^- = 0.30$ meq/l

From the table: $pK'_2 - pK'c = 2.3$

$p(Ca+Mg) = 2.8$

$p(Alk) = \underline{3.5}$

Total = 8.6

were not for cooling with overtree systems.

Several factors affect the rate of lime accumulation and properties of the lime precipitated on the fruit. As indicated, the dominant factor is the lime-deposition potential. The rate of water application and the speed of sprinkler rotation will also have an effect. The higher the rate of application, the more fruit washing takes place and, therefore, more of the lime formed is washed off the fruit surface. The higher the rate of evaporation, the more rapidly the Ca^{2+} and HCO_3^- become concentrated and the more rapidly lime will form.

Under irrigation conditions, the longer the trees are subject to wetting the less lime forms. This would also hold under cooling conditions; however, since intermittent cooling is probably optimum, the length of time between cooling sequences will also be important. The longer the time before rewetting, the drier the fruit becomes and the more difficult it is to remove lime formed during the previous cooling. The optimum length of time between cooling sequences will depend on equipment capacities, orchard design, and weather conditions.

Theoretically, under conditions of optimum overtree cooling, all the water applied would be evaporated from leaf and fruit surfaces. Therefore, even at very low lime-deposition potential, some precipitation will be formed. Under these conditions, levels below 2 meq/l may represent a significant threat for precipitation formation. The level of lime-deposition potential that can be managed without formation of significant lime will depend upon the overtree system and management of the system. Therefore, experimentation is probably the only means to determine the actual potential for lime precipitation with relatively low lime-deposition potential water in a given orchard.

It is apparent that to reduce actual precipitate remaining on the fruit at harvest one must either 1) reduce the lime-deposition potential, or 2) manage the system to minimize the amount of precipitate remaining after each cooling episode. A producer will have to experiment with his or her cooling

TABLE 4. Water quality analysis and lime deposition potential for a potential water supply for orchard cooling.

pH	7.7	Ca^{2+}	2.7 meq/l
EC	0.43 mmhos/cm	Mg^{2+}	1.2 meq/l
CO_3^{2-}	0.8 meq/l	Na^+	0.6 meq/l
HCO_3^-	3.4 meq/l		

Lime Deposition Potential 2.7 meq/l

TABLE 5. Lime-deposition potential of the irrigation water and subsequent irrigation management recommendations (Halvorson and Dow, 1975).

Lime Deposition Potential *meq lime (CaCO3)/liter*	(ppm Ca^{2+} + CO_2)	Water Application Rate *inches per hour*
2	100	No limitations
2-3	100-150	More than 0.2
3-4	150-200	More than 0.2 and irrigate only at night
over 4	200 or more	Not recommended for overhead irrigation

system to determine the management that maximizes cooling while minimizing precipitate formation. There are several ways that the quality of the water can be altered to reduce the lime-deposition potential.

The use of cooling as a management tool may affect significantly overall irrigation and nutrient management. Growers must do an effective job of monitoring soil moisture to assure that optimum soil moisture conditions are maintained. If less water is reaching the orchard floor than expected and irrigation is reduced, the soil may actually become too dry during periods of cooling.

On the other hand, if excess water is being applied over long cooling sets, soils may become saturated. Prolonged periods of saturation in the root zone can lead to poor root function and increased incidence of root disease. Over-application of water may also increase leaching loss of mobile nutrients such as nitrate. Leaching of nitrate may cause reduced nitrogen supply to the tree, as well as represent a potential for nitrate contamination of ground water.

IMPROVING WATER QUALITY

There are currently several different means of altering water quality available to the grower. Each method has its advantages and disadvantages. There does not appear to be any one method that will work best under all conditions and system designs. Each method must be evaluated as to its ability to reduce the precipitation problem, its effects on the trees, its long-term effect on soil's physical and chemical properties, and its cost effectiveness under a grower's management system.

Dilution

The dilution of poor quality water with high quality water has been effective in improving overtree irrigation results; however, dilution does not eliminate the total amount of Ca^{2+} or HCO_3^- in the water. As the water is evaporates during cooling, these ions are concentrated and precipitation can occur. For dilution to be used successfully in overtree cooling systems, the system must be operated to apply large amounts of water frequently to minimize precipitate on the fruit. These high

application volumes may have some significant negative impacts on soils and roots.

Sulfur burners

Sulfur burners or sulfurous generators currently are being used to improve water quality. As with other acid treatments, the sulfur burner works by removing HCO_3^- from the water supply. A sulfur burner burns elemental sulfur to produce acid to neutralize a percentage of the HCO_3^- in the water source according to the following:

Equation 3:
$$S + O_2 \rightarrow SO_2$$

Equation 4:
$$H_2O + SO_2 \rightarrow H_2SO_3$$

Equation 5:
$$H_2SO_3 \rightarrow H^+ + HSO_3^-$$

Equation 6:
$$HCO_3^- + H^+ \rightarrow H_2O + CO_2$$

In the combustion chamber, the sulfur burns with oxygen from the air and produces the gas sulfur dioxide (SO_2). As can be seen in Equation 4, in the SO_2 gas-scrubbing chamber, the SO_2 is dissolved in the irrigation water which passes through the chamber. This concentrated solution of hydrated SO_2, often referred to as sulfurous acid, results in a pH of about two to three, and is fairly corrosive. However, almost as soon as this concentrated solution forms, it is injected into the main irrigation stream. Upon injection into the main stream, half of the acidity is released as H^+ *(Equation 5)*. These H^+ ions react with the HCO_3^- in the solution and eliminate it by conversion to H_2O and CO_2 *(Equation 6)*. If enough sulfur is burned to drop the pH of the irrigation water to 6.3 to 6.5, much of the HCO_3^- and all of the CO_3^{2-} in the water will be removed. There will be some HCO_3^- remaining in the water and therefore some precipitation potential will exist. It is generally suggested that irrigation water pH be maintained at approximately 6.5 to minimize corrosion problems.

By significantly reducing the level of

HCO_3^- in the water, the lime deposition potential of the water is significantly reduced. The pH 6.5 water also helps remove any precipitate that is formed on the fruit surface. Water used for overtree cooling must be continually treated because the pH 6.5 water will not remove well-attached precipitate.

The other half of the acidity formed in the sulfur burner reaches the soil as the bisulfite (HSO_3^-) ion *(Equation 5)*. Once the HSO_3^- ions enter the soil, they react with oxygen chemically or are transformed by soil microorganisms *(Thiobacillus)* into SO_4^{2-} ions and H^+. These acidic H^+ ions can react with and dissolve any lime in the soil. This process is important on soils where Na^+ from the irrigation water has created sodic problems as described above. The released Ca^{2+} ions will increase Ca^{2+} concentration in the soil solution, replacing the Na^+ from the exchange sites. The additional soil acidification may be helpful on calcareous soils where micro-zones of lowered pH may increase the availability of micronutrients such as iron.

The acidity added to the soil by sulfur burners may have a negative effect on acid soils or poorly-buffered soils where the pH can be decreased easily. Under these conditions, long-term use of sulfur burners may necessitate the use of lime to maintain optimum soil pH.

Acid additions

Acids may be added directly to irrigation water to reduce the HCO_3^- levels. The addition of acids removes a portion of the HCO_3^- through the same chemical reaction as the acid from the sulfur burner. Two materials that have been used for this purpose are sulfuric acid and N-phuric.

Sulfuric acid may be added directly to the water supply to lower the pH to approximately 6.5 and thus improve water quality. Sulfuric acid is a very strong and corrosive acid and requires special equipment for injection and must be handled with care. Special handling procedures should be established for worker protection and to minimize the potential for spills. Because sulfuric acid is a strong acid, relatively small quantities are required for pH modification *(Table 6)*. All of the acidity added with sulfuric acid reacts with the HCO_3^- in the water and therefore, there is very little effect on soil pH.

The material N-phuric can also be utilized to low water pH. The material is a mixture of urea and sulfuric acid. The most common mix is referred to as 15-49, containing approximately 49 percent sulfuric acid. The biggest advantage of this material is that it is considered noncorrosive and is much safer to handle than sulfuric acid.

Some soil acidification will be obtained through the conversion of urea to nitrate. The one disadvantage of this material appears to be its nitrogen content. Late-season cooling may lead to nitrogen additions that are greater than optimum and that may stimulate fall growth.

Chemical treatments

As the interest in overtree evaporative cooling has increased, additional compounds have been tested to see if they could effectively decrease the potential for lime formation. A number of these compounds may be available

TABLE 6. Quantities of 95% H_2SO_4 required to neutralize 90% of the bicarbonate (HCO_3^-) of irrigation water. Additional acid will be required for those waters containing carbonate (CO_3^{2-}) (Stroehlein and Halderman, 1975).

HCO_3^- Content	Acid Required		
	Per acre-foot of water		
ppm	ppm	lbs	gal
50	38	103	7
100	76	206	13
200	152	412	27
400	304	824	55

in the near future. One such compound currently on the market is Orchard Chelant #841 by CH_2O International. This product is not reported to chelate Ca^{2+} in the water.

It is recommended at rates as low as 0.5 ppm, which would be much too low to effectively chelate Ca^{2+} levels in problem waters. Orchard Chelant #841 is reported to distort mineral crystal formation and thus lower adhesion to the fruit.

Anything that interferes with the formation of the crystal structure of a precipitate can reduce the binding between crystals and thus increase the solubility of the precipitate and potentially improve its washability. More testing is needed to determine the potential of this type of material. To date it appears that this type of material would be most effective with waters having very low lime-deposition potential.

SUMMARY

As environmental concerns and demands for water increase, the use of less water and poorer quality water in agriculture will increase. Producers will have to adjust their management practices to optimize the use of this water. Knowing what is in the water will be critical in developing management plans to produce high quality fruit.

Increased use of marginal and poor quality water for orchard cooling will require treatment of these waters to ensure fruit quality. Producers should look at all available options to determine which treatment package fits their water, orchard system, and management strategy. Planning for treatment should be an essential part of design and layout of any new operation or update of existing orchards. Optimum results will only be obtained when the water treatment fits the management objectives and careful attention is paid to application of the treatment.

REFERENCES

Ayers, R.S. and D.W. Westcot. 1985. "Water Quality for Agriculture." FAO Irrig. and Drain. Paper 29, Rev. 1.

Halvorson, A.R. and A.I. Dow. 1975. "Interpretation of chemical analysis of irrigation water." Washington State University Co. of Agric. Cooperative Extension Mimeo 3522(SR). Pullman, Washington. 5 pp.

McNeal, Brain L. 1982. "Managing poor water quality and associated soil problems." In. *Water Management and Irrigation of Tree Fruits: Proceedings of the Short Course.* Wash. State Univ. Pullman, Wa. 99164. p. 181-200.

Oster, J.D. and J.D. Rhoades. 1979. "Infiltration as influenced by irrigation water quality." *Soil Sci. Soc. Amer. J.* 43:444-447.

Rhoades, J.D. 1977. "Potential for using saline agricultural drainage waters for irrigation." *Proc. Water Management for Irrigation and Drainage.* ASCE, Reno, Nevada. 20-22 July 1977. pp. 85-116.

Stroehlein, Jack L. and Allan D. Halderman. 1975. "Sulfuric acid for soil and water treatment." Arizona Agri-File Q-357. College of Agri. Univ. of Arizona. Tucson, Arizona.

Stromberg, L.K. and S.L. Tisdale. 1979. "Treating irrigated arid-land soils with acid-forming sulphur compounds." The Sulphur Institute. Washington, D.C. 20006. Tech. Bull. 24.

U.S. Salinity Laboratory Staff. 1954. "Diagnosis and Improvement of Saline and Alkali Soils." *USDA Handbook No. 60.* U.S. Gov. Print. Office, Washington, D.C.

Vomocil, James A. and John Hart. 1990. "Irrigation water quality". FG 76 Oregon State University, Corvallis OR.

PART FOUR

System design considerations

Design and sealing
of on-farm ponds

Thomas L. Spofford
Agricultural Engineer
United States Department of Agriculture, Soil Conservation Service, West National Technical Center, Portland, Oregon

Prior to the selection of a pond site and construction, various elements should beconsidered. Considerations should include but not be limited to:

1. What capacity of pond is needed to meet the objective?
2. Is there an available and adequate water supply?
3. Is extra storage needed to compensate and store the sediment load delivered with the water supply?
4. Is there adequate room at the site and are all property rights available to allow construction?
5. Will the pond present a public safety hazard; what safety precautions are necessary?
6. What permits will be needed?
   - Dams 10 feet or greater in height require a WA dam safety permit from the Dept. of Ecology.
   - The assurance of continued use of the water may require a WA water right from the Dept. of Ecology.
   - Permits may be required from the county under their hydraulic and shoreline ordinances.
   - Construction may require a Corp of Engineers 404 permit.

PLANNING AN EARTH-FILL POND

Foundations

It is possible to construct a safe earth-fill dam on almost any foundation if the foundation has been thoroughly investigated and the design and construction procedures are adapted to site conditions. Some foundation conditions require construction measures that are relatively expensive which, in the case of small farm ponds, cannot be justified. Sites with such foundation conditions ordinarily should be abandoned.

The most satisfactory foundation is one that consists of, or is underlain at a shallow depth by a thick layer of relatively impervious consolidated material. Such foundations cause no stability problems. Where a suitable layer occurs at the surface, no special measures are required. It is sufficient to remove the topsoil and scarify or disk the area to provide a bond with the material in the dam.

Where the impervious layer is overlain by previous material, a compacted clay cutoff extending from the surface of the ground into the impervious layer is required to prevent possible failure by piping and to prevent excessive seepage.

Where the foundation consists of highly

pervious sand or sand-gravel mixture and any impervious clay layer is beyond economical reach with available equipment, a detailed investigation should be made. While such a foundation might be satisfactory insofar as stability is concerned, corrective measures will be required to prevent excessive seepage and possible failure.

Foundation cutoffs

Where the foundation consists of pervious materials at or near the surface, with rock or impervious materials at a greater depth, seepage through the pervious layer should be reduced to prevent piping and excessive losses. Usually a cutoff joining the impervious stratum in the foundation with the base of the dam is needed.

The most common type of cutoff is one constructed of compacted clayey material. A trench is cut parallel to the centerline of the dam to a depth that extends well into the impervious layer. The trench is extended into and carried up the abutments of the dam as far as pervious material, that might allow seepage under the embankment, exists. The trench should have a bottom width not less than 4 feet but the equipment necessary to obtain proper compaction generally governs the minimum dimension. The sides of the cutoff should be no steeper than 1 to 1. The trench should be filled with successive thin layers of relatively impervious material, each layer being thoroughly compacted at near optimum moisture conditions before the succeeding layer is placed. Any water collected in the trench must be removed prior to the start of backfill operations.

Embankment top width

A conservative top width for dams under 10 feet in height is 10 feet. The top width should be increased as the height of the dam increases. State standards and specifications need to be consulted for local requirements.

Where the top of the embankment is to be used for a roadway, the top width should provide for a shoulder on each side of the traveled way to prevent raveling. The top width in such cases should not be less than 14 feet.

Embankment side slopes

The side slopes of a dam depend primarily on the stability of the material in the embankment. The greater the stability of the fill material, the steeper the side slopes may be. Unstable materials require flatter side slopes.

Freeboard

Freeboard is the added height of the dam provided as a safety factor to prevent waves or runoff from overtopping the embankment by storms greater than the design frequency.

Freeboard is defined as the vertical distance between the elevation of the water surface in the pond when the spillway is discharging at its designed depth and the elevation of the top of the dam after all settlement has taken place. Where the maximum length of a pond is less than 660 feet, a freeboard of not less that 1.0 foot should be provided. Freeboard is also needed when filling the pond by pumping or gravity to prevent overtopping. Freeboard is best controlled by installing a spillway to safely dispose of excess waters above the design depth..

Allowance for settlement

Settlement is the consolidation of the fill materials and consolidation of foundation materials due to the weight of the dam and the increased moisture caused by the storage of water. The extent of settlement or consolidation depends on the characteristics of the materials and construction methods used in the construction of the dam and foundation. To account for this settlement, the design height of earth dams must be increased by an amount equal to the estimated settlement. The increase should not be less than 5 percent of the overall dam height.

PLANNING AN EXCAVATED POND

Shape and capacity

Excavated ponds may be constructed to almost any shape desired, however a rectangular shape usually is the most convenient for excavation equipment.

The amount of water volume needed generally determines the required capacity and size.

Selecting pond dimensions

The selected dimensions of an excavated pond will depend upon the required capacity and available space for installation. The maximum depth will depend on the climatic conditions, the nature of the materials to be excavated, and the type of equipment to be used in excavating the pond.

The width of an excavated pond will not ordinarily be limited, except that the type and size of the excavating equipment may become a limiting factor. For example, if a dragline is used, the length of the boom will determine the maximum width of excavation that can be made allowing for the proper placement of waste material.

The minimum length of the pond should be that needed to obtain the required pond capacity. However, this length may need to be increased to meet the needs of the excavating equipment, such as a carryall.

Side slopes of an excavated pond should not be greater than the natural angle of repose of the materials being excavated.

Estimating the volume of an excavated pond

After the dimensions and side slopes of the pond have been selected, it is necessary to estimate the volume of excavation.

The volume can be estimated with sufficient accuracy by use of the formula:

$$V = (A + 4B + C) \div 6 \times D/27$$

Where:

V = Volume in cubic yards.
A = Area at the proposed water surface, in square feet.
B = Area at the mid-depth point (1/2 D), in square feet.
C = Area of bottom of the pond, in square feet.
D = Average depth of the pond, in feet.
Z = Side slope
27 = Factor converting cubic feet to cubic yards.

Example

Assume a pond with a depth (D) of 12 feet, a bottom width (W) of 40 feet and a bottom length (L) of 100 feet.

The side slope at the ramp end (Z_2) is 4:1 and the remaining slopes (Z_1) are 2:1. The volume excavation (V) is computed as follows:

Top length = $D(Z_1) + D(Z_2) + L$
$\quad = 12(2) + 12(4) + 100$
$\quad = 172$ feet
Top width = $D(Z_1)$ (2 SIDES) + W
$\quad = 12(2)(2) + 40$
$\quad = 88$ feet
A = 88 x 172
$\quad = 15,136$ square feet
Mid-length = $1/2D(Z_1) + 1/2D(Z_2) + L$
$\quad = 6(2) + 6(4) + 100$
$\quad = 136$ feet
Mid-width = $1/2D(Z_1)$ (2 SIDES) + W
$\quad = 6(2)(2) + 40$
$\quad = 64$ feet
4B = 4(64 X 136) = 34,816 square feet
$\quad$ C = 40 X 100 = 4,000 square feet
(A + 48 + C) = 53,952 square feet

Then V = 53,952 ÷ 6 x 12 ÷ 27
$\quad = 3,996$ cubic yards
$\quad$ (or 4,000 cubic yards)

The volume of water that can be stored in the pond is 4,000 cubic yards X 0.00062 ac. ft./cu. yd., or 2.48 acre feet.

To convert to gallons multiply 4,000 cubic yards by 202.0 to get 808,000 gallons.

Disposal of waste material

The placement or disposal of the excavated material should be planned in advance of construction. Proper disposal will prolong the useful life of the pond, improve its appearance, facilitate easier maintenance and the establishment of vegetation. The waste material may be stacked, spread or removed from the site as conditions warrant.

The waste material, when not removed from the site, should be placed in a manner such that its weight will not endanger the stability of the pond side slopes and so that rainfall will not wash the material back into the pond. Stacked material should be placed uniformly with side slopes no steeper than the natural angle of repose of the soil. A berm width equal to the depth of the pond, but not less than 12 feet should be established and maintained between the toe of the waste bank and the edge of the pond. In the case of large ponds, it is often desirable to stack the waste material along two sides of the pond to reduce the height of the banks.

SEALING PONDS, RESERVOIRS: SEALING METHODS

Excessive seepage loss in farm ponds is usually due to the selection of a site where the soils are too permeable to hold water. This may be the result of inadequate site investigations in the planning stage. However, the need for water may be so important as to justify the selection of a permeable site. In such cases, plans for reducing seepage loss by sealing should be part of the design.

The problem of reducing seepage loss is one of reducing the permeability of the soils to a point where the loss become tolerable. Losses may be reduced by the methods discussed below. The choice will depend largely on the proportions of coarse grained sand and gravel and fine grained silt and clay in the soil.

A thorough investigation of the materials to be sealed should be made by a gelogist, soil mechanics engineer or soil scientist before the method of sealing is selected. In some cases it may be necessary to have a laboratory analysis of the materials.

Sealing by compaction alone

Certain pond areas containing a high percentage of coarse grained material can be made relatively impervious by compaction alone. The material is well graded from small gravel or coarse sand to fine sand, clay, and silt. This method of sealing is the least expensive and very effective on silt and clay soil materails.

The soil should be scarified to a depth of 8 to 10 inches with a disk, rototiller, pulverizer or similar equipment. All rocks and tree roots must be removed.

The loosened soil should be rolled under optimum moisture conditions to a dense, tight layer with four to six passes of a sheepsfoot roller. Site soil material specific optimum moisture is determined from a soil compaction curve developed by an engineer or experience technician.

The thickness of the compacted seal should not be less than 8 inches for impoundments up to 10 feet in depth. Since seepage loss varies directly with the depth of water impounded, the thickness of the compacted seal should be increased proportionately when the depth of water exceeds 10 feet. This will require compacting the soil in two or more layers not exceeding 8 inches in thickness over that portion of the pond where the water depth exceeds 10 feet.

Use of clay blankets

Pond areas containing high percentages of coarse grained soils but lacking sufficient amounts of clay to prevent high seepage losses can be sealed by blanketing. The blanket should cover the entire area over which water is to be impounded. It should consist of material containing a wide range of particle sizes varying from small gravel or coarse sand to fine sand and clay in the desired proportions. Such material should contain approximately 20 percent of clay particles by weight.

The thickness of the blanket will depend on the depth of water to be impounded. The minimum thickness of the blanket should be 12 inches for all depths of water up to 10 feet. The minimum should be increased by 2 inches for each foot of water over 10 feet.

Clay blankets require protection from cracking that result from drying or freezing and thawing. A cover of gravel, 12 to 18 inches thick, placed over the blanket may be used for this purpose. Blanketed areas should be protected by a cantilevered pipe or rock riprap where flow into the pond is concentrated.

Sealing with bentonite

Seepage loss in well-graded coarse grained soils may be reduced by the addition of bentonite. Bentonite is a fine-textured colloidal clay that will absorb several times its own weight in water. At complete saturation it will swell from 8 to 15 times its original volume. When bentonite is mixed in the correct proportions with the coarse grained material, compacted, then saturated, the particles of bentonite will fill the pores in the material and make it nearly impervious. A laboratory analysis of the material is essential to determine the amount of bentonite that should be applied per unit of area. Rates of application range from 1 to 3 pounds per square foot, depending on site conditions. bentonite, upon drying, will return to its original volume and leave cracks in the pond area. For this reason, Bentonite is not recommended for ponds where a wide fluctuation in the water level is expected.

The soil moisture level in the area to be treated should be optimum for good compaction. If the area is found to be too wet, sealing operations should be postponed until moisture conditions are satisfactory. If the material is too dry, water should be added by sprinkling. Optimum moisture is derived from the soil compaction curve.

Bentonite should be spread uniformly over the area to be treated at the rate determined by the laboratory analysis. It is then mixed thoroughly with the soil to a depth of at least six inches with a rototiller, disk, or similar equipment. The area then must be compacted with four to six passes of a sheepsfoot roller.

Treated areas subject to inflow should be protected by riprap or other mechanical means.

Some sources of bentonite are indicated on page 136.

Treatment with chemical additives

Excessive seepage loss often occurs in fine grained clay soils because of the arrangement of the clay particles which form a honeycomb structure. Such soils are said to be aggregated and have a relatively high permeability rate. The application of small amounts of certain chemicals to these aggregates may result in collapse of the open structure and rearrangement of the clay particles. The chemicals used are called dispersing agents.

For chemical treatment to be effective, the soils in the pond area should contain more than 50 percent of fine grained material (silt and clay finer than .074 mm diameter) and at least 15 percent clay finer than .002 mm diameter. The soils should contain less than 0.5 percent soluble salts (based on dry soil weight). Chemical treatment is not effective in coarse grained soils.

Due to rapid technological advancements, new chemical additives are being developed constantly. Some of these may prove useful in reducing seepage loss.

Use of flexible membranes

Another method of reducing excessive seepage loss is the use of flexible membranes of polyethylene, vinyl, and butyl rubber.

Thin films of these materials are structurally weak, but if kept intact, they are almost completely watertight. Polyethylene films are less expensive and have better aging properties than vinyl. Vinyl is more resistant to impact damage but repairs require patching by heat sealing. Butyl rubber can be joined or patched with a special cement.

Flexible membranes must be protected from mechanical or animal damage if they are to remain serviceable for any period of time. To achieve protection, all polyethylene and vinyl rubber membranes should have a cover of earth, or earth and gravel, not less than 6 inches thick.

The minimum normal thickness should equal or exceed the value shown in Table 1 for the soil material being covered and the type of membrane used.

The area lined should be drained and allowed to dry until the surface is firm. This is necessary to support the workers and equipment that must travel over it during installation of the lining.

All banks, side slopes and fills within the area to be lined should be uniformly sloped

TABLE 1. Below is a chart for determining membrane thickness.

Soil material not coarser than:	Polyethylene	Vinyl	Butyl Rubber
Sands, clean or silty	8 mil	8 mil	15 mil
Gravels, clean, silty or clayey	15 mil	15 mil	30 mil

no steeper than 1 to 1 for exposed lining and 3 to 1 for covered lining. The cover material may slide on the lining if placed on steeper slopes.

Earth materials used to cover the membrane should be free of large clods, sharp rocks, sticks, and other objects that would puncture the lining. The cover should be placed to the specified depth without damage to the membrane.

Bentonite sources
(known sources and not all inclusive)

Central Oregon Bentonite Co.
Roberts Rt
HC 67 BOX 500
Prineville, OR
(503) 477-3351

H & H Bentonite and Mud Inc.
628 Yucca Dr.
Grand Junction, CO
(303) 243-9960

Hebb Resources International
N 2128 Pines Rd, Suite 17-1
Spokane, WA
(509) 926-1036

Mitchell Lewis & Staver
E 2502 Trent
Spokane, WA
(509) 534-0343

United Pipe and Supply
1100 Walla Walla
Wenatchee, WA
(509) 662-7128 or 1 -800-772-7855

Operating chemigation and fertigation systems

T.W. Van der Gulik, P. Eng.

Resource Management Branch
British Columbia Ministry of Agriculture, Fisheries and Food, Abbotsford, B.C. Canada

Chemigation is the term used to define the practice of applying chemicals to a crop through an irrigation system. In agriculture, the chemicals applied are generally fertilizers to promote crop production and plant growth.

Trickle irrigation systems are used to apply fertilizers directly to the plant roots of crops tree fruits, vegetables, small fruits and berries. In drier climates, the utilization of fertigation techniques is the only viable method of applying fertilizers to crops using trickle irrigation systems. Insufficient rainfall will not ensure incorporation of broadcast fertilizers into the soil under a trickle irrigation regime in these drier climates.

The term chemigation also applies to the application of herbicides, insecticides, fungicides, nematicides and growth regulators through sprinkler and trickle irrigation systems. While these types of chemicals currently are not applied extensively in British Columbia, Canada, some are in other irrigated regions of the world.

The application of fertilizers imposes minimal health concerns and risks to water purveyors. However, the potential to apply other chemicals is seen as a greater risk. Potential contamination of the water source due to backsiphonage and backpressure are possible if an unexpected shutdown of the irrigation system should occur while injection is taking place. This risk can be minimized if proper backflow prevention devices are installed and inspected and if good chemigation practices are followed.

The intent of this chapter is to provide information on the design and operation of chemigation systems.

CHEMIGATION CONSIDERATIONS

The goal of a chemigation system is to apply the proper amount of chemical to the target area in a safe, efficient and uniform manner. The following precautions must be taken to achieve this goal:

- assure personal protection
- be aware of the danger to the environment
- calibrate the injection equipment
- apply the correct amount of chemical at the right time
- apply the chemical at the correct concentration
- use a well-designed and -maintained irrigation system

Subsequent sections in this chapter will

explain how the above precautions can be met. Keep in mind that the chemical cannot be distributed more evenly than the water is applied by the irrigation equipment.

Advantages

The application of chemicals through an irrigation system offers many advantages to the farmer. Advantages obtained depend on the type of irrigation system used and type of chemical being applied.

Sprinkler system advantages

- Reduces cost of chemical application. With chemicals such as herbicides, application through an irrigation system may save 50 percent of the application costs.
- Reduces energy consumption. Energy consumption by chemigation application methods compared to conventional methods may be reduced by up to 90 percent.
- Ensures timely application of chemicals. Fertilizers and other chemicals can be applied to the crop at the most opportune time, even if the field is not trafficable by farm implements. Nutrients can easily be applied to the crop throughout the growing season at specified rates and intervals.
- Improves application uniformity. Irrigation systems that are properly designed and operated can apply chemicals more uniformly than aircraft and can be as uniform as ground sprayers.
- Reduces chemical use. Studies have shown that less fertilizer is required when nutrients are applied more efficiently, more often and when required by the crop. The same applies to herbicides and pesticides. The potential for chemicals to be leached into groundwater is therefore reduced.
- Reduces labor costs. One operator can apply chemicals easily and efficiently to large acreages.
- Reduces machinery equipment needs. Chemigation saves wear on tractors and sprayers.
- Reduces soil compaction. Soil conditions are improved and mechanical damage to the crop is reduced as there is less

movement of vehicles over the field.
- Improves operator safety. Since the operator does not have to be in the target area, exposure of the operator to herbicides, pesticides and insecticides applied through an irrigation system is greatly reduced.
- Improves crop production. Chemigation systems may simplify cultural practices and improve crop production and quality if used correctly. Timely fertilizer applications can significantly increase crop yields.

Trickle system advantages

Trickle irrigation systems offer additional benefits to sprinkler systems in applying nutrients and systemic pesticides. As water is applied directly to the plant's root zone, nutrients can be efficiently applied. Trickle systems may not be compatible with herbicides or insecticides as the chemical is not applied evenly over the entire ground surface. An exception would be spray emitter systems which could be used for weed control on some crops. The following are advantages of trickle irrigation systems:

- Ensures incorporation in drier climates. Fertigation is the only method of ensuring that fertilizers are incorporated into the soil when trickle systems are used to irrigate crops in arid regions, such as the interior of British Columbia. Fertigation is therefore a necessity instead of an option for agricultural practices in these regions.
- Ensures efficient application because of higher application efficiencies. Since trickle irrigation systems apply water directly to the plant's root system, better uniformity of fertilizer application to the crop can be attained.
- Increases fertilizer availability to the crop. Fertilizers are applied in a form by which they can be taken up easily by the plant.
- Allows for modification of fertilizer application for crop maturity. Nutrients can be applied throughout the growing season with precalculated amounts and frequencies to meet crop demand at various growing stages.
- Injection systems are required for

maintenance of the trickle system. The addition of chlorine and acids to a trickle system is required to prevent algae and precipitate buildup in the emitters and lateral lines. The same injection equipment may be used for chemigation.

Disadvantages

Disadvantages of chemigation include but may not be limited to the following considerations.

- Chemigation is not viable for all chemicals. Not all chemicals are soluble enough to be applied as a solution and some chemicals may not act as intended under an irrigation application regime. Therefore, more than one method of chemical application must be retained.
- Specified use and application is limited to the product label. A herbicide, pesticide or insecticide may only be applied to a field or crop in Washington or British Columbia as described on the product label. Application through an irrigation system must be specified on the label.
- The addition of safety equipment is required. To prevent the possibility of backpressure or backsiphonage into a potable water source, approved cross connection control equipment must be installed and proper procedures followed.
- A change in management techniques is required. Personnel in charge of the chemical application must fully understand the calibration of injection equipment and the operation of the injector, irrigation system, check valves and backflow prevention equipment.
- Equipment must be portable. If a farmer has more than one field, duplication of equipment will be required unless the injection system, solution tank and safety equipment are connected as one unit and can easily be transported from field to field.
- Timing of application may be limited by weather conditions. Sprinkler irrigation systems are susceptible to drift in windy conditions that will affect uniformity and effectiveness of the application. Applications should be limited to good weather conditions.

- Unwanted chemical residue on crops may occur with sprinkler systems.
- Chemical solutions may be corrosive to irrigation equipment.
- Using an irrigation system to apply chemicals may irrigate the crop at a time when it is not required or when the soil is already too wet.
- The acidity of the soil may be increased by the injection of some types of fertilizers into an irrigation system. This is especially true for trickle irrigation systems, which concentrate the fertilizer application to a small area.

Irrigation system design

Many irrigation system design factors must be considered for chemigation if good application uniformity is to be obtained. While there are many operation characteristics that need to be understood as well, it is virtually impossible to achieve good uniformity if the irrigation system is not designed correctly in the first place. This section provides minimum criteria for the design of irrigation systems to be used for chemigation.

Irrigation system location

Proximity of the irrigation system to dwellings, surface water sources such as ditches, streams and lakes, neighboring crops, roadways, playgrounds and residential areas must be carefully considered. The safety of people, wildlife, domestic animals and other nontarget areas must be considered.

Crop type

Selection of an irrigation system is often determined by the type of crop to be irrigated.

Trickle irrigation systems are often used for tree fruits, grapes, strawberries and other horticultural crops because of water application efficiency and the ability to control fertilizer application directly to the plant's roots. High density orchard plantings require quick tree response after planting and early fruit development to realize a return on capital investment. It is imperative that plantings use fertigation to apply plant nutrient requirements. Injection of herbicides and pesticides by trickle system is not generally effective.

Overhead and undertree sprinkler systems are also popular on orchards and vineyards for a variety of reasons. Overhead sprinkler systems used for irrigation, frost protection or crop cooling purposes on tree fruits can be adapted to chemigation. However, the coefficient of uniformity for most overhead systems designed for these purposes is not adequate for chemigation. (A minimum application uniformity of 85 percent should be achieved.)

Soil type

The maximum infiltration rate of water into the soil and available water storage capacity of the soil differ with soil type. Soil types can vary significantly over an entire field, requiring a change in the operation of the irrigation system. Coarse-textured soils can have high infiltration rates but can store very little water within the plant's root zone. Conversely, fine-textured soils can store large amounts of water but have low infiltration rate capabilities. High application rates on fine-textured soils increase runoff potential, while excessive amounts of irrigation on coarse-textured soils increase the potential for leaching of chemicals below the crop root zone and into the groundwater.

Chemigation systems must be operated within the limits of the soil types present to reduce the potential for runoff and for leaching.

An understanding of soil water-holding capacity is also important to ensure that the chemical added is moved into the soil to an appropriate depth with respect to the plant rooting volume. The section, "Irrigation system operation considerations," provides further information on calculating the depth of chemical penetration into the soil.

Topography

Field topography can cause pressure differences along an irrigation lateral, which affect application uniformities. Trickle systems are most susceptible to pressure differences caused by elevation or friction loss. Sprinkler irrigation systems can also be affected if the elevation changes are in excess of 16.5 feet or more.

For chemigation systems, varying the nozzle size along a lateral to accommodate pressure fluctuations is not an acceptable method of rectifying this problem. Pressure or flow regulators on each sprinkler head are required to ensure uniform discharge for each sprinkler along the lateral. Pressure-compensating emitters are recommended to maintain system uniformity for trickle systems.

Drift and runoff potential

Drift and runoff are the two leading causes of chemical losses from chemigation systems. Environmental conditions during application, sprinkler types, type of chemical being applied and climatic conditions after application all affect the magnitude of chemical losses.

Water discharged from a sprinkler nozzle under pressure emerges as a fine spray. Part of the spray is evaporated within the wetted area, intercepted by vegetation and soil, or carried away by wind outside the intended target area. Wind drift can be a potentially hazardous situation. Chemigation should not be carried out if wind conditions are strong enough to cause significant drifting to nontarget areas.

Runoff depends not only on the irrigation system application rate and soil infiltration rate but is also influenced by factors such as field slope, surface vegetation, crop cover and soil surface residue. Irrigation systems applying chemicals must be designed and operated to prevent any runoff from occurring.

Irrigation system characteristics

The physical characteristics of the irrigation system will determine the type of injection system, selection of chemicals that can be applied, application rate and duration of application. Irrigation systems can be divided into two categories, stationary and continuous move systems.

Stationary systems include handlines, wheel moves, solid-set sprinklers, trickle and microsprinkler systems. These types of systems irrigate a block of land at a constant application rate over time. A batch of chemicals can therefore be mixed and applied during the irrigation interval. The duration of application will be determined by the type of chemical being applied. Some chemicals must be incorporated to be effective, requiring application of enough water to move the chemical into the soil. Other chemicals, such as nitrate nitrogen, are very mobile and should be left near the soil surface to avoid potential groundwater problems. Chemicals intended for foliar applications should only be applied by overhead sprinkler systems during the end of an irrigation set with a minimum amount of flushing.

On continuous move systems, the chemical injection rate must be matched with the rate of travel.

Irrigation systems used for chemigation must be in good working order and managed in an environmentally sensitive manner. *All chemigation systems must have appropriate safety equipment installed to prevent backflow to potable water supplies.*

The following parameters must be considered in the design of chemigation systems.

Sprinkler systems

To ensure maximum uniformity, sprinkler irrigation systems used to apply chemicals must be designed and operated to achieve a minimum coefficient of uniformity of 80 percent and preferably 90 percent. Even for uniformities of 90 percent, there can still be a three to one ratio between individual field measurements in the depth of water applied. Further information on determining the coefficient of uniformity can be found in the *B.C. Sprinkler Irrigation Manual.* A coefficient of uniformity of 80 percent can only be obtained by designing sprinkler systems to the following minimum standards. The following standards should apply for chemigation systems:

1. The maximum pressure variation along the lateral must not exceed 20 percent of the sprinkler operating pressure. Flow control nozzles must be used if pressure fluctuations exceed the 20 percent allowance. Another option is to use pressure regulators at sprinkler heads operating at pressures exceeding the normal operating range.
2. The sprinkler spacing along the lateral should not exceed 50 percent of the wetted diameter. The spacing between laterals should not exceed 60 percent of the sprinkler wetted diameter.

3. The sprinkler is operated within the manufacturer's recommended pressure range that is sufficient to provide adequate stream breakup for proper dispersal.
4. The sprinkler head must rotate a minimum of two times per minute.
5. Sprinkler irrigation systems must be operated for at least 15 minutes to achieve uniform application. A 30-minute injection time would attain better uniformity but may be too long for some chemicals.

Trickle

Trickle irrigation systems generally have a coefficient of uniformity exceeding 80 percent providing the system has been designed correctly. Trickle systems operate at efficiencies in the 85 to 90 percent range compared to sprinkler systems that are only 65 to 75 percent efficient. Therefore, these systems are superior to sprinkler systems in the application of fertilizers and systemics. However, trickle systems are limited in their ability to apply herbicides and insecticides.

The following factors need to be considered in the design of a trickle system used for chemigation.

1. Emitters should be spaced to irrigate as much of the plant's root volume as possible.
2. An appropriate emitter should be selected for the terrain, crop type and water quality being used. Emitter flow characteristics and product durability for the conditions should be considered. An emitter with a manufacturer's variance coefficient of less than 0.05 should be selected. Emitter flow rates at the beginning and end of the zone should be tested to confirm that discharge rates are within acceptable limits.
3. On sloping terrain, nonleaking emitters should be used to prevent over-application at the end of the laterals.
4. Emitter operating pressure range should be kept within plus or minus 10 percent of the emitter operating pressure. If the trickle system is operating on a slope, pressure- compensating emitters should be used.
5. The injection system must be located

before the filtration system so any precipitates that may form will have an opportunity to be filtered out before entering the irrigation system.

Irrigation system operation

To operate a successful chemigation program, the most difficult obstacle that must be overcome by the operator is to ensure good application uniformity. As indicated in the previous section, the irrigation system must be designed to distribute the water as uniformly as possible to achieve even application of chemicals.

Physical characteristics of irrigation systems which affect the uniformity of chemical injection include the following:

- Solute dispersion occurs as the chemical travels along the irrigation pipeline. The friction effect of the pipe walls on the fluid motion causes this dispersion. A heavy dose of chemical injected into an irrigation system diffuses as the chemical travels along with the irrigation water.
- The irrigation mainline contains a significant amount of water. The travel time for the chemical to reach the discharge point and the time required to flush the system must be considered.
- The operating flow rate for each zone will be different.
- For stationary systems, uniformity of application generally increases with the length of set time. Chemicals that require a short application duration may be difficult to apply uniformly.

Irrigation system layout and the travel time of chemicals through the system must be known to ensure good application uniformity and adequate flush times for the laterals on chemigation completion.

The following procedures should be used as guidelines in the operation of chemigation systems.

1. Prepare a worksheet showing zones, flow rate per zone, area covered or plants per zone, injection rate and injection time. This is useful for future reference.

2. The irrigation lines should be filled completely and pressurized before starting chemigation.

3. Solid-set sprinkler systems should preferably be operated for one hour to achieve good application uniformity. This may not be possible for all chemigation applications, but the minimum application duration suggested is 15 minutes.

4. The system should be flushed after chemigation has been completed. The irrigation system must be operated long enough to clear all lines of the chemical being applied. If the irrigation system is shut down before all the chemicals have exited the lateral lines, extra chemical will be applied at low spots where water drains through emitters or sprinklers. Chemical that was intended for the end of the lines will not reach the target area. A flushing time of 30 minutes should be sufficient for most systems, although systems with lengthy and large mainlines may require longer durations for system flushing.

   A dye test should be conducted to determine the length of time required for the last of the chemical to exit the final sprinkler or emitter. The amount of flush time can be reduced by injecting the chemical at the zone control.

5. Mixing a solution separately for each zone reduces the likelihood of error during the application process and allows for proper flushing of the irrigation system to increase application uniformity. If a controller with the capability of programming injections during scheduled irrigations is used, a large batch tank of chemical can be mixed for all zones. The amount of chemical applied to each zone will then be controlled by adjusting injection times.

6. When applying chemicals that may damage the crop foliage, the sprinkler irrigation chemigation system should be operated for at least one hour after chemical injection has ceased.

7. Post-injection treatments may be required to prevent the accumulation of algae, slime or precipitates that may plug

trickle irrigation systems. High carbonate and/or iron concentrations in some irrigation waters may react with fertilizers and cause insoluble calcium or iron compounds. Certain bacteria can also fix iron as a byproduct of metabolism and produce slime or jelly-like material inside the trickle irrigation lines. Algal growth may also be enhanced by the addition of nutrients in the water. Special maintenance procedures such as chlorination, adding algaecides, bactericides and pretreating water with chelating agents may be required when performing fertigation with a trickle irrigation system.

8. The acidity of the soil should be monitored, especially when applying ammonium fertilizers through a trickle irrigation system. Acidity will be dependent on the buffering capacity of the soil. Selection of an appropriate fertilizer source will reduce acidity problems. Treatment with lime may also be an alternative.

Chemical application depth

The amount of water applied by the irrigation system must be stored within the plant's root zone. Any moisture that is applied that exceeds the holding capacity of the soil will cause leaching beyond the plant's rooting depth. The specific depth in the soil to which chemicals are applied can be determined from the application rate of the irrigation system, the duration of irrigation, soil texture and soil moisture content before the chemigation is applied. *(See Example 1, Solid set sprinkler - fertilizer application, page 162)*

Table 1 can be used to determine the soil moisture content of the soil using the hand feel method. Other methods such as oven drying can be used if accurate measurements need to be made.

Table 2 shows the depth of penetration into the soil for one inch of water application for different soils at various moisture contents.

For example if an irrigation system is applying one inch of water to a sandy loam soil that has a moisture content at 50 percent of field capacity, the water applied will move to a depth of 16 inches.

TABLE 1. Hand feel moisture test. (From Chemigation in the Pacific Northwest, WSU)

Degree of Moisture	Feel	Amount of Available Moisture
Dry	Powder dry	None
Low	Crumbly, won't hold together	25% or less
Fair	Somewhat crumbly but will hold together	25 - 50%
Good	Forms ball; will stick slightly with pressure	50 - 65%
Excellent	Forms a ball, is pliable; sticks readily; a clear water sheen will come to the surface when the ball is squeezed in the hand	75 - 100%
Too Wet	Can squeeze free water	Over field capacity

TABLE 2. Depth of water penetration (inches) per inch of water applied.

Soil Moisture Content	Sand 1.0 in/ft	Sandy Loam 1.5 in/ft	Loam 2.1 in/ft	Clay 2.4 in/ft
75%	48	32	23	20
50%	24	16	12	10
25%	16	11	8	7

System and injector calibration

To ensure that the chemical is being applied at the proper concentrations, it is important that the application rate and zone flow rates of the irrigation system are known. Over-application of chemicals is expensive, is not environmentally friendly and may even be harmful to the crop, defeating the entire purpose of applying the chemical in the first place.

Under-application may not achieve the desired effect of the chemigation program. Calibration of the injection system to the irrigation system is imperative if the two are to operate harmoniously. See "Calculating injection rates" for further information on calculating injection rates and calibrating various irrigation systems.

Additional information on the design of irrigation systems in the province of British Columbia can be obtained from the *B.C. Trickle Irrigation Manual* and the *B.C. Sprinkler Irrigation Manual.*

CROSS CONNECTION CONTROL IS IMPORTANT FOR SAFETY

Why is chemigation a potential hazard?

The introduction of chemicals into an irrigation system presents a potential hazard to public health. The irrigation system acts as a cross connection between the chemical solution tank and the potable water source. The cross connection can be to an irrigation district mainline, municipal water line, stream, lake, river or groundwater. All of Washington and British Columbia's fresh water supplies are considered a potable water source to some user.

A cross connection is any connection or structural arrangement between a potable water system and any nonpotable water system or chemical source through which backflow can occur. Any temporary or permanent devices through which backflow can occur are considered cross connections. The water source can be subjected to the chemical being injected into the irrigation system by two backflow processes, backpressure and backsiphonage.

Backsiphonage

Backsiphonage is caused by low pressure or a reduced pressure in the supply piping. Principal causes of backsiphonage are:

- creation of a severe hydraulic gradient by undersized piping in the supply line;
- pipeline breakages in the district mainline which is lower than the customer service point;
- reduced mainline pressure caused by a high water withdrawal rate such as fire fighting or mainline flushing;
- reduced mainline supply pressure caused by pump or power failure.

Backpressure

Backpressure occurs when the user system is operating at a higher pressure than the potable water supply system. Major sources of backpressure are:

- booster pumps on the user system used to increase flows and pressure requirements;
- interconnection with other piping systems operating at higher pressures;
- connections to pressurized systems such as boilers.

In low-pressure trickle irrigation systems, backpressure can be caused by either elevation differences in the system or chemical injection pumps.

Degree of hazard

The safety devices that must be installed on an irrigation system will depend on the degree of hazard the system imposes on potable water supplies. There are three degrees of hazard that must be considered.

Severe: An existing or probable cross connection involving any substance in sufficient concentration to cause death, spread disease or with a high probability of causing such effect.

Moderate: An existing or probable cross connection involving any substance that has a low probability of becoming a severe hazard but constitutes a nuisance or is aesthetically objectionable if introduced into the water supply.

<u>Minor</u>: An existing or probable cross connection between a potable water supply line and a tank or other water supply that has a low probability of becoming contaminated.

A chemical injector installed on an irrigation system is considered a severe hazard as fertilizers, herbicides or insecticides can be introduced into the potable water supply system. The irrigation system generally is cross-connected to a potable water supply, whether these are surface water supplies, groundwater, irrigation districts or municipal water systems. *An approved backflow prevention device must be installed on all irrigation systems that are injecting chemicals.*

Backflow prevention device selection

There are many types of backflow prevention devices available, some that protect against backsiphonage only and others that protect against both backsiphonage and backpressure. Chemigation systems must use either a double check valve assembly or a reduced pressure backflow device, depending on the water source.

Inspection requirements

Before the first irrigation application of the season, the owner or operator must have the backflow prevention device inspected by a certified tester to ensure that it is an approved device, installed correctly and in proper operating condition. In British Columbia, a copy of the test report should be provided to the Water Authority within 30 days of completion of the test and before operation of the chemical injection system.

The owner or operator must provide to the Water Authority upon initial installation of the backflow prevention device a certificate showing:

- date of installation
- type, model and size of backflow prevention device installed
- copy of the certified tester's inspection certificate

Nonapproved backflow devices for chemigation

An atmospheric vacuum breaker or a pressure vacuum breaker do not provide adequate protection against all forms of backflow. They, therefore, are not considered approved backflow prevention devices for a chemigation system.

An atmospheric vacuum breaker (AVB) allows air to enter the downstream line when the line pressure is reduced to a gauge pressure of zero or less. The AVB must be installed downstream of the last shutoff valve (no valves can be installed downstream of the AVB) and a minimum of 15 centimeters (6.8 inches) above the highest outlet on the nonpotable system. *An AVB must not be used where continuous operating pressure is applied for more than 12 hours in any 24-hour period as the relief valve may stick in the closed position and cause malfunctioning.*

The pressure vacuum breaker (PVB) has an atmospheric vent valve which is internally loaded by a spring. A spring helps open the valve and the PVB can therefore be installed on the pressure side of a shutoff valve and used in situations that are operating under continuous pressure. A PVB must be installed 30 centimeters (13.6 inches) above the highest outlet on the non-potable water system.

Acceptable uses for atmospheric and pressure vacuum breakers include situations where nonpotable water is pumped into an irrigation system that is cross-connected to an irrigation district or municipal pipeline or irrigation system applications that do not have a chemigation system installed. Common applications are on automatic home or industrial underground sprinkler systems and agricultural trickle and sprinkler irrigation systems that do not use chemigation systems. *Vacuum breakers are effective against backsiphonage only and cannot be used in backpressure situations.*

Approved backflow devices for chemigation

Double check valve assembly

A double check valve assembly (DCVA) consists of two approved check valves, internally loaded either by a spring or weight, which are installed as a unit between two tightly closing shut-off valves. The DCVA is effective against backflow caused by backpressure or back-siphonage. *A DCVA provides acceptable protection from backpressure and backsiphonage for irrigation systems with an approved chemigation system that use a stream, river, lake or other natural surface water source as a water supply.*

The DCVA must be installed upstream of the chemical injection system at a location that is readily accessible for testing purposes.

Figure 1 shows the configuration of a double check valve assembly.

DCVA installation
for irrigation systems

1. Wherever possible, the DCVA shall be installed aboveground with adequate space to simplify maintenance and testing. It shall be inspected and tested after installation to ensure it is installed correctly and operating satisfactorily.
2. The DCVA must be tested by a certified tester before every irrigation season.
3. If possible, a DCVA should not be installed in a pit because any leaky test cocks would then become cross connections when the pit is flooded. If the unit must be installed in a pit, provisions for pit drainage must be provided. Test cock tappings should also be plugged to reduce

the danger of leaks if the device does become submerged. The vault should be large enough to provide free access for testing or repairing the device.

4. DCVAs larger than 2.5" shall have support blocks to prevent damage.
5. A strainer with a blow-out tapping should be installed ahead of the DCVA.
6. The DCVA must be drained in the fall and protected from freezing. The manufacturer can provide recommendations on how to drain each water-trapping cavity of the device.
7. The lines should be thoroughly flushed before installation of the DCVA. Most failures during testing are caused by debris fouling either the first or second check valve seats.

Figure 2 and Figure 3 provide details on acceptable methods of installing a DCVA on an irrigation system.

Reduced pressure principle
backflow prevention device

A reduced pressure principle backflow device (RPBD) consists of two independently acting, internally loaded check valves separated by a reduced pressure zone. The device should be installed as a unit between two tightly closing shut-off valves. The RPBD is effective against backflow caused by backpressure and back-

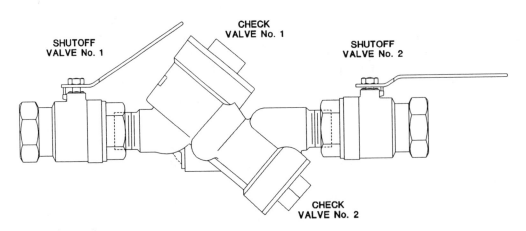

FIGURE 1. A double check valve assembly

siphonage and is designed to be used in situations that are considered very hazardous.

An RPBD should be used as a backflow prevention device for any irrigation system using an approved chemigation system that is drawing water from an irrigation district mainline, municipal waterline, well or other groundwater source.

Figure 4 shows a typical reduced pressure principle device.

RPBD installation

1. The preferred method for a RPBD is to be installed aboveground with adequate space to ease maintenance and testing. It shall be inspected and tested after installation to ensure it is installed correctly and operating satisfactorily.
2. The RPBD must be tested by a certified tester before every irrigation season.
3. If possible, the RPBD should not be installed in a pit below ground level. Flooding of the pit could cause a direct cross connection through the relief valve. If installation in a pit is absolutely necessary, adequate drainage must be provided.
4. RPBDs larger than 2.5" shall have support blocks to prevent damage.
5. Horizontal installation of the RPBD is suggested.
6. The RPBD should be sized hydraulically to avoid excessive pressure loss.
7. Because of the nature of a reduced pressure backflow preventer, fluctuating supply pressures on an extreme low flow or static flow condition may cause nuisance dripping and eventual fouling of the device.
8. A strainer with a blow-out tapping should be installed ahead of the RPBD.
9. The RPBD must be drained in the fall and protected from freezing. The manufacturer can provide recommendations on how to drain each water-trapping cavity of the device.
10. The lines should be thoroughly flushed before installation of the RPBD. Most failures during testing are caused by debris fouling either the first or second check valve seats.

Figure 2 and Figure 3 provide information on the proper installation of an RPBD on an irrigation system.

Pesticide, herbicide and insecticide application guidelines

The safety requirements for chemigation systems will depend on many circumstances. These include:

- water supply source;
- irrigation system pressure source;
- type of injector;
- chemical injected; and
- type of irrigation system.

Application of pesticides, herbicides and insecticides is considered much more hazardous than general fertigation. Precautions outlined in this section must be taken for the application of these products. Chemigation systems applying any product must follow all the safety standards outlined in various sections of this chapter. If applying a pesticide, herbicide or insecticide, the following procedures must be followed:

- The product label must clearly specify that the product can be applied through an irrigation system. Applying a product through an irrigation system that does not have this method of application specified on the label is an offense under federal and state regulations
- Pesticides, herbicides, insecticides, fertilizers or surfactants, when applied through an irrigation system, cannot be mixed or combined with other products.
- Only positive displacement pumps or venturi injection systems that are compatible with the chemical to be injected can be used for these products.
- Irrigation must not be carried out for at least 24 hours after chemigation has been completed.
- Application of these chemicals through an irrigation system cannot occur if the target area is within 30 meters (100 feet) of a residential dwelling, park, playground, stream, river or lake.
- For pesticide or insecticide application

the irrigation system must be capable of covering the entire field in one day. *Solid-set sprinkler or center pivot systems are the only acceptable types of irrigation systems that can be used with these products.* The irrigation system must be operated at normal pressures as recommended by the manufacturer. Nonuniform distribution of treated water can result in crop injury, ineffective application or illegal pesticide residues in the crop. The application rate and coefficient of unifor-

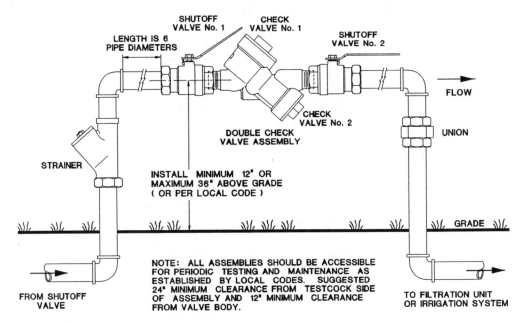

FIGURE 2. DCVA or RPBD installation, above ground.

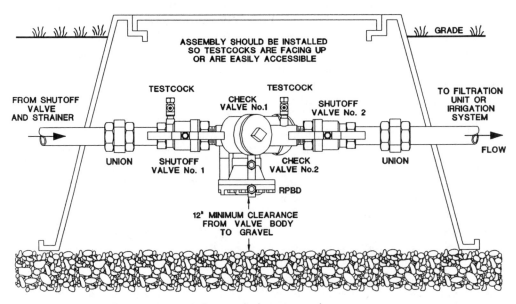

FIGURE 3. DCVA or RPBD installation, below ground.

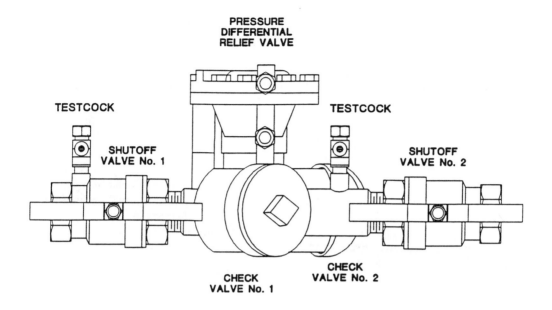

TOP VIEW

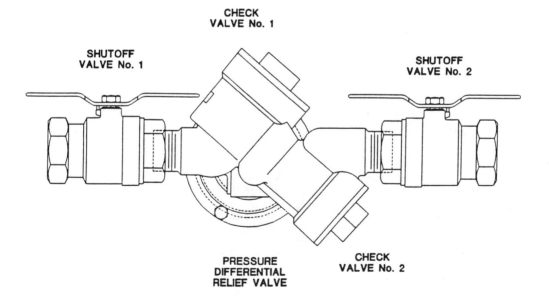

SIDE VIEW

FIGURE 4. A reduced pressure backflow prevention principle device.

mity of the irrigation system must be known before chemigation is attempted.

- Application must be done under minimal wind conditions to allow good distribution, prevent drift and minimize evaporation of the product. Wind conditions must be less than 1.25 miles per hour during the entire time of application to prevent drift off the target area.

- A person knowledgeable of the irrigation system and responsible for its operation must be present during the treatment application to stop pesticide injection and make necessary adjustments should the need arise.

Injection system requirements

The following guidelines should be followed to ensure that an injection system is installed in a safe and correct manner.

- Injection on the suction side of the irrigation pump is prohibited. The injector must be located on the discharge side of the irrigation pump downstream of the backflow preventer.

- Only positive displacement pumps or venturi injection systems that are com-patible with the chemical to be injected can be used with pesticides, herbicides and insecticides. Pitot tube or pressure differential injection systems may be used with fertilizers.

- The injection system could shut off unex-pectedly while the irrigation system con-tinues to operate. Overflow of the tank could occur, resulting in chemicals being spilled onto the ground. The chemical injection line must contain a functional, automatic quick-closing check valve to prevent the flow of water from the irriga-tion system back through the injector into the chemical storage tank.

- A functional, normally closed solenoid valve should be located on the intake side of the injector and be interlocked with the power system and irrigation con-troller to prevent fluid from being with-drawn from the chemical supply tank when the irrigation system is shut down. The solenoid valve can be interlocked directly with the irrigation controller if an electric injector pump or irrigation pump is not used on the system.

- If an electric irrigation pump is used on the irrigation system and an electric

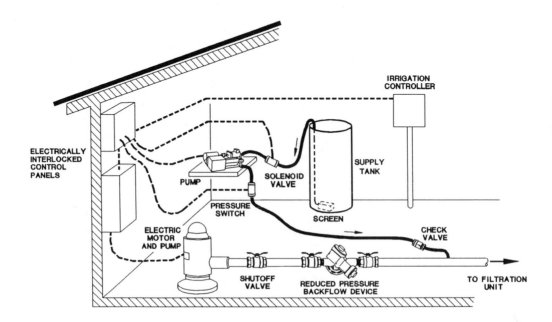

FIGURE 5. Injection system safety features.

positive displacement pump is used to inject the chemicals, the controls for the injector and irrigation pump must be functionally interlocked to stop chemical injection automatically when the irrigation pump shuts down. This applies to injection systems operating with any type chemical.

Figure 5 shows a schematic of the injection system safety features if the irrigation system includes an irrigation pump and injector pump.

Backflow prevention requirements

Pumping systems from a self-contained pond or reservoir

Some irrigation systems in Washington and British Columbia pump from a self-contained storage reservoir that is filled from a ditch or stream by a lift pump.

If the water source is a self contained pond or reservoir, a 50-cm (23 inch) air gap must be maintained between the maximum water surface elevation of the pond and the pipeline used to fill the pond. If the air gap cannot be maintained, then a double check valve assembly must be installed according to the procedures shown in "Backflow prevention device selection," page 145.

The irrigation pump discharge line must contain a functional quick-closing check valve and a vacuum breaker and drain located between the pump and check valve to prevent the backflow of treated irrigation water into the pond or reservoir.

The irrigation pumping system must contain a functional pressure switch that will shut down the irrigation pump should the system pressure reach a point where chemical distribution is adversely affected. A foot valve shall also be installed on the suction line to prevent the suction line from draining back into the water source.

The guidelines shown under pesticide application and injection system requirements shall also apply as shown in those sections.

Pumping systems from streams, lakes or other natural sources

If the irrigation system is pumping directly from a canal, drainage or irrigation supply ditch, lake, stream or other natural watercourse an approved double check valve assembly backflow prevention device must be installed on the irrigation mainline between the irrigation pump and the injection system.

In addition to the double check valve assembly (DCVA), the pumping system must include a foot valve on the suction line.

The irrigation pumping system must contain a functional pressure switch that will shut down the irrigation pump should the system pressure reach a point where chemical distribution is adversely affected.

The guidelines shown under pesticide application and injection system requirements shall also apply as indicated in those sections.

Pumping systems from wells

An irrigation system drawing from groundwater must install an approved reduced pressure principle backflow device (RPBD) between the irrigation pump and the chemical injector.

In addition to the RPBD, the pumping system must have a foot valve at the bottom of the intake line to prevent the discharge column from draining back into the water source.

The irrigation pumping system must contain a functional pressure switch that will shut down the irrigation pump should the system pressure reach a point where chemical distribution is affected adversely.

The guidelines shown under pesticide application and injection system requirements shall also apply as indicated in those sections.

Pumping systems from irrigation districts or other water authorities

If the irrigation system is pumping from an irrigation district or other water purveyor mainline, an approved reduced pressure principle backflow device must be installed between the water authority's mainline and the irrigation pump.

In addition to the RPBD, the pumping system should include a check valve on the discharge side of the irrigation pump.

The irrigation pumping system must contain a functional pressure switch that will shut down the irrigation pump should the system pressure reach a point where chemical distribution is affected adversely.

The guidelines shown under pesticide application and injection system requirements shall also apply as indicated in those sections.

Irrigation systems operating from irrigation district or municipal mainlines

If the irrigation system is operating directly from an irrigation district or other water purveyor mainline, an approved reduced pressure principle backflow device must be installed between the irrigation district service and the chemical injector system.

The guidelines shown under pesticide application and injection system requirements shall also apply as shown in those sections.

Systems operating on a self-contained gravity-feed system

An irrigation system operating on its own gravity feed system where the elevation difference between the irrigation intake and the chemical injector exceeds 10 meters (33 feet) need not use a backflow prevention device if a venturi or other passive type of injector is used. If an injector pump is used, the elevation difference between the intake and the injector must exceed the pressure capability of the injector pump, otherwise a DCVA assembly must be installed between the intake and the chemical injector.

If the gravity feed irrigation system also functions as a potable water source, then injection must take place downstream from the potable connection and a DCVA must be installed between the injector and the potable water connection on the water supply mainline.

The guidelines shown under pesticide application and injection system requirements shall also apply as shown in those sections.

Additional precautions

Personal protection

The use of insecticides, nematicides and other chemicals are hazardous and require that safety procedures be followed by the operator. The following precautions should be taken by chemigation operators:

- Wear rubber boots, gloves and other appropriate protective equipment at the injection site.;
- Use a separate injection system to apply insecticides from that used for fertilizers.;
- Read the label to determine the safe field re-entry interval.;
- Ensure that the injection site is out of the spray range of the irrigation system. Some sprinklers may have to be plugged to ensure the injection site or the operators are not wetted down..

Field posting

Children, farmworkers and other people may be tempted to take a drink from an irrigation sprinkler or trickle emitter on a hot summer day. The orchard should be posted with signs warning that water cannot be consumed if fertigation or any form of chemigation is done.

A backflow prevention device is considered to be in working order only if it is tested annually by a certified technician.

INJECTION EQUIPMENT

The injector is the heart of the chemigation system. There are many types of injectors available, all with their own advantages and disadvantages. Some types of injection systems are not recommended because of the safety hazards that are inherent with those systems. This section provides information on the selection of an appropriate injection system.

Injector selection

Proper selection of a chemical injector and the chemical solution tank must include consideration of the following:

- type of irrigation system;
- crop grown;
- irrigation system flow rate;
- irrigation system operating pressure;
- injection rate;
- type of chemical to be injected;
- determination of whether a fixed volume ratio of fertilizer to water is needed;
- source of power;
- duration of operation;
- expansion requirements; and
- safety considerations.

Injectors can be classified into two types of feeder systems: constant rate feeders and constant ratio feeders. Constant rate feeders inject at the same discharge rate even if the irrigation system flow rate changes. A constant ratio feeder will inject the chemical at a constant ratio in proportion to the irrigation system flow rate. The concentration of chemical in irrigation water for a constant ratio feeder will therefore remain the same, and the injection time for each zone will remain constant.

The following steps are useful for the selection of a chemical injector:

1. Determine the flow rate of the largest zone. The injector selected must be capable of injecting sufficient volume to achieve the concentration of chemical desired in the irrigation water. Another check is to ensure that the injector is capable of completely injecting all of the chemical in the desired time frame.
2. Determine operating sequence. Will more than one zone be treated at a time? If so, then a constant ratio feeder may have an advantage in that the injection time for each zone will remain constant. If only one zone at a time is being treated, then it may be more convenient to inject the required weight or volume. A constant rate feeder or diluter works well for this.
3. Determine the operating characteristics of the irrigation system. If water is delivered to the irrigation system via a pump, an injector pump must be interlocked with the main irrigation pump. An injector pump also must be capable of exceeding the operating pressure of the irrigation system. A passive injection system may also have different backflow prevention requirements in specific situations. See "Cross connection control," page 144, for further information.
4. Determine the availability of power. The type of injector used will depend on whether an electrical power source is available at the injection site.
5. Determine the type of chemicals that are to be injected. The injector must withstand the corrosivity of the injected chemical.

Injectors can also be categorized into two different types: passive and active injectors. A discussion on the various types of injectors follows.

Passive injectors

Passive injectors use the energy supplied by the irrigation system or the atmosphere to inject the chemicals. Examples of passive injectors are a venturi, pitot tube, utilization of the suction side of an irrigation pump and taking advantage of pressure differentials.

Injection on suction side of irrigation pump

A centrifugal pump draws water into the impeller by creating a negative pressure in the suction pipe. Atmospheric pressure then forces water up the suction pipe and into the pump volute. The same principle can be used to draw fertilizer solutions into the irrigation system. This system is risky and potentially hazardous, as any chemicals that are being injected during a pump or power failure would then enter the water supply. This method of injection is not recommended for any chemigation system application in British Columbia.

Other problems that can be encountered with this type of injection system are:

- any air entering through the connection to the suction line can cause malfunctioning and damage
- extra pump maintenance may be required because of the metal's exposure to the chemicals.

Diluter systems

Batch tank or diluter systems are simple and easy to operate but are labor-intensive and require good management to ensure that uniformity of application is achieved. Pitot tube and pressure differential injectors are two types of diluter systems.

Pitot tube injector

The pitot tube injection system consists of a small open-ended pipe placed in the irrigation pipe with one end facing the water flow and the other facing away from the water flow.

(See Figure 6) This practice creates a flow of water between the two pipe ends. The water can be circulated through an airtight pressure supply tank that contains the fertilizer or chemical. Dry fertilizers are often used with this injection system.

The rate at which the fertilizer is injected will vary as the fertilizer in the tank becomes diluted. This type of injection system is therefore not applicable to continuously moving irrigation systems such as travelling guns or center pivots. The proper use of a pitot injector requires that:

-   a batch of fertilizer be mixed for each set and the entire batch is applied during that irrigation set;
-   each set is sufficiently long to allow all of the fertilizer that is mixed to be applied;
-   the supply tank must withstand the maximum operating pressure of the irrigation system.

Pressure differential injection system

Pressure differential injectors consist of a pressurized tank connected to the irrigation mainline through two ports. This type of injection system is also known as a diluter injection system.

The inlet port is connected to the mainline on the upstream side of the pressure-reducing valve. The outlet port is connected to the downstream side of the pressure-reducing valve. *(Figure 7)* The pressure-reducing valve on the irrigation mainline is used to create a pressure difference between the inlet and outlet ports of the pressurized tank. The difference in pressure creates a flow of water through the tank. The chemical in the tank is slowly diluted over the injection time until it has all been applied.

This type of injection system is used where a specified amount of chemical is to be applied to an irrigated zone. As the chemical is diluted over time, the injector cannot be operated if the irrigation system is switching from one zone to another. A new chemical mixture must be added to the injector every time a new zone is irrigated. This type of injection system is trouble-free and inexpensive and works well for small systems operating at less than 50 gallons per minute.

Pressure differential systems are also available with a diaphragm to separate the incoming

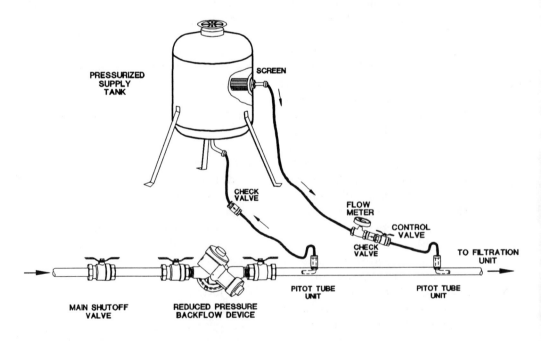

FIGURE 6. A pitot tube injector

water from the fertilizer. The concentration of the injected solution then remains the same. This type of system is generally used for smaller operations such as small greenhouses.

Venturi principle injection system

Venturi injectors operate by creating a vacuum when water is forced through a constriction. The vacuum sucks the chemical into the irrigation water stream at the point of constriction. Venturi are most commonly installed on a bypass to a pressure-reducing device such as a regulator or a gate valve *(Figure 8)*.

To operate effectively, venturi must have a pressure drop of 20 to 50 percent of the inlet pressure and are therefore not effective where supply pressures may be low. The primary advantage of a venturi system is the low cost.

The rate of chemical injection is dependent upon the flow rate through the venturi which is affected by the operating pressure, venturi size, construction and any flow con-

strictions or flow control devices that may be installed on the venturi discharge line. The injection rate can be adjusted by varying the flow through the injector, adjusting the system operating pressure or adjusting the controls on the discharge line. A metering valve on the suction line may also be used to control the injection rate. Once established, the rate of injection will remain constant for a zone. As the chemical is not diluted while it is injected, the concentration of the chemical mix is also constant.

Table 3 provides information on the injection capacities of various size venturi injectors for different operating conditions and flows through the injectors. Specifications from the injector company should be used in making the final selection of an injector.

Active injectors

Active injectors use an external energy source or a mechanical moving part to create pressures exceeding the irrigation mainline pres-

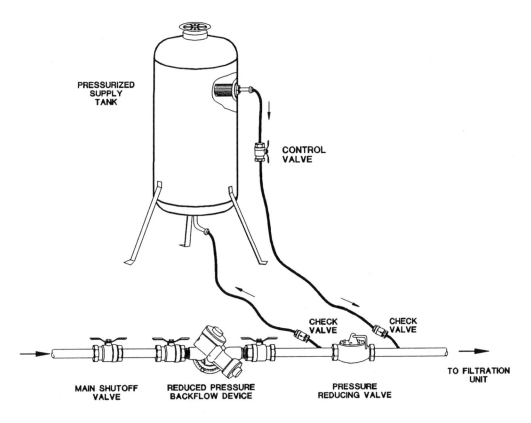

FIGURE 7. A pressure differential injection system.

sure to inject the chemical. The main types of active injectors are pumps and compressor systems.

Injection pumps

Injection or metering pumps use gear, rotary, piston or diaphragm to develop the pressures exceeding the irrigation system pressure to inject the chemical. Injection pumps, within the minimum to maximum operating range, should have a delivery accuracy of plus or minus one percent. The pumps should be easily adjusted for different injection rates and be constructed of noncorrosive materials.

Injection pumps are available in constant rate and constant ratio feeder systems. A constant rate system will deliver a constant injection rate irrespective of the irrigation system flow rate. Constant ratio feeders inject chemicals at a rate determined by the flow of the irrigation system. The concentration of chemical in the irrigation water therefore remains the same.

The injection pump selected should have a capacity that is consistent with the application rate of chemicals to be injected. Pumps should not be operated at the maximum or minimum output as pumping accuracy is affected and pump damage could occur. Figure 9 shows a metering injection pump.

Diaphragm pumps

Diaphragm pumps are more expensive than piston injection pumps but offer distinct advantages over other types of injection units.

- They have a small number of moving parts;
- Limited areas of the components are exposed to the chemicals injected. This reduces the potential for corrosion, wear and leakage, lowering maintenance costs and enhancing environmental safety; and
- The injection rate is easily adjusted while the pump is operating.

Piston pumps

Piston pumps are available in single and dual injection heads with a wide range of injection capacities. Piston pumps are used most commonly in situations that require a high injection rate. These pumps have distinct disadvantages for chemigation:

- Piston seals are subject to accelerated wear;
- Calibration of most piston pumps is timeconsuming. Altering the injection rate requires stopping the pump and altering the stroke length mechanically. The pump must then be restarted and the

TABLE 3. Venturi injector selection. (From Mazzei Injector Corporation.)

Model	Size In/Out	Pressure Differential	Flow through Injector @ 50psi (gpm)	Injection rate L/hr	gal/hr
283	1/2"	26%	0.5	23	6
384	1/2"	25%	2.1	38	10
484	1/2" -3/4"	18%	3.4	64	17
584	3/4"	18%	6.4	95	25
878	1"	16%	12	227	60
1078	1"	16%	17	284	75
1583	1 1/2"	18%	34	680	180
2081	2"	18%	101	1890	500
384-x	1/2"	50%	2.1	132	35
885-x	1"	32%	12	530	140
1585-x	1 1/2"	35%	36	1325	350
2083-B	2"	67%	29	4275	1130

injection rate checked. Some models offer variable-speed drives to adjust injection rates; and

- Piston pumps lose suction capabilities proportionally as stroke length of the piston is reduced to pump smaller amounts. It is more efficient and consistent to operate within the middle capacities of the pump.

Water-powered injectors

Water-powered injectors are considered active injectors although an external energy source is not used. The energy of the pressurized water in the irrigation system is used to drive the injector. Water powered injectors are available in turbine (impeller) or piston drive.

A turbine water-driven injector does not expel water but does utilize some irrigation supply pressure to drive the unit. *(See Figure 10)* The irrigation system design and injector selection must consider the additional losses to ensure that adequate pressure is available to

operate the system and injector. These types of injectors are available in single- and double-head models.

Piston-operated units use a small amount of the pressurized irrigation water supply to drive the piston. The drive water that is expelled from the piston is usually three times the quantity of the injected solution. The injection rate is set by controlling the amount of water entering the piston drive. Piston drive units do not reduce the irrigation system pressure. Figure 11 shows a piston-drive injection system.

Compressor injectors

Another form of active injection is to use compressors to pressurize a tank with a diaphragm containing the fertilizer mix. The pressure in the tank is set higher than the irrigation system pressure to allow chemical flow from the tank into the irrigation system. Control valves on the discharge line are used to control the injection rate from the tank.

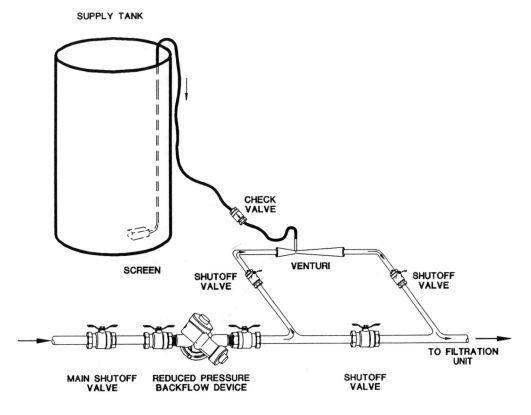

FIGURE 8. A venturi injection system.

This system is not commonly used because of the expense of purchasing and linking all the components required. The system does not offer any major advantages over other types.

Injector calibration

Proper operation of a chemigation system requires calibration of the irrigation and injection system. "Calculating injection rates" *(see page 160)* covers the calibration of an irrigation system using chemigation in more detail. Procedures for the calibration of an injector are provided here.

It is always good to calibrate one's own injection system rather than rely on the manufacturer's specifications. Manufacturer's suggestions may eliminate the process of trial and error, but conditions at the site will never be the same as in a factory setting. The injection system should be calibrated with the irrigation system operating under normal conditions and the injection supply tank located in its permanent position.

Calibration tubes

A stop watch and graduated cylinder are required to perform the injector calibration. The calibration container should be clear, large enough to hold a volume sufficient for five minutes of injection and calibrated in milliliters or ounces. The calibration container is filled and the injector is allowed to pump from it for a specific period. Alternately, the time required to pump a fixed volume from the container may be measured.

The injector is calibrated by measuring the amount of material pumped from the calibration tube over the time interval measured with the stop watch. This method is superior to pumping into a container as pressure is always maintained against the injection pump.

Although not as accurate as a calibration container, the injection rate can also be found by measuring the amount of chemical solution removed from the supply tank. This method is acceptable for batch fertigation but

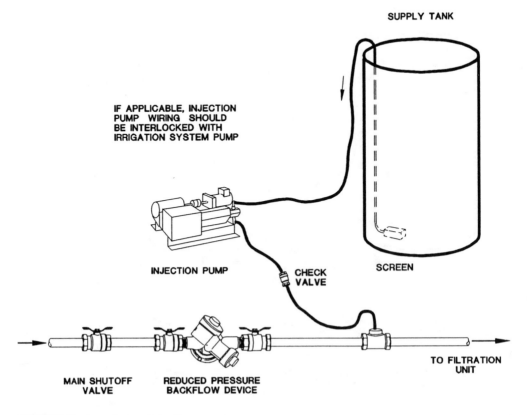

FIGURE 9. A metering injection pump.

should not be used for the injection of pesticides or herbicides or for continuous moving irrigation systems.

Venturi, pitot tube or pressure differential injection systems need not be accurately calibrated if these injectors are only used for batch-type fertilizer injection. However, the injection of herbicides or pesticides will require accurate knowledge of the injection rate.

CALCULATING INJECTION RATES

Proper operation of a chemigation system requires appropriate equipment and accurate calculations to determine the correct application rate. This section (Calculating Injection Rates) provides detail on calibrating chemigation systems and calculating system injection rates.

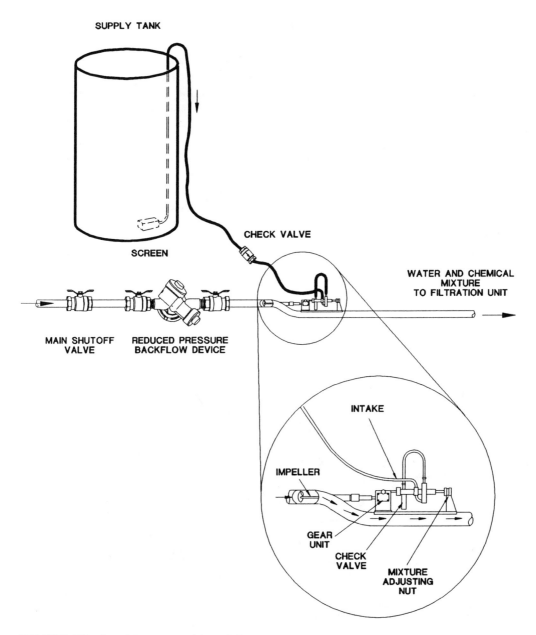

FIGURE 10. A turbine water-driven injector.

Determining a method of calculating injection rates

There are four different methods that can be used to determine how much chemical must be added by the injection system. Usually it is not practical to adjust chemigation rates by adjusting the injection rate. With venturi, for instance, the injection rate will be fixed by the operating pressures of the irrigation system. With variable speed metering pumps, it will be necessary to reset injection rates or solution concentrations to adjust for unequally sized zones. It is more practical to use alternative procedures for controlling application rates. Four different methods could be used, depending on the type of chemical, injector, type of irrigation system, zone size and number of zones.

1. Weight method: Weigh out the desired weight of material to be applied, dissolve in a convenient amount of water, and inject until it has all been applied. Knowledge of the injection rate will be required to ensure that the concentration in the irrigation lines is not too strong and that the time for injection is not too long.

2. Volume method: Similar to the weight method except that the concentration of the liquid solution must be known to calculate how much volume to apply.

3. Injection rate method: This procedure is explained in the "Calibrating an injection pumping system."

4. Injection time method: The time required to inject the amount of chemical is calculated from the injection rate and solution concentration using the same equation as for the injection rate method shown in "Calibrating an injection pumping system."

Calibrating an injection pumping system

Calibration of a chemigation system involves the following basic steps:

1. Determine the area to be treated or the number of plants to be treated with a trickle irrigation system;

2. Determine the amount of chemical to be applied per acre or per plant;

3. Calculate the total amount of chemical to be applied;

4. Determine the length of injection time in

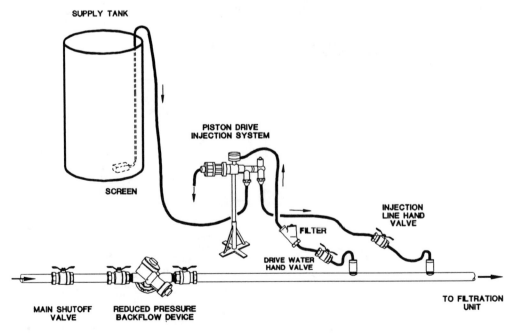

FIGURE 11. A piston driven injection system.

hours. Factors that will influence this are the length of the irrigation set time, irrigation system application rate, transit time from the injection point to the target area and the amount of chemical to be applied;

5. Select the chemical composition to be used and mixture concentration; and

6. Set the injection flow rate on the injector.

The injection rate may be predetermined by the capacity of the injector or the flow rate of the irrigation system. The desired injection rate can also be calculated by using the following formula if all of the parameters are known.

Equation 1:

$$Ic = \frac{Qc \times A}{C \times T}$$

where:

Ic = Chemical injection rate (gal/min)

Qc = Quantity of chemical to be applied to target area (lbs/acre)

A = Area (acre)

C = Concentration of injected solution (lbs/gal)

T = Injection duration (min.)

The method of calibrating chemigation systems using different irrigation systems and chemicals is best exemplified through the following examples. Consideration must be given to batch versus continuous injection and the target area effectively covered by the irrigation system.

Batch chemigation examples

Irrigation systems such as solid-set sprinklers and trickle operate in a batch mode. These systems irrigate a block of land at a constant rate for a fixed period. Batch chemicals can therefore be mixed and applied to these blocks during irrigation.

The amount to be applied is easily determined for a batch application process. The timing of application of a batch system is most critical if the chemical is to be applied to a specific area of the plant's root zone. This is determined by the type of chemical used and the duration of application.

Example 1:
Solid-set sprinkler - fertilizer application

Solid-set systems irrigate blocks of land controlled by a single valve. The following example provides the calibration sequence for a solid-set sprinkler system.

The system has the following particulars:

- 5/32" x 3/32" nozzle operating at 45 psi;
- 6.5 gpm flow rate per sprinkler;
- 90 ft. wetted diameter;
- 45 ft. x 55 ft. spacing;
- 20 sprinklers operating in the zone;
- zone flow rate is 130 gpm; and
- irrigation set time is 12 hours.

Calcium nitrate fertilizer is to be used to apply 50 kilograms of nitrogen per hectare (45 lbs. per acre) to a mature orchard crop on a sandy loam soil. The moisture content of the soil is at 25 percent of the available water storage capacity. The nitrogen is to be applied to a depth of 300 millimeters (12 in.).

Area to be treated

For a sprinkler system, the area to be treated is calculated by using the sprinkler spacing and number of sprinklers. Water application will occur outside this calculated area, but it is expected that the same amount will be returned to the target area from the next set.

Equation 2:

Treated area

= no. of sprinklers x sprinkler spacing ÷ 43,560 ft²/acre

or

= 20 x 45 x 55 ÷ 43,560

= 1.14 acres

= 0.46 hectares

Amount of chemical to be applied per hectare/acre

From Table 4, the following information can be obtained on calcium nitrate.

- 15.5% N
- solubility   - 180 g/100 g H_2O
            - 1.8 kg/l *(this value is interpreted from the table using a temperature of 20°C);*
- $CaCO_3$ equivalency is -20.

Calcium nitrate will not acidify the soil, as a negative amount of calcium carbonate is required to neutralize the acidic effect.

To apply 50 kilograms of nitrogen per hectare (45 lbs. per acre) the weight of calcium nitrate fertilizer will be:

Equation 3:

$$Q_c = \text{desired amount of N / Ha}$$
$$\div \quad \text{percentage N in fertilizer}$$
$$= \quad 50 \div 0.155$$
$$= \quad \text{323 kg of calcium nitrate / hectare (290 lbs./acre)}$$

Total amount of chemical to be applied

Equation 4:

Amount applied
$$= \quad \text{rate per hectare x no. of hectares}$$
$$= \quad \text{323 kg/ha x 0.46 hectares (290 lbs./acre 1.14 acres)}$$
$$= \quad \text{149 kg   (329 lbs.)}$$

At a solubility rate of 1.8 kg/L the minimum volume of solution will be:

Solution volume
$$= \quad \text{total amount to be applied} \div \text{solubility rate}$$
$$= \quad \text{149 kg} \div \text{1.8 kg/L}$$
$$= \quad \text{83 l   (22 gal.)}$$

A tank capable of 83 liters (22 gallons) of chemical storage is required if calcium nitrate is to be used as the nitrogen source. The nutrient mixture concentration can be diluted if the solubility of the calcium nitrate is reduced due to fertilizer coatings. A larger tank will then be required.

Length of injection time

An injection time of one hour is selected to ensure that the chemical is applied as uniformly as possible. The chemical is to be applied during part of the normal 12-hour set time so there is ample time to inject the product. Step 6 shows the methodology for calculating when the chemical should be applied if a specified depth is desired.

Injection rate

Equation 5:

$$I_c = Q_c \times A \div C \times T$$

where
$$I_c = \quad \text{chemical injection rate (L/min.) (gal./min.)}$$
$$Q_c = \quad \text{323 kg/ha (290 lbs./acre)}$$
$$A = \quad \text{0.46 ha (1.14 acres)}$$
$$C = \quad \text{1.8 kg/L (15 lbs./gal.)}$$
$$T = \quad \text{60 minutes}$$

$$I_c = \quad 323 \times 0.46 \div 1.8 \times 60$$
$$= \quad \text{1.38 l/min (.37 gal./min.) (1.5 quarts/minute)}$$

The maximum concentration of injected solution in the irrigation lines selected for this example is one percent. The irrigation system flow rate is 130 gallons per minute or 490 liters per minute.

The concentration of solution in the irrigation line is:

Solution concentration
$$= \quad \text{injection rate} \div \text{system flow rate}$$
$$= \quad 1.38 \div 490$$
$$= \quad \text{0.0028 or approximately 0.3\%.}$$

For this example, a 1.38 l/min (.37 gal./min.) injection rate is well within the one percent fertilizer concentration limit that was set.

Depth of penetration

Equation 6:

Application rate
$$= \quad \text{96.3 x gpm} \div \text{sprinkler spacing}$$
$$= \quad \text{96.3 x 6.5} \div \text{45 ft. x 55 ft.}$$
$$= \quad \text{0.25 in./hr.}$$

Total application
$$= \quad \text{application rate x time}$$
$$= \quad \text{0.25 in./hr. x 12 hrs.}$$
$$= \quad \text{3 inches applied}$$

Depth of water penetration

$$
\begin{aligned}
&= &&\text{total application x} \\
& &&\text{(Table 3 value)} \\
& &&\text{(25\% moisture content} \\
& &&\text{on sandy loam)} \\
&= &&\text{3 in. x 11 in./ inch applied} \\
&= &&\text{33 inches}
\end{aligned}
$$

Desired depth of chemical is 12 inches
Amount of irrigation required

$$
\begin{aligned}
&= &&(12 \text{ inches} \div 33) \times 12 \text{ hrs.} \\
&= &&4.4 \text{ hours of irrigation} \\
& &&\text{required after injection begins}
\end{aligned}
$$

The chemical injection must be started 7.6 hours after the irrigation set begins and be completed one hour later. The chemical will then have 4.4 hours to infiltrate into the soil to a depth of 12 inches during a 12-hour irrigation set.

Example 2
Trickle system - granular fertilizer

Trickle systems irrigate the plant's roots directly and should be designed to irrigate blocks of the same maturity, crop and soil type. For this example, a first-year planting of tree fruits requires 15 grams (0.5 ounce)of phosphorus to be applied. The following parameters are used for this example:

- the orchard is high density with plant spacings of 5 feet and rows spaced 12 feet apart;
- the rows are 250 feet long (50 plants per row);
- one zone irrigates 20 rows at one time;
- each tree is supplied by two 2 l/hr (.5 gal./hr.)emitters;
- a normal irrigation is approximately nine hours of operation per day during peak conditions for a mature crop. For a first-year crop, the operating time is estimated to be two hours per day.

The grower wishes to apply 15 grams (0.5 ounce) of actual phosphorus to each plant over the growing season, in eight equal applications one week apart. Monoammonium phosphate will be used as the phosphorus source.

1. Number of plants to be treated
   Number of plants

$$
\begin{aligned}
&= &&\text{plants per row x number} \\
& &&\text{of rows} \\
&= &&50 \times 20 \\
&= &&1{,}000 \text{ trees}
\end{aligned}
$$

2. Amount of chemical to be applied per application
   From Table 4, the following information can be obtained on monoammonium phosphate.
   - 11% N
   - 22% actual P (Note phosphorus fertilizers often provide the amount of phosphorus as P_2O_5. To convert from P_2O_5 to actual P, divide P_2O_5 by 2.3)
   - Solubility - 43 g / 100 g H_2O
                  - 0.43 kg/L
   - $CaCO_3$ equivalency is 58

Monoammonium phosphate has an acidifying effect on the soil. Liming may be required if this fertilizer is used extensively.

The amount of actual fertilizer to be applied per application is:

Amount applied

$$
\begin{aligned}
&= &&\text{amount per tree x number} \\
& &&\text{of trees} \\
&\div &&\text{number of applications x \% P} \\
& &&\text{in fertilizer} \\
&= &&15 \text{ g/tree (.5 oz.) x } 1{,}000 \\
& &&\text{trees} \\
&\div &&(8 \times 0.22) \\
&= &&8{,}522 \text{ g (284 oz.)} \\
&= &&8.5 \text{ kg (19 lbs.)}
\end{aligned}
$$

Volume of solution

The minimum volume of solution required to dissolve this amount of fertilizer will be:

$$
\begin{aligned}
&= &&\text{total amount to be applied} \\
&\div &&\text{solubility rate} \\
&= &&8.5 \text{ kg} \div 0.43 \text{ kg/l} \\
&= &&19.8 \text{ l (5.3 gal.)}
\end{aligned}
$$

The minimum storage tank size required is therefore 20 liters (6 gallons). In this example, 30 liters is used to dissolve the 8.5 kilograms of fertilizer.

The solution concentration is therefore 8.5 kilograms divided by 30 liters equals 0.28 kilograms per liter (19 lbs./7.8 gal. = 2.4 lbs./gal.).

Injection rate

All of the chemical is to be injected in one hour. The injection rate is therefore 30 l/hr. (7.8 gal./hr.).

The maximum concentration of injected solution into the irrigation lines is selected to be one percent. The flow rate of this zone is:

$$1,000 \text{ trees x 4 l/hr/tree}$$
$$= \quad 4000 \text{ l/hr}$$
$$(1 \text{ gal./hr./tree}) = (1.000 \text{ gal./hr.})$$

Concentration of chemical in the irrigation lines is:

TABLE 4. Granular fertilizer properties, below, may be used for calculating examples.

Fertilizer	Molecular compound	Percent element	Solubility g/100 g H_2O	Temp °C	Equivalent $CaCO_3$
Ammonia	NH_3	82% N	90	0	148
Ammonium nitrate	NH_4NO_3	34% N	118`	0	62
			187	20	
			590	80	
Ammonium sulphate	$(NH_4)_2SO_4$	21% N	71	0	110
		24% S	95	80	
Calcium carbonate (limestone)	$CaCO_3$		0.006	0	
Calcium metaphosphate	$Ca(PO_3)_2$		0.001	0	
Calcium nitrate	$Ca(NO_3)_2 . 4H_2O$	15.5% N	134	0	-20
			364	100	
Calcium sulphate	$CaSO_4 . 2H_2O$		0.24	0	
Copper sulphate	$CuSO_4 . 5H_2O$		32	0	
Diammonium phosphate	$(NH_4)_2HPO_4$	18% N	25	0	70
		20% P			
Dicalcium phosphate	$CaHPO_4 2H_2O$		0.02	0	
Magnesia	MgO		0.0006	0	
Magnesium sulphate	$MgSO_4 . 7H_2O$		85	0	
Manganese sulphate	$MnSO_4 . 4H_2O$		105	0	
Monoammonium phosphate	$NH_4H_2PO_4$	11%	43	0	58
		22%P			
Monocalcium phosphate	$CaH_4(PO_4)_2H_2O$	20% P	varies		
Potassium chloride	KCl	60% K_2O	28	0	neutral
			51	80	
Potassium nitrate	KNO_3	13% N	13	0	-26
		46% K_2O	169	80	
Potassium sulphate	K_2SO_4	53% K_2O	8	0	neutral
Sodium nitrate	$NaNO_3$	16% N	73	0	-29
Urea	$CO(NH_2)_2$	46% N	67	0	71
			108	20	
			167	40	
Zinc sulphate	$ZnSO_4 . 6H_2O$		70	0	

=	injection rate
÷	system flow rate
=	30 l/hr
÷	4000 l/hr (or 1 gal./hr./tree)
=	0.0075 or 0.75 percent

This injection rate is therefore acceptable.

The amount of nitrogen applied to each tree can also be calculated. The N concentration in the fertilizer is 11 percent vs. 22 percent for phosphorus. A total of 7.5 grams (0.26 ounce) of N is therefore applied to the crop over the eight applications.

Irrigation and pest management

Mike Willett

Washington State University Cooperative Extension

Yakima, Washington

Questions about impacts of irrigation practices on pest problems were first raised in the Washington State fruit industry over 60 years ago, prompted by the conversion of existing surface irrigation systems to sprinklers. This discussion has been repeated at intervals over the last six decades as we began to more fully explore the potential usefulness of delivering water under pressure to targeted locations throughout the orchard.

Most of this discussion has revolved around the impacts of delivery systems which wet all or substantial portions of the tree canopy. In the future, we may spend more time discussing the impacts of delivery systems which deliver water in ways that create a drier orchard environment and/or intentionally stress trees. This chapter will focus on whole orchard, insect, disease, and environmental impacts in the relationship between pest management and irrigation.

Whole orchard impacts

While it is better to discuss the impacts of irrigation on specific insects or diseases separately, it is also important to note that changing irrigation methods can significantly affect the orchard environment. Years ago the switch from surface irrigation methods to sprinklers increased the potential for soil residual herbicide and insecticide movement into the tree root zone. In cases where the soil residue was arsenic from lead arsenate sprays, it was speculated that increased leaching of this element played a major role in orchard replant problems in Washington State.

Based on observations by Dr. Ed Proebsting at the WSU Irrigated Agriculture Research and Extension Center, drip-irrigated research orchards had less shoot growth but usually had more mite problems. Dr. Stan Hoyt, entomologist at the WSU Tree Fruit Research and Extension Center in Wenatchee, attributed increased mite problems to lower populations of apple rust mite, which are an essential early season food source for predatory mites. It was his observation that in the more arid areas of the state, rust mite populations were generally lower. This combination of lower rust mite populations and increased dustiness in orchards without a well-watered cover crop, helped elevate mites to pest status.

When a drip or other low-volume irrigation system is used intentionally to withhold water and/or create regulated water stress in tree crops, shoot growth can be dramatically reduced. Few detailed studies have been done to look at the impact of this reduced shoot growth on pest populations. Research on pear using plant growth regulators to reduce shoot growth resulted in lower pear psylla populations and a reduction in second bloom on Bartlett. If the research results on reducing secondary bloom in Bartlett pear can be duplicated using deficit irrigation, there may be some hope for reducing fireblight susceptibility in this variety, as most infection occurs through secondary bloom.

The impact of regulated deficit irrigation on flush-feeding pests of apple should be a target of future research. Research on regulated deficit irrigation in grapes demonstrated a reduction in leafhopper populations under low-volume irrigation treatments.

Impact on pesticide residues

Fruit growers in the Pacific Northwest began widespread adoption of overhead sprinklers in the 1960s. These systems were used for a variety of purposes, including bloom delay, frost protection, summer cooling, pesticide delivery, and to reduce pest density and damage. However, although increased pest damage was reported, some of this damage was caused less by a direct promotion of pest damage but rather by a reduction of pesticide residues in the canopy of these crops. Various studies have demonstrated that 30 to 90 percent of pesticide residues can be removed by overtree irrigations ranging from one to four inches of water. Losses differ depending on the pesticide tested and seem to vary substantially even with the same pesticide.

A thorough study by Dr. Frank Howell and Jay Maitlen of the USDA-ARS in Yakima, Washington, offers the most complete guidelines for using a specific pesticide, azinphosmethyl, with overhead sprinklers. Recently deposited residues were more susceptible to erosion than older residues. A single irrigation (about four inches) can remove all protection against codling moth. Irrigation at 13 days after application had no observable effect on residues. To maintain maximum residues, growers should apply pesticides after irrigation and wait as long as possible before irrigating again. If the orchard is in a moderate to high codling moth pressure area, overhead

irrigation may be incompatible with acceptable codling moth control.

A number of spray adjuvants have been tested for the prevention of pesticide removal by rainfall or sprinkler irrigation. In a test in southern Oregon, Biofilm® failed to reduce azinphosmethyl wash-off. The polyterpene compounds (Nu-Film-17® or Nu-Film-P®) have been shown to extend pesticide residues after real or simulated rainfall. Other products exist for this purpose. No direct comparison data exist for these products under overhead sprinkling or evaporative cooling regimes as practiced on tree fruits in the Pacific Northwest.

Both growers and researchers have attempted to make foliar applications of pesticides using overtree irrigation systems to apply the pesticides. Research done in southern Oregon in mature Bartlett and d'Anjou orchards demonstrated that control was poor and resulted from a 10-fold reduction in pesticide residues compared with the same pesticides applied by a speed sprayer. In this trial, the overtree sprinklers were spaced 25 feet apart on the square. Improvements in delivery system uniformity might improve the performance of this pesticide application method. An improved technique for charging the system with pesticides would have to be found to avoid excessive dilution and runoff of the pesticide by water applied immediately before or after application. Additionally, a more targeted system of water delivery would have to be found to minimize application to nontarget areas.

Perhaps the most serious question surrounding the removal of pesticide residues by overtree sprinkling is the environmental fate of these materials after they are removed from plant surfaces. While most of the chemicals we currently use on tree fruits are relatively short-lived in the soil, their use and the virtually immediate wash-off which can happen under evaporative cooling regimes seems wasteful. Additionally, unless the evaporative cooling system is designed and operated to prevent soil saturation and runoff, these residues may be carried out of the orchard and end up in surface water supplies.

Direct impacts on insects and diseases

Codling moth

Although most reports about the interaction between codling moth control and overtree irrigation have focused on the erosion of pesticide residues, early workers speculated that rainfall may have an effect on the ability of codling moth to infest fruit. To test if overhead sprinkler applications could aid in the control of codling moth, former Yakima County Cooperative Extension Agent Bill Hudson and Dr. Hal Moffit of the USDA-ARS, Yakima, tested this concept in a heavily infested orchard in Yakima in the early 1970s. Because codling moth is reported to be most active from dusk until total darkness, the plot was sprinkled from 7:00 pm until 11:00 pm each night, beginning April 5 and continuing until September 10. At the end of the season, the sprinkled plot had 4.3 percent damage and the adjacent untreated, unsprinkled section of the orchard had 43 percent damage after applying 55 inches of water during the season.

It is still uncertain why overtree irrigation reduced codling moth damage. Pheromone traps continued to catch moths. The water may wash eggs or newly hatched larvae off the fruit in addition to interfering with normal flight activity. More research should be conducted to determine how sprinkling controls codling moth. This technique could be another tool in our codling moth control arsenal, particularly with the increase in the use of daily overtree cooling as an option for orchard management.

Spider mites

In 1968 and 1969, Bill Hudson also studied the effects of overtree sprinkling on spider mite populations as part of his M.S. thesis. His conclusion was that overtree sprinkling was effective in keeping populations of McDaniel mite and apple rust mite below the economic injury level, but was ineffective against European red mite. While sprinkling effectively washes mites and eggs off the upper portions of the leaves, European red mites were able to migrate to the lower surfaces of the leaves and continue to lay eggs. More European red mites were removed when immature mites were the dominant life stage present.

Pear insect pests

Based on work from Medford, Oregon, in Bartlett and d'Anjou blocks which received five to six summer irrigations there were no reductions in pear psylla densities, spider mite levels, or natural enemy populations. There was a three- to four-fold reduction in pear psylla honeydew damage and, in one year, a 50 percent reduction in pear rust mite damage in overtree sprinkled plots. The authors of this study concluded that the greatest potential for the use of overtree sprinklers in pear pest management was to wash off pear psylla honeydew residue.

Apple scab

There is a clear and widely understood relationship between leaf wetness, air temperature, and the development of apple or pear scab in those regions where these diseases exist. The use of overtree irrigation to initiate or prolong leaf wetness periods, creating scab infection periods, has been reported both in the literature and by grower experience. Growers are cautioned to use the shortest possible irrigation sets and to avoid overtree irrigation during those periods when even a minimal irrigation set may result in an infection.

To determine what these minimal infection requirements would be, growers should refer to the Mills table for apple scab infection prediction found in crop protection guides published for each region. It is extremely important that infections be avoided during the primary infection period, which, for apple scab, extends from bud break until about mid-June.

Primary infection is the form of scab which results from inoculation by overwintering scab spores produced in fallen leaves on the orchard floor. If infection can be prevented during this period, overtree irrigation can be used with relatively little risk of infection during the rest of the season. Research in South Africa has demonstrated that fruit becomes increasingly resistant to apple scab as it grows. This information can be used to time fungicide applications if preventing fruit scab is the primary concern. Foliar scab infection periods seem to follow Mills table guidelines throughout the season. Obviously, if natural or induced infections occur, they can be controlled with available fungicides. Concern about using additional fungicides may be a reason to avoid the use of overtree sprinklers during the early season.

Fireblight

Studies have reported increased fireblight when overtree irrigation was used for bloom delay. Other reports indicate that when overtree sprinklers were used for irrigation purposes, increased fireblight can occur but is largely confined to the edges of the block or fringe areas that receive insufficient wetting.

Crown rot and sprinkler rot

There have been numerous reports of increased crown or collar rot from the use of overtree sprinklers for evaporative cooling, but in the early 1970s, some growers felt that converting from undertree sprinklers to overtree sprinklers for irrigation helped alleviate the crown rot problem by keeping the crown area drier. Crown rot is caused by the water mold fungus *Phytophthora cactorum* and requires free water for the movement of spores. Infection is more likely in wet soils than in dry soils, although some severe infections have been noted in shallow soil areas of orchards which have highly fluctuating soil moisture levels. Because of the great variability in evaporative cooling systems, some of these may be creating extremely wet orchard soils and some may not. To reduce the risk of crown rot, prolonged saturation of orchard soils should be avoided.

Sprinkler rot of immature pear fruit is a persistent and occasionally severe disease in the Pacific Northwest. This disease is also caused by *Phytophthora cactorum* and is spread by contaminated irrigation water. *Phytophthora* can be isolated from many irrigation canals in the state, where it overwinters in silt on canal bottoms. Infection occurs when irrigation water containing the infective zoospores is applied to the fruit. The required wetting periods are very short. Treating the water with as little as one ppm of copper can control the disease, but may have an effect on fruit finish of copper susceptible cultivars. The disease can also occur on apples. Golden Delicious is the most susceptible apple cultivar.

Powdery mildew

In a survey done of growers using evaporative cooling in Washington State, powdery mildew had not increased as a result of cooling. Previous reports from Washington and other areas also indicated no effect of overtree irrigation or, at best, a slight reduction in fruit infection.

REFERENCES

Collins, M.D., P.B.. Lombard and J.W. Wolfe. 1978. "Effects of evaporative cooling for bloom delay on 'Bartlett' and 'Bosc' pear tree performance." *J. Amer. Soc. Hort. Sci.* 103(2):185-187.

Harley, C.P. and E.L. Reeves. 1930. "Observations of apple and pear diseases under overhead irrigation." *Proc. Wash. St. Hort. Assoc.* 26:48-50.

Howell, J.F. and J.C. Maitlen. 1987. "Accelerated decay of azinphosmethyl and phosmet by sprinkler irrigation above trees and its effect on control of codling moth based on laboratory bioassays as estimated by laboratory simulation of insecticide deposits". *J. Econ. Entomol.* 4(4):281-288.

Hudson, W.B. and B.P. Beirne. 1970. "Effects of sprinkler irrigation on McDaniel and European red mites in apple orchards." *J. Entomol. Soc. British Columbia.* 67:8-13.

Hudson, B. 1974. "Fruit Facts." *Good Fruit Grower.* 25(9):20.

Lombard, P.B., P.H. Westigard and D. Carpenter. 1966. "Overhead sprinkler system for environmental control and pesticide application in pear orchards." *HortScience.* 1(3 and 4):95-96.

Lombard, P.B., P.H. Westigard, J.G. Strang, R.B. Allen, and D.N. Joy. 1982. "Effect of nitrogen and daminozide on shoot growth for pear psylla supression and on 'Bartlett' pear performance." *HortScience.* 17(4)668-669.

Mitchell, P.D., P.H. Jerie and D.J. Chalmers. 1984. "The effects of regulated water deficit on pear tree growth, flowering, fruit growth and yield." *J. Amer. Soc. Hort. Sci.* 109(5):604-606.

Olcott-Reid, B., T.B. Sutton and C.R. Unrath. 1981. "Evaporative cooling irrigation influences disease, insect and mite pests of `Delicious' apple." *J. Amer. Soc. Hort. Sci.* 106(4):469-974.

Proebsting, E.L., J.E. Middleton, and S. Roberts. 1977. "Altered fruiting and growth characteristics of `Delicious' apple associated with irrigation method." *HortScience* 12(4):349-350.

Sanderson, P.G. 1993. "Overtree cooling survey summary." Personal communication.

Schwabe, W.F.S. 1982. "Wetting and temperature requirements for infection of mature apples by *Venturia inaequlis* in South Africa." *Ann. Appl. Biol.* 100:415-423.

Stang, E.J., D.C. Feree, F.R. Hall, and R.A. Spotts. 1978. "Overtree misting for bloom delay in `Golden Delicious' Apple." *J. Amer. Soc. Hort. Sci.* 103(1):82-87.

Sugar, D. and P.H. Westigard. 1993. "Over-tree irrigation in pear orchards influences persistence of foliar residues of four pesticides." *HortScience.* 28(10):1020-1021.

Sugar, D. and P.B. Lombard. 1981. "Pear scab influenced by sprinkler irrigation above the tree or at ground level." *Plant Disease.* 65(12):980.

Trichilo, P.J., L.T. Wilson and D.W. Grimes. 1990. "Influence of irrigation management on the abundance of leafhoppers (Homoptera: Cicadellidae) on grapes." *Env. Entomol.* 19(6):1803-1809.

Westigard, P.H., U. Kiigemagi and P.B. Lombard. 1974. "Reduction of pesticide deposits on pear following overtree irrigation." *HortScience.* 9(1):34-35.

Westigard, P.H., P.B. Lombard and R.B. Allen. 1979. "Effects of overtree irrigation on density and damage of pear pests." *J. Econ. Entomol.* 72(6):839-840.

Designing multipurpose water application systems

Robert G. Evans, Ph.D.

Irrigated Agriculture Research and Extension Center
Washington State University, Prosser

A multipurpose water application system in the Pacific Northwest (PNW) will include irrigation as well as various other uses. Examples of typical multipurpose systems are: undertree frost protection and irrigation; overtree frost protection and irrigation; or drip irrigation with fertigation.

The design and operation of any water application system, but especially for multipurpose projects, is where everything must come together. If it all doesn't mesh properly, there will be unsatisfactory compromises between competing uses, and water management will be extremely difficult. Multipurpose systems must be comprehensively engineered from the very beginning of the orchard planning process.

In addition to hydraulic considerations, a proper design must facilitate good water management and orchard cultural practices. Flow rates between different uses can vary as much as fivefold. Thus, the overall complexity of a design increases tremendously with each additional proposed use of a water application system. Consequently, designing a multipurpose water application system that works efficiently for all uses will be complicated and difficult.

Designs should be done by certified professionals with experience in multipurpose systems, it is a wise investment. One shouldn't hesitate to ask for references, make site visits, and to check them out. A few extra dollars for a good design can have a significant long-term payback in terms of labor savings, reduced disease problems, reduced water costs and improved management flexibility.

Orchards in the PNW are typically planted on sloping and/or irregular terrain to maximize cold air drainage during frost. In addition, soils are often sandy, and land-smoothing is usually not an option. These and other factors make pressurized sprinkle and microsprinkle systems the preferred water application methods. Although there are gravity furrow (rill) systems used on some PNW orchards, they are not typically part of multipurpose systems and, thus, are not included in this chapter. Consequently, the following discussion is directed towards the use of pressurized water application systems in PNW orchards.

This chapter brings together much of the information presented in other sections of this book. The following is not intended to be a design manual or to be all-inclusive, but to serve more as a checklist of some of the more important items to consider and to provide appropriate field level design parameters.

SELECTING A WATER APPLICATION SYSTEM

Numerous general questions, as well as specific cultural and crop considerations, must be addressed when choosing a water application system. The responses will select the type of system, establish design parameters, influence final cost, and the eventual, obtainable level of management.

General considerations

Factors to be considered in selecting a water application design will include: available labor (cost/quantity), available capital, soils (depths, types, variations, saline/sodic), field size, field shape, topography, water supply (quantity and seasonal availability), climatic factors, and personal preference.

Cultural considerations will include: varieties and spacing, specific spray programs, chemigation, pruning programs/practices, fertilizer applications, tillage program, cover crop/soil erosion problems, soil compaction and harvesting methods/procedures. Crop factors that should be considered are: frost protection, crop cooling, fruit quality, dis-

ease/pest control (e.g., existing pressure from fireblight and apple scab), water quality, trellising/training systems, cold hardiness and winter survival. All of these parameters must be considered at one level or another and compromises made before selecting the type of water application system(s). Unfortunately, evaluations of these factors are often based on short-term economics rather than good horticulture.

What should the system do?

In addition to irrigation, a water application system for an orchard can be used for: frost protection; enhancing red fruit color by overtree evaporative cooling (EC); control of fruit temperatures to reduce sun scald by overtree EC; chemigation; and, a combination of one or more of these uses. Table 1 presents general guidelines for designing specific, individual systems. Obviously, the system design will depend on the extent each of these uses is included and what the grower can afford. Overall design parameters will generally be dictated by the most restrictive proposed use of a multipurpose system, usually cooling or

TABLE 1. Guidelines for individually designing orchard sprinkle-microsprinkle systems on a total area covered basis (multipurpose needs are often additive).

	Overtree Frost[1]	Undertree Frost[2]	Irrigation	Overtree EC[3]
Average application rate, gpm/ac	≥70	≥40	≥8	≥40
Water supply, hrs/week[4]	60-80	50-70	25-160	60-100
Chemical injection	No	No	Sometimes[5]	Usually[5]
Water treatment[6]	Screens	Screens	Screens filters	Screens, pH[7]
Water quality	Marginal concern	Marginal concern	Major concern	Major concern
Uniformity	≥80%	≥70%	≥70%	≥80%
Cycling?	No	No	Okay	Yes

1= *Not recommended for stone fruits. Never use with wind machines.*
2= *Can be used with wind machines and/or heaters to supplement.*
3= *A separate irrigation system is often appropriate*
4= *Water supply over time period it is required (weeks, months, season, etc.)*
5= *Make sure injected chemicals are compatible, must follow labeling, and that all required chemigation safety devices are installed.*
6= *Chemical and/or biological control (eg., chlorine) treatment will usually be required for low volume, small orifice systems sued for irrigation (eg., drip/micros) and/or undertree microsprinkle frost.*
7= *pH control 6.5 to 6.6 usually required for overtree EC in central Washington.*

frost protection, although chemigation may also be a significant constraint.

Sometimes the use of a system is changed by replacing sprinkler heads or nozzles. However, even that simple modification can greatly affect pressure distributions throughout the entire piping network, water application uniformities, pumping efficiencies and application efficiencies. Any changes in system operating parameters between uses must be addressed in the initial design since it may not be possible to economically correct any deficiencies at a later date.

Multipurpose system or multiple systems?

There are an increasing number of water-application systems being installed on top of other water-application systems for a specific use. For a number of reasons, it is sometimes necessary to install multiple water-application systems for multiple uses. It must be determined early in the planning process if it is hydraulically required, economically feasible or otherwise advantageous to have separate or partially separate systems for various uses. Some examples of multi-system configurations in PNW orchards include: undertree sprinkle frost protection and irrigation; overtree (OT) sprinkle cooling with undertree sprinkle for frost protection and irrigation; overtree sprinkle cooling with undertree sprinkle frost protection and drip irrigation/fertigation; overtree sprinkle cooling with drip irrigation (over tree maintains cover crop) and fertigation; and, overtree sprinkle frost and cooling (at least 70 gallons per minute per acre) with undertree sprinkle irrigation.

Water quantity

Timing, availability and reliability of long-term water supplies must be determined. Published estimates of seasonal irrigation requirements for noncooled mature orchards in central Washington with a cover crop (EB 1513: James, *et al.*, 1988) range from 35 to 48 inches. Windy areas will require larger seasonal water deliveries than more protected, cooler areas. Adequate water must be available for all proposed uses (including irrigation requirements) at the right times.

Most of the canal and on-farm delivery systems in the PNW are generally designed to satisfy the requirements of furrow irrigation (maximum delivery 6-9 gpm/ac continuous flow to farm's total cropped area) which is also adequate for standard sprinkle systems. These flows are usually combined and used to irrigate smaller areas (sets), often at rates above 100 gpm/ac and the water use is rotated over

TABLE 2. Comparison of application rates, shown in depth (inches) per hour at nozzle and gpm/ac, plus the hours needed to apply approximately one week's peak crop evapotranspiration (ET_C) at an 80% efficiency. (Note that peak ET_C approaches 0.4 in/day and there are 168 hours/wk).

Application Rates		Hours to apply 2.8 in @ 80% efficiency
8 gpm/ac	0.02 in/hr	194.4 [1]
15 gpm/ac	0.03 in/hr	106
30 gpm/ac	0.07 in/hr	53
45 gpm/ac	0.10 in/hr	35
60 gpm/ac	0.13 in/hr	26
80 gpm/ac	0.18 in/hr	19.4
125 gpm/ac	0.28 in/hr	12.5

1= *Note that during peak ET periods, this rate may result in deficit water applications for irrigation and additional water must be extracted from soil water.*

ET_C= *Crop Evapotranspiration*

several days to cover the entire cropped area. Other uses also require high rates of water applications, but over much larger areas on a daily basis for limited time periods during the season. These other uses include overtree and undertree frost protection as well as overtree cooling. Therefore, many PNW orchardists are buying extra water, drilling wells and/or building large holding ponds/storages for supplemental water and/or unused allocations. Depending on the design and time of year, the required water supplies for multipurpose systems can be additive. Table 2 is presented to give some perspective to the various application rates and the corresponding gpm/ac for scheduling and other uses.

Water requirements can be extremely large. Figure 1 presents the estimated net per-acre weekly water-storage deficit for different uses with a constant field delivery rate of 7.5 gpm/ac (75,200 US gal/wk/ac), which is typical of many canal water supply operations. As can be seen, a 40 gpm/ac use for 73 hours/week will produce a net storage deficit

of about 100,000 gallons per acre for that week. Consequently, use must be estimated over the total anticipated period (days, weeks, months) and deficits summed to determine total storage size requirements. The use with the highest water requirements will determine the maximum storage size in multipurpose systems.

The following simple equation can be used to estimate net water storage deficits in gallons per acre for an average usage rate over a week at any field delivery rate *(see also Figure 1)*:

$$[(Use \times Hours) - (Delivery \times 168)] \times 60$$
$$= Net\ Deficit\ (US\ gallons/ac)$$

Use and delivery in the equation refer to average rates (gpm/ac) for that specific block, and "hours" refers to the time used in the week. The points where the lines in Figure 1 intersect the x-axis (y-axis = 0) are the break-even hours of operation (0 deficit) where total use equals the total weekly delivery. The results of Figure 1 (or the equation) need to

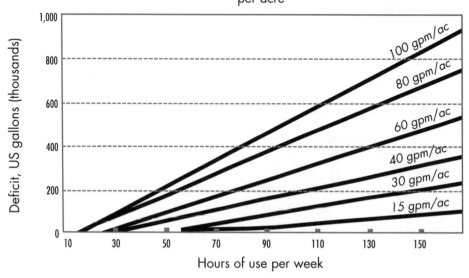

Weekly deficit per use rate
7.5 gpm/ac constant delivery
per acre

FIGURE 1. Estimated weekly net water removed from pond/storage (deficit/week/acre) for various usage rates with a constant field delivery of 7.5 gpm/ac (Note: 168 hours/wk, 60 minutes/hr, 27,154 US gal/ac-in).

be multiplied by the number of acres under the use to calculate total required storage volume per week. One shouldn't forget to consider the time needed to initially fill the storage at the field delivery rate, particularly for frost protection when available time may be compressed. Perhaps the storage should be partly filled in the fall in these cases.

Water quality

As discussed in other chapters, the mineral content and composition of the water supply from all sources (wells, canals, and reuse ponds) must be considered. The potential for soil salination must be assessed. Fertigation and injection of other chemicals requires a knowledge of the water chemical constituents and characteristics (e.g., pH, electrical conductivity, Ca^{++}, Mg^{++}, Na^+, $CO_3^=$, HCO_3^- and SAR) to ensure compatibility between chemicals as well as help determine chemical water treatment needs and procedures. Sometimes it is possible to apply some soil amendments prior to planting to ameliorate negative water quality problems (e.g., gypsum)

Eventual soil-sealing effects caused by excessive sodium is a concern with most deep wells in central Washington. High evaporation rates with overtree EC can leave excessive surface deposits of calcium carbonates and silicates on the fruit depending on the chemical composition of the applied water. Mineral deposition tends to be more significant at lower application rates (e.g., <30 gpm/ac) because less is washed from the fruit during EC. Drip/trickle systems require treatment for biological contaminants, but may also require chemical treatment for control of precipitates or other potential plugging agents.

Soils

A watering system must match the soil type under it. This is true for irrigation as well as broad area uses such as cooling or frost protection. Sometimes soil infiltration capacities will be exceeded and saturated soils (waterlogging), runoff, or deep percolation become big problems. This is a design problem for irrigation systems and it is often a very large concern with multipurpose systems such as frost protection and evaporative cooling that apply water at high rates. In addition to environmental pollution considerations, soil waterlogging can result in increased orchard disease and many physiological disorders.

Soil salinity may also affect a design. It is recommended that complete soil chemical analyses be conducted as an initial part of the planning process for water application as well as cultural reasons. Salination and shifts (up or down) in soil pH may also develop because of the quality of the water supply and as a result of various water treatment or chemical or fertilizer management programs. These factors can be somewhat addressed in the design, but management will be critical. Growers must monitor the soil chemistry throughout the life of the orchard in all cases.

Fields with many soil types make it especially difficult to manage and schedule irrigations because of the wide disparity in soil water-holding capacities. It is possible, however, to design and install a separate pressurized irrigation system on each major soil type in a field (most easily with microirrigation, but also possible with big sprinklers.) Closely matching irrigation to each soil offers tremendous advantages in terms of management flexibility, reduced leaching and water conservation. Even though the technology is available, it is seldom implemented because of short-term economic and perceived cultural constraints.

It should be noted that with proper design and controls, drip, microsprinkler or sprinkler systems will work on any soil type. The most difficult design and operational problems occur on extreme soil types: very sandy (dune sand, sugar sand) and heavy clays.

Sands

Sprinkler systems are often preferred over drip for orchards on sandy soils because of wider distribution patterns and increased size of wetted volumes resulting in greater nutrient availability and extended rooting patterns. Drip will also work well on very sandy soils but tends to have narrow wetted volumes and takes more management and better control systems. Leaching of nutrients will be a major concern for any watering system on sandy soils.

Clays

Heavy soils present design and management difficulties because of low infiltration rates, runoff problems, and increased chance for waterlogging with associated disease and physiological problems. Application rates should be low to match soil intake. Drip systems generally work well for irrigation on these soils. Frost protection and overtree cooling present big design challenges because of the high application rates.

Water management of multipurpose systems

The management of multipurpose watering systems must be coordinated and carefully integrated. However, the ability to manage water is limited by the commitment of the irrigator to good water management and the ability of the watering and control systems to implement any management program. Growers should always manage the soil water by some form of scientific irrigation scheduling to maintain optimal growing conditions.

Irrigation scheduling

Because irrigations are always required in the arid PNW fruit-growing regions, irrigation scheduling provides a logical focal point around which various other cultural activities can be integrated and compromises are implemented. In addition, a scientifically-based irrigation scheduling program becomes absolutely essential when a grower is attempting to minimize total seasonal water deliveries when using multipurpose systems, especially for EC. The relative contribution of each use towards meeting crop evapotranspiration (ET_C) must be assessed, usually by soil water monitoring.

Past irrigation-scheduling practices such as calendar scheduling or fixed rotations (e.g. every 10 days) will usually not be appropriate for multipurpose systems. All water applications must minimize chemical leaching, especially under chemigation (adequate leaching for flushing excess salts out of the root zone is usually not a PNW problem). Substantial and detrimental soil-water deficits may develop under EC systems, but may not be readily evident because of the luxurious appearance of cover crops, particularly at higher application rates under pulsed systems. Estimating actual irrigation needs by traditional methods under these conditions can be difficult.

Daily records on flow rates, pressures and total water applications across the system should be kept for maintenance as well as evaluation of system operation and management for future improvement. Soil water levels must be monitored on a regular basis.

Controls

High levels of control that allow irrigation of each zone (or soil type) according to individual, specific requirements are generally more efficient and result in less runoff or deep percolation. They are required for shallow and/or widely varying soils, and may also be mandated by disease or pest problems. Evaporative cooling will necessitate good controls and valving. All control wires, computer interfaces, and data communication links should be carefully planned from the start and designed into the overall system.

Computerized data collection and system-monitoring systems and programs are commercially available and will become more common in orchards. Microprocessor controls can reduce labor, monitor climatic conditions and soil moisture, monitor water-application system performance (flows, pressures, or pond water levels), and initiate some action such as turning pumps on or off, call an operator when there is trouble, and/or initiate frost protection or cycled cooling. The technology is available.

Flow measurement

Knowledge of water application amounts and timing is critical for good water management of multipurpose systems. Totalizing and rate-of-flow measurement should be installed for the entire system to make sure the system is operating correctly and to assist in irrigation scheduling efforts. It is advantageous to have a flow meter on each block.

GENERAL MULTIPURPOSE SYSTEM DESIGNS

The most rigorous and restrictive designs will probably be for overtree frost protection because of high flow rates, large pipe sizes and the need to operate the entire block at one time without cycling. Cycled overtree evaporative cooling likely ranks next in difficulty, with irrigation relatively being the simplest.

The majority of problems with designing multipurpose systems will be in the areas of pumping plants, pipe sizing, and valving. In addition, the design of pulsed or cycled systems, such as cooling and some drip installations, presents additional and unique problems.

Pumping plants

Centrifugal and turbine pumps used for pressurized agricultural water-application systems are specialized machines designed to operate efficiently within narrow flow and pressure ranges. They will usually not operate satisfactorily at both the lower and upper limits of multipurpose systems. It is important to work with a trained pump expert in selecting and designing the pumping system for multipurpose applications.

Operating a single pump under the big flow rate variations common to multipurpose systems may be very inefficient, resulting in high power costs, and cause excessive wear to impellers and bearings, resulting in high maintenance costs and premature replacement of pumps. The use of a single pump for multipurpose systems is not recommended. There are two other options: preferably purchase separate, compatible pumps for each use, which must be carefully matched to the system; or, in case of deep wells, purchase a variable-speed/variable-frequency pump. It should be noted, however, that variable-speed pumps are expensive, are also designed to operate efficiently in a narrow range, and changing impeller speeds will affect flows, pressures and efficiency (although probably not quite as much as for single-speed pumps over the same flow range). Booster pumps may be required to maintain pressures within the proper limits.

Multiple electric pump systems or extra-large pumps to handle the highest flow conditions will often have high standby or demand charges from the utility company. In some cases it may be more economical to purchase a large, stationary diesel-power plant for the larger pumps that operate for relatively short time periods each year (e.g., for frost control).

Pipe sizing

Piping and valving must be sized to handle the maximum expected flow rate, which increases the cost, although not as much as the cost of two separate systems. Large pipe sizing often creates substantial pressure, elevation and flow control problems at the lower flows that must be addressed by additional special valving (e.g., pressure sustaining or check valves). It is often desirable to have separate submains for the proposed use and irrigation.

Sizing of laterals (piping supplying water to individual heads) is usually not different for frost protection, cooling or irrigation unless different sprinkler heads are used for each use. Looped hydraulic systems, where water feeds into laterals from both ends, may have large hydraulic benefits but can increase costs. Polyethylene pipe is often more economical at smaller diameters (e.g., less than 1.5 inches diameter) than PVC, especially for field laterals on trellises.

Valving

Valving is essential for all water application systems. Valves are typically used (but not limited) to: turn blocks on and off; drain the piping system for winter; provide pump protection during startup and stopping; assure chemigation safety, including backflow prevention for chemigation and well-head protection; control pressures; prevent excessive drainage from high points to low points in a block and throughout the entire piping network (laterals, submains and mainlines); and, protect the piping system from excessive pressure conditions and provide air/vacuum relief.

With multipurpose systems, valving should be selected that has the capacity for maximum flows with acceptable headlosses, but will still operate satisfactorily at the lowest flow rates. Sometimes it is not possible for a valve to operate under these conditions and special manifolds and additional valves may be required. Zone pressure-control valves such as pressure-regulation valves (downstream pressure is controlled depending on flow) or pressure-sustaining valves (upstream pressure is constant regardless of flow) are quite often required for multipurpose systems. Some valves may do both. The selection and location of this type of valving is best left to experts.

Each solenoid valve should have provisions for manual isolation so that the entire system does not have to shut down to fix local problems in small blocks. Continuous-bleed air relief, vacuum relief (to prevent siphoning), and pressure-relief valves should be installed in appropriate locations (e.g., ends of mains and submains or high points). Gate valves should be installed to isolate control valving for maintenance. Solenoid and other control valves should be slow closing to avoid water hammer problems.

Flush valves and drains should be installed for winter maintenance. Provisions should also be made to drain lines above each check valve, solenoid and pressure-control valve (and bonnet), and any low points in pipelines to prevent freeze damage.

Pulsed systems

There are two situations where pulsing of watering systems are often required: drip with chemigation and overtree evaporative cooling. Properly controlled drip will minimize leaching by frequent pulsing (e.g., hourly) to match water use (ET_C). Pulsed (cycled) EC systems at higher flow rates (e.g., 30 gpm/ac or more) are preferred for their cooling efficiency in reducing sun scald and for water conservation.

Pulsed or cycled systems at any flow rate generally present numerous design challenges, particularly with respect to pipe sizing and pressure controls. These systems may operate for short periods (e.g. 10 to 45 minutes) several times each day. Water will drain from the highest elevations in the block through the lowest sprinkler heads every time the system is turned off causing severe waterlogging of soils in low areas and wasted water; and the system must refill each time resulting in nonuniform applications. In addressing these problems, it might be wise to:

1. Break the blocks under each solenoid valve into several smaller, relatively equal elevation subblocks with individual, spring-loaded check valves to prevent drainage from higher elevation blocks. This also provides for more rapid filling since the entire system does not have to be recharged for each pulse.

2. After the initial fill, the entire system for a block should be designed to fill in 5 percent or less of the total pulse on-time (e.g. a 15-minute pulse should fill the entire block in less than 40 seconds). Mechanical check valves or other water elevation controls should be used (e.g. design each block to be as level as possible) to keep the piping, laterals and risers full so that water in lines does not have to be replaced for each pulse. This also reduces drainage.

3. Solenoid valves should have manual overrides and should be of the highest quality as they must dependably open and close several thousand times over their useful life. They should take two to 10 seconds to open and to close, depending on valve size to avoid "water hammer."

If cooling is pulsed based on fruit temperature, then the piping, water supply, and pumps must be sized to meet the occasional demand of the entire system being on at one time. Pressure control may be a problem. When cycling between blocks, the pumps, piping and valving must be designed to handle the increased local flows and maintain required pressures.

Chemical injection

As addressed in earlier chapters, there are several reasons to inject chemicals into watering systems. Microirrigation systems require chlorine for sanitation. Nutrients are injected to match crop requirements, increase nutrient use efficiencies and reduce costs. Soil water content may affect the efficacy of many applications. An assessment of expected injection rates and types of chemicals should be made before the system is designed. Chemigation requires high uniformity of application (e.g., distribution uniformity of at least 90 percent).

Preventing calcium carbonate precipitation by pH control (e.g. acid, sulfur burners) or specialized chelates is generally required for drip and cooling systems using ground water supplies and is often needed with canal (river) water. Injection equipment (pumps, tubing) must be able to withstand the specific chemicals being injected. All chemicals and chemical mixtures should also be checked to avoid phytotoxic effects, as well as for compatibility to prevent precipitations and maximize efficacy. Chemicals should usually be injected upstream of the filters (except possibly for some acids) and be adequately mixed. Except for chlorine treatments for microirrigation, the systems must be flushed of the chemicals before shutting down or draining the pipes.

Special chemigation safety devices are required for *all* chemical injection systems under federal and state laws and regulations. There can be no reverse flows, system drainage or backsiphoning. Injection of any pesticide into an irrigation system *must be allowed on the label* and may also be subjected to additional state regulations beyond label specifications. (Growers should check out regulations and thoroughly understand them before attempting chemical injection.)

DESIGN AND MANAGEMENT OF PRESSURIZED SYSTEMS

Advances in equipment for pressurized-irrigation installations and microprocessor controls make it possible to design economically a water application system that allows the orchardist to write a water management prescription for each area in an orchard. The arid climate of many of the fruit-growing regions in the Pacific Northwest provides an opportunity to very carefully control the amount and timing of water that is available to the plants.

If properly done, this can have beneficial effects on several critical crop factors including fruit quality, disease, and pests. It is also possible to apply various fertilizers and some labelled chemicals through certain irrigation systems with great efficacy, lowering the total amount of chemical used as well as protecting the environment. However, there is no single, perfect water-application system for all uses and there is a wide range of equipment available, with advantages and disadvantages for each situation.

The design of multipurpose water-application systems must first consider specific design requirements of each of the proposed uses. The overall design must then satisfy all of the diverse, combined criteria. With this in mind, general design and operation considerations of individual uses are discussed below.

Basic hydraulic criteria

System hydraulic capacity for irrigation should be based on peak evapotranspiration demands in mid-summer of a mature planting, usually 0.35 to 0.50 inches per day, depending on application efficiencies. Other uses for these sprinkle systems such as overtree evaporative cooling, will increase the design hydraulic capacity of these systems. A common mistake, especially with microirrigation systems, is to undersize piping and valving so the system is unable to meet the demands of mature trees.

Sprinkler systems should always be designed such that the pressure differential between any two points in a block is more than 20 percent (plus or minus 10 percent). Flow variations from individual sprinkler heads should not vary by more than 10 percent (plus or minus five percent) throughout a block caused by pressure. The effect of surface elevation (affects pressure) on flow variation cannot be neglected as can be seen in Figure 2. Pressures can be managed by proper pipe sizing, special valving, or carefully controlling elevation differences within blocks. Numerous pressure taps or gauges should be placed throughout the entire piping system for maintenance and trouble shooting, particularly on low volume and/or low pressure microsprinkle and misting systems.

The maximum allowable flow velocities in pipes should be less than five feet per second at the maximum expected flow rates. Flow rates (gpm) for a given pipe size should not exceed the general limits presented in Figure 3. To protect the piping system, thrust blocks should be used at all elbows, tees, control valves, and dead ends, especially when pumps are larger than 10 to 15 horsepower.

Sprinkle equipment

To be technically correct, "sprinkle" is the method, while "sprinkler" is the water application device, although these terms are often used interchangeably. Sprinkler heads are usually described by whether it is a rotating or fixed head with three general nozzle types: constant-diameter nozzles, constant-discharge nozzles or diffuser nozzles. Heads may be rotating or fixed. The rotation mechanism can be impact (spring-driven), gear-driven or reaction drive (e.g., spinners, rotators). Fixed heads are fans, jets, or sprayer types.

Each individual sprinkler type has advantages and disadvantages under different conditions. Selection of a particular sprinkler or microsprinkler should be dictated by the design requirements for uniformity, spacing, application rates and costs. Equipment selection is often a matter of personal preference, but a competent designer should be able to accommodate the operational quirks of any particular device into a system that considers physical constraints (e.g., soils, tree spacing, expected tree height, field size, topography).

Water distribution patterns are quite different at various pressures for the same sprinkler. A designer selects specific equipment based on assessing sprinkler distribution patterns at various spacings and pressures to achieve as uniform a depth as possible over the area covered by adjacent heads. Therefore, it is absolutely critical that all sprinkler heads operate as near to their design pressures as possible to minimize flow variations (Figure 2) and maximize uniformity. This is particularly true for multipurpose systems with high uniformity requirements.

Constant-flow nozzles may reduce flow variations caused by pressure changes. But, changing pressures also influence throw diameters and may cause variations in water-droplet sizes, affecting their susceptibility to wind with resulting negative impacts on uniformity.

For overtree frost protection and evaporative cooling, the application of water to the canopy should have a water-application uniformity coefficient (UCC; a statistical measure of the uniformity of the depth of applications) of not less than 80 percent, and a design UCC of 90 percent is often recommended for windy areas. Undertree sprinkle systems used for frost protection should have a UCC of at least 70 percent, but 80 percent is preferred. A UCC of 70 percent is usually adequate for irrigation, although undertree microsprinkle systems may be substantially less, depending on the coverage patterns. A general rule of thumb for sprinkler spacing that will usually result in acceptable UCCs is to keep spacing between heads along a lateral equal to the wetted radius of throw, and the perpendicular distance between adjacent laterals should not be more than about 60 percent of the wetted diameter (1.2 X radius). The distribution uniformity (DU), a statistical measure of sprinkler/emitter performance, should always be greater than 80 percent. (See Chapter 18 for descriptions and definitions).

Sprinkler risers should have enough support to prevent vibration or sway that would affect uniformity. Overtree systems usually require steel risers. Weeds and tall grasses can substantially affect the uniformity of undertree sprinkle and microsprinkle systems.

Sprinkle irrigation systems

Undertree and overtree sprinkle and microsprinkle are the most common water application systems in PNW orchards, mainly because of the desire to maintain permanent cover crops for improved infiltration, reduced soil compaction and erosion control as well as to reduce labor costs, and provide some frost protection or crop cooling. Typically PNW systems are solid-set systems that are permanently installed with buried mainlines and laterals. Few of them are automated. Portable aluminum sprinkle systems are sometimes used, usually in new plantings as temporary measures. Impact sprinkler heads are probably the most common.

Most canal deliveries in central Washington range from six to nine gallons per minute per acre based on peak demands of furrow (rill) irrigation over large areas (e.g., 40 acres or more). A design application rate of about 8 gallons per minute per acre over the total area is recommended for drip and microsprinkle systems that wet a small portion of the root zone in order to meet peak ET_C. Lower rates rely on soil water storage to supplement irrigation applications during peak ET_C periods. (Irrigations will be about 24 hr/day, 7 days a week at 7.5 to 8 gpm/ac to equal maximum peak demand.)

When designing multipurpose water-application systems it is wise to design irrigation with an application rate of at least 15 gallons per minute per acre (and the corresponding water supply) over the area so that there is sufficient capacity to irrigate at night or other times and to provide for needed management flexibility. Irrigation application rates below 15 gallons per minute per acre may require separate water application systems in multipurpose situations.

Overtree sprinkling for frost protection

Overhead or overtree sprinkling is the field system that provides the highest level of frost protection, and it does so at a very reasonable cost. However, there are several disadvantages, and the risk of damage can be quite high if the system should fail in the middle of the night. It is the only method that does not rely on the inversion strength for protection and with

proper design may even provide some protection in advective frost conditions.

These systems are generally suitable for irrigation, frost protection and evaporative cooling (EC) for red color and sunscald reduction. Water requirements are quite high *(see Table 1)*, which limits their adoption, plus large pipelines and big pumps increase costs. The entire block or orchard should be sprinkled at the same time when used for cold-temperature protection. Some tree species/cultivars (e.g., most stone fruits) may not be able to support the ice loads. These systems are never used with wind machines for frost protection.

Generally, adequate levels of protection require that 70 to 80 gallons per minute per acre (0.15 - 0.18 in/hr) of water (on a total protected area basis) be available for the duration of the heating period. Targeting overtree applications to apply water only to the area covered by the tree canopy (e.g. one microsprinkler

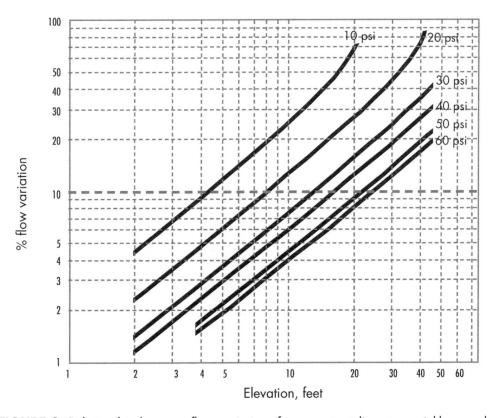

FIGURE 2. Relationship between flow variations from constant-diameter sprinkler nozzles and elevation changes at various inlet operational pressures (log-log graph).

per tree) can reduce overall water requirements to about 50-55 gallons per minute per acre, but the water applied directly to the tree must still be at least 0.15 inches per hour. Protection under advective conditions may require application rates greater than 100 gallons per minute per acre, depending on wind speeds and temperatures. Based on a computer model developed at North Carolina State University, Figure 4 presents approximate protection levels that can be achieved with overtree sprinkling at different application rates and wind speeds. As can be seen, the amount of water required to protect under extreme temperature and advective conditions can be very high and is usually not practical.

TABLE 3. Suggested starting temperatures for overtree sprinkling for frost protection, based on wet bulb temperatures, to reduce the potential for bud damage from evaporative dip.

| Wet Bulb Temperatures | | Starting Temperatures | |
°F	°C	°F	°C
≥26	≥ -3.3	34	1.1
24 to 25	-4.4 to -3.9	35	1.6
22 to 23	-5.6 to -5.0	36	2.2
20 to 21	-6.7 to 6.1	37	2.8
17 to 19	-8.3 to -7.2	38	3.3
15 to 16	-9.4 to -8.9	39	3.9

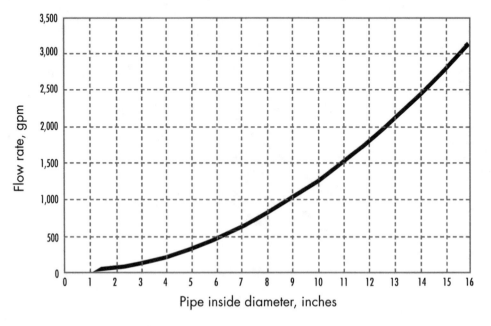

Maximum flow rate at 5 fps

FIGURE 3. Guidelines on flow-rate capacities of each pipe size at a maximum allowable flow velocity of five feet per second.

Overtree frost protection is probably the most restrictive design because the entire block must be capable of being irrigated at one time without cycling. Mainlines, pumps and motors (3-5 BHP/ac) must be sized so that the entire orchard or block can be sprinkled at one time. A smaller pump is often installed for irrigation purposes and the block watered in smaller sets.

Water supplies capable of sustaining 60 to 80 hours of frost protection per week are required because these systems typically start earlier and run longer than undertree frost protection systems. They start earlier because of initial air temperature dips caused by droplet evaporation and turn off later because of the need to sprinkle until most of the ice is off the tree after sunrise. Table 3 presents suggested starting temperatures for overtree sprinkling for frost protection.

Because of the need to have a continuously wet, dripping canopy, it is generally recommended that individual sprinkler heads rotate at least once every 60 to 90 seconds. Precautions should be taken so that ice does not build up on the actuator springs (impact heads) or in the bearings and stop sprinkler head rotation.

Cycling

Under mild to moderate frost-protection conditions (e.g., dew point temperature is greater than critical bud temperatures and low wind speeds of two miles per hour or less, cycling of OT frost systems is possible if, and only if adequate computerized controls are available to monitor bud temperatures and to cycle water applications; there are still adequate water and the hydraulic capacity to operate the entire system at one time over extended periods (if the bud temperatures approach critical levels); and, the buds and tree maintain unfrozen (free, dripping) water at all times. This is a high risk option. Cycling can save substantial amounts of water under marginal frost conditions. However, water application rates must still be at least 0.15 inches per hour. The general recommendation is that overtree sprinkle systems for frost protection should not be cycled.

Undertree (UT) sprinkling for frost protection.

Even though there is relatively little information on the design and operation of undertree sprinkling systems for frost protection, they are commonly used by PNW orchardists. They are lower risk and present fewer disease problems (e.g., fireblight) than overtree systems since little water comes in contact with buds. They don't work in advective conditions.

Research and experience have shown that the success of undertree systems (with and without wind machines) is influenced by five main factors. These are (in approximate order of importance):

– the height and strength of the temperature inversion;
– the level of protection is directly proportional to the amount (mass) of water applied and the temperature of the applied water;
– the volume of air flow moving into the orchard (advection) which can remove about half the heat;
– release of latent heat from the freezing of the applied water; and,
– radiation heat fluxes from the soil.

Other important, but less significant, parameters are the height and type of cover crop and soil moisture. The relative contribution of any one factor will vary with site and climatic conditions at the time. Heat is lost as it rises above the canopy and by natural air drift or advection carrying it out of the orchard. Any practice that reduces these major losses will increase the effectiveness of the method.

Water-droplet sizes appropriate for irrigation are also adequate for UT frost protection. It has been found that producing large amounts of very fine water droplets is not a significant factor in undertree frost protection.

The transfer of heat to the frosty buds is by radiation, convection and by any condensation which occurs on the coldest (radiating) plant tissues. The radiant heat and condensation (latent) heat have little effect on the thermometer, which may not accurately reflect the effective protection levels. However, ambient air-temperature increases of about 1.5 to 2°F at about 12 feet high are common, although increases up to 3°F have been found under very strong inversion conditions. Undertree systems are very compatible with wind machines or heaters (at the borders) and the individual heat contributions appear to be additive.

Much of the heat from the freezing and the cooling of water is carried into the ground by infiltrating water. Part goes into warming the air, and part into evaporation (which always occurs, even at these low temperatures, and only slightly increases the humidity). It is estimated that at least 75 percent of the potential heat is lost with conventional undertree systems (most probably in the infiltrating water). If the water applications aren't adequate, total heat losses can approach 100 percent.

Most of the systems use small, low-trajectory, (7° or less) sprinkler heads at 30 to 50 pounds per square inch. Applications range from 0.08 to 0.12 inches per hour (40-55 gpm/ac) or a little more than half of overtree requirements. The systems are usually turned

on around 32°F to 34°F, or earlier if expected dew points are low (e.g., if the dew point is at or below the critical bud temperatures—in which case damage may occur anyway), in order to raise the humidity as much as possible and prevent freezing of the risers and heads. Rotation speed of individual undertree sprinkler heads is not as critical as for overtree frost protection systems, but should probably complete rotations about once every 1 to 2 minutes.

Warm water

Using warm water is a definite advantage for undertree frost protection systems. In fact, because of the great inefficiencies in keeping and getting all heat from freezing water into the orchard air, it has been experimentally determined that almost all the heat measured in an undertree sprinkled orchard under freeze conditions can be accounted for by just the heat released by the water as it cools to 32°F. Figure 5 presents the amount of heat that can be expected from warm water in undertree frost conditions. Thus, the warmer

OT sprinkler application rates to protect to various temperatures

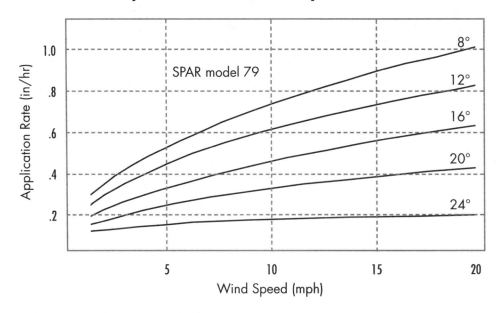

FIGURE 4. Rough approximation of ambient air protection levels that might be expected from overtree sprinkling. (adapted from Parsons and Tucker, 1984)

the water, the lower the application rate to achieve the same protection levels. Using oil to heat the water before it is applied may be a much more efficient use of oil than to use it in heaters. Common sources of warm water in the PNW include well water that is often in excess of 65°F and shallow ponds that act as solar collectors and warm cold canal water as high as 70-80°F.

Overtree sprinkling for cooling

An overtree EC system can be selected for enhancing red fruit color and control of fruit temperatures to reduce sun scald. The final design of the system will depend on the extent to which each of these factors is included, what is practical, if sufficient water is available, and what is affordable.

For improved early red color, it is usually sufficient to begin applying water over the fruit and canopy four to six weeks before expected harvest date. Depending on application rate and uniformity, it is believed that optimum red color benefits will be achieved by starting EC about 30 to 40 minutes before

and continuing about 60 to 90 minutes after sundown. Fruit temperatures will drop several degrees below ambient air temperatures, even at low application rates (e.g., 20 gpm/ac or less). Some growers also use EC for one to two hours in the morning, starting just before sunrise, for additional color, but there are no data to support this practice.

It is often expensive and difficult to retrofit existing irrigation systems for overtree EC. Many growers are installing two systems, an overtree sprinkle system for cooling, and a trickle or undertree sprinkle system for irrigation. Undertree sprinkle systems can also be used for frost protection. This dual system approach is preferable, but is more expensive. The use of undertree sprinkling for cooling is not effective and is not recommended.

Design recommendations for overtree evaporative cooling systems are: 1) the direct application of free water to the plant and operating the system to maximize evaporative efficiency while minimizing the total application of water; and 2) pulsing the water on and off so that free water is continually evaporating

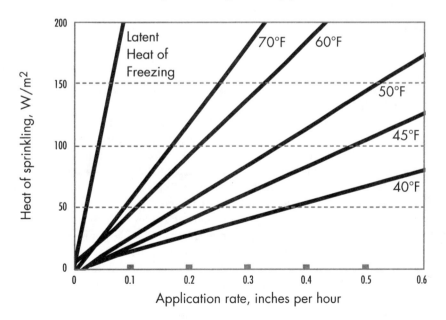

Heat of sprinkling vs. application rate

FIGURE 5. Relationship between water temperature of the applied water and the amount of heat that is released as it cools to the freezing point (typically growers should try for about 80-100 W/m^2 of heat from the water).

from the fruit and leaf surfaces. Overtree EC systems which usually average 30 to 60 gallons per minute per acre are not suitable for OT frost protection, which requires an average of at least 70 gpm/ac.

Recent research at WSU-Prosser shows that higher application rates (at least 40 gpm/ac) work better than lower rates in reducing fruit temperatures. Rapid wetting of the fruit and then letting the water evaporate directly from the surface is effective in reducing fruit temperatures and conserving water. Application rates (*average rate* over all cooled blocks in the system) of 40 gallons per minute per acre or less may not minimize sun scald on extremely hot days. It may be necessary to operate all blocks simultaneously to protect adequately for sun scald.

Droplet sizes should be large enough to penetrate the canopy and wet all crop surfaces. Some type of control system is required to pulse or cycle the water applications based either on time sequences (e.g. 15 minutes on, 30 off as water cycles between three blocks) or on fruit temperatures (core or skin). Cycling will reduce the potential for waterlogging or deep percolation.

Systems in windy areas need to be designed for higher application rates and shorter intervals between pulses because of higher evaporation rates and distortion of sprinkler patterns. Droplet sizes need to be larger and sprinkler spacing must be closer than in less windy areas.

Evaporative cooling is not a water conservation measure and will require extra water. Total seasonal water application amounts will be from 25 percent to 40 percent greater (equavalent to 12 to 18 more inches/season) than historical actual irrigation requirements. Cooling is a very inefficient use of water and, by design, most is lost to the atmosphere.

It must be emphasized that EC is *not* a replacement for crop water use. It reduces the actual daily water use (ET_C) of the tree by only 15 to 20 percent depending on climatic conditions. These complicating factors make scientific irrigation scheduling absolutely necessary. Irrigations must be in addition to EC, usually at night.

As a general rule for sun-scald reduction,

it is better to divide a block into two 40-gallon-per-minute-per-acre (or 3 at 60 gpm) cycled cooling sets than to have one 20-gallon-per-minute block that would be on continuously. Hydro-cooling (excessive applications) should be minimized. Misting systems (20 gpm/ac or less) do not reduce sun scald.

Controls

Automation is usually required to pulse or cycle EC water applications based either on time sequences or on fruit temperatures. Some EC systems are cycled based on air temperatures, fruit temperatures and/or time while others are operated on a continuous basis (usually based on air temperatures) during the heat of the day.

Research shows that starting EC based on air temperatures is a very poor procedure. Research has shown that fruit can warm much more quickly (e.g., 15°F to 20°F warmer) and cool off more slowly than ambient air temperatures. It is recommended that initiation and cycling of all EC should be based on fruit core, skin temperatures, or other alternative measurements (e.g., simulated fruit) that reflect actual conditions of sun-exposed fruit. Cycling based on temperature measurements from exposed fruit will require higher flow rates and/or water storage capacities in the event that all blocks turn on at the same time because of timing or when evaporation rates exceed the average application rate (system operates continuously) across the orchard.

Overtree sprinkling for bloom delay

Overtree evaporative cooling in the spring is intended to delay bloom which ostensibly keeps the buds hardy until after the danger of frost has passed. It has been found to delay bloom of apples, peaches, pears and other crops; however, it has not been successful as a frost control measure on deciduous trees because of water imbibition by the buds causing them to lose their ability to supercool. This results in critical bud temperatures that are almost the same as those in nondelayed trees. In other words, although bloom is delayed, there is no delay in critical bud temperatures and, thus, no frost benefit. Bloom delay is not recommended for deciduous trees. Water logging of soils and leaching of nutrients is often a serious problem with cooling for bloom delay. These systems should have application rates greater than 40 gallons per minute per acre, and uniform water coverage of the trees and buds is necessary (UCC plus or minus 80%). Water supplies should be sufficient to water 50 to 80 hours per week for a two- to three-week period.

Microirrigation systems

Microirrigation is a broad term that includes pressurized drip/trickle and microsprinkler/microsprayer systems that operate on a daily or alternate day basis (high frequency). Solid-set, high-frequency microirrigation provides a way to deliver water to fruit trees that has distinctly different characteristics compared to more traditional PNW irrigation methods. These characteristics have been used to solve some specific problems (i.e., use of high salinity water, application of fertilizers and/or systemic pesticides, and adjustment for water shortages) and can be creatively used for others.

Generally, drip systems are not considered multipurpose except with respect to chemical applications, but may provide an acceptable irrigation alternative with overtree cooling systems. Trickle/drip systems can be buried or lie on the surface of the ground. These systems generally irrigate only 25 percent to 50 percent of the total cropping area (25 to 60% of root zone). However, a few microsprinkler systems can irrigate the entire orchard floor. Depending on management, these systems can be quite efficient and are greatly preferred when chemicals (e.g., water soluble fertilizers) are to be injected. The use of drip/trickle systems in PNW orchards is quite limited, with most used on some stone fruits and pears, primarily because of the difficulty in maintaining cover crops.

Because of low pressures and chemigation requirements, hydraulic limitations are tighter than for sprinkle systems. Pressures should not be permitted to vary by more than 10 percent (plus or minus 5%) and flows by more than five percent (plus or minus 2.5%). Distribution uniformity should always be greater than 90 percent. Management will be very different from traditional sprinkle or furrow irrigation.

Drippers, foggers, misters and many microsprinklers require good filtration and special water treatment (e.g., chlorine) to reduce the incidence of plugging. As a general rule there should be a least two emitters per tree (especially if tree spacing is greater than 3.5 to 4 ft). Turbulent path emitters are much preferred over long path emitters (e.g., spaghetti tubing).

Usually any positive response to trickle irrigation has been attributed to or associated with reduced or minimized plant water deficits. In general, research has shown increases in vegetative growth and yields of young trees when compared to more traditional irrigation techniques. Reports on the acceleration of the onset of yield caused by trickle irrigation have been mixed. Increased yields on young trees is most probably due to an increased early tree size that translates more sites for flower formation which, in turn, produces more fruit. However, under proper management, high-frequency microirrigation techniques can have a very beneficial effect in new plantings by minimizing any water and/or nutrient stresses (with fertigation).

Combining low-volume irrigation (microirrigation techniques) and fertigation will affect water and mineral distribution and consequently the root development of trees in the orchard. Soil acidification may quickly become a problem with acid-based fertilizers and alternatives such as calcium nitrate should be considered. Since only a small percentage of the root zone is wetted, soil fertility should be monitored (including micronutrients) and a balanced fertilization/fertigation program (possibly supplemented by foliar applications of micronutrients) must be carefully implemented. Some micronutrients, such as boron, should never be injected through a microirrigation system.

Microirrigation management requires precise information on the amount of water and nutrients that the crop is using and it is site, soil and climate dependent. Make sure that the chemicals being injected are compatible with each other and the water chemistry so that precipitates do not form and plug emitters. Injection of labelled pesticides (if available) requires a sophisticated level of controls and management.

Controlled root volumes

Efficient root concentration within a limited wetted soil volume is readily achievable with microirrigation in arid areas like central Washington. Benefits of maintaining concentrated root systems under an emitter are: 1) improved water availability because of the reduced importance of soil hydraulic conductivity; 2) efficient application of water by minimizing losses caused by evaporation and deep percolation; 3) efficient application of fertilizers and other water-soluble chemicals, particularly those that tend to be fixed by the soil particles (e.g., potassium and phosphorus); and, 4) inducing physiological root-restriction effects such as reduced vegetative to reproductive growth ratio, increased fruits per unit shoot length ratios, precocity, and improved fruit quality caused by better light penetration.

There are substantial economic, as well as environmental, advantages from successful implementation of low-volume irrigation/fertigation programs. Economically, there are water and fertilizer savings and reduced weed-control costs, as well as improved productivity resulting from improved control of the root environment with respect to water potentials and soil-mineral concentrations.

Environmental advantages result from reduced chemical usage and the minimization of groundwater contamination by greatly reducing excess percolation of water transporting undesirable chemicals and minerals below the root zone. However, the benefits depend on the level of management.

Deficit irrigation

A part of the controlled root-volume concept is regulated deficit irrigation (RDI). Research conducted in Washington State and Australia has shown that carefully managing the severity and duration of water stress of fruit trees can be advantageous. This technique carefully stresses the trees during specific growth stages and has been found to increase fruitfulness

and increase soluble solids as well as substantially reduce annual water diversions.

Regulated deficit irrigation is made possible by the practical ability to achieve high-frequency irrigation regimes (e.g., microirrigation methods) and the capacity to restrict soil water by controlling the application amount and/or the wetted volume of soil available to the roots. Regulated deficit irrigation requires that full allocations of late-season water be available to finish the crop and that the system be designed to apply at least peak crop water use on a daily basis throughout the entire growing season. Automation is desirable. Additional information on RDI can be obtained from Cooperative Extension personnel or at Washington State University Research and Extension Centers.

Subsurface drip irrigation

These systems offer several advantages to growers because of their potential for: 1) reducing soil erosion; 2) saving water through greatly increased water-application efficiencies (no evaporation); 3) reducing labor costs through automation; 4) better weed control and reduced tillage with little, if any, herbicide use; 5) controlling crop water deficits for improved yields; and, 6) use of the system for efficient application of fertilizers and plant-systemic pesticides (if labeled). These systems require numerous safeguards to prevent plugging and facilitate maintenance, but have numerous advantages.

Controls

Automation of these systems is generally less expensive than sprinkle systems because of smaller pipe and pump sizes. However, the selection of the controls and operational criteria will directly affect the resulting water-application efficiencies and the potential for leaching. Under all forms of high-frequency irrigation, the real questions concerning irrigation management are not only when to irrigate but also how much to apply and how to evaluate accurately the water status of the tree. This is true with trickle irrigation in general since water is applied to a small percentage of the total root zone area, and especially when it is desirable to establish and manage plant water deficit levels at any selected growth stage.

A high level of water management is absolutely necessary to minimize the potential for movement toward the ground water when chemicals (e.g., labeled pesticides and fertilizers) are applied through subsurface drip systems. The control criteria that theoretically has the lowest potential for leaching is to utilize electronic tensiometers or other soil-matrix potential (SMP) sensors to switch irrigations on or off within a narrow SMP range (e.g., 1 cb). This practice may apply 10 or more small, pulsed irrigations per day. It tends to maintain a relatively constant SMP, a constant wetted volume of irrigated soil and should be considered when chemicals are being injected.

Microsprinklers for frost protection

There are many misconceptions concerning the use of low-volume undertree and overtree sprinkle systems for cold temperature modification in orchards. The benefits of microsprinklers attributed to their small droplets and purported radiation-loss reducing fogs have often been misrepresented and many spurious claims have been made with respect to the level of protection.

In most cases, the benefits that have been attributed to small droplets and fogs were actually due to already high humidities in the general air mass (the microsprinklers may not have even had any positive contribution to protection in these marginal situations), where the high dew point provides a heat source (condensation) that greatly limits the rate of air temperature decrease.

Nevertheless, with correct spacings, nozzles, pressures and application amounts, undertree microsprinklers can deliver the same amount of heat as other more common undertree sprinkle systems. If overtree microsprinklers are targeted, as discussed previously, and apply adequate water to the tree (e.g., at least 70 gpm per acre of targeted area), they can work as well as any other sprinkle system.

Overtree microsprinkle misting systems (not to be confused with high pressure [100 psi or more] systems that produce thick blankets of very small suspended water droplets that fill an orchard with fogs several feet thick,

and have other problems) should *not* be considered for overtree frost protection because of the very low application rates (e.g., 15 gpm/ac or less).

There is absolutely no scientific evidence that these types of microsprinkle misting systems trap heat, reflect heat or dam cold air away from the block. They do not apply adequate water amounts to provide sufficient latent heat for bud/flower protection that is necessary for overtree sprinkling conditions. It is a physical fact that the heat for overtree frost protection must come from the applied water. If water applications are inadequate, and latent plus sensible heat releases cannot meet evaporative demand as well as maintain bud temperatures above critical levels, there will be frost damage. If used, these systems should have good filtration and biological control (e.g., chlorination) of algae and bacteria. Overtree misting for frost protection is a high risk option and is not a recommended practice.

SOME FINAL THOUGHTS

Alls growers have their own favorite types of irrigation systems and equipment. However, environmental, water supply and fruit quality considerations are forcing many to step outside their comfort zones in these areas. Commercially available irrigation equipment and microprocessor controls are making it possible to specifically manage each area of an orchard for maximum horticultural benefit.

Designing a basic irrigation system requires that the designer have a broad level of skill and knowledge. However, multipurpose designs make even greater demands on a designer's talents. Selecting and paying for a professional who is experienced and competent to design any water application system, and multipurpose systems in particular, is a wise investment. The designers should be professional agricultural engineers, or at least certified by the Irrigation Association for design of these systems.

Registered professional consulting engineers may be required for many elements in the project (e.g., ponds and pumping plants). Growers should not be afraid to tell the engineer/designer exactly what they want; after all, they are the ones who have to live with the systems after they're installed. Hopefully, this chapter will provide a list of design options.

When comparing two or more designs, one must make sure that all the designs contain the same elements, valving, pump sizes and safeguards. If there is a big difference in price, there are *always* reasons for the cost differences. It may be a mistake, but it is usually because the designs and their capabilities are different. One must find out why and where the differences occur. It is always a good idea to take the competing designs to another independent professional agricultural engineer for evaluation.

The overall design of multipurpose systems must be addressed from the very beginning of the orchard-planning process. The design of a water application system will determine the maximum potential performance level for any proposed use, whereas management dictates the actual benefits received and any ecological impacts. Properly designed automation/controls combined with a good system design will lead to more efficient watering, improved water management and reduced leaching of nutrients and chemicals to ground water.

REFERENCES

American Society of Agricultural Engineers. 1981. *Design and Operation of Farm Irrigation Systems.* ASAE Monograph, M.E. Jensen (Editor). ASAE, 2950 Niles Road, St. Joseph, Michigan. 829 p.p.

American Society of Agricultural Engineers. 1990. *Management of Farm Irrigation Systems.* ASAE Monograph, G.J. Hoffman, T.A. Howell and K.H. Solomon, Editors. ASAE, 2950 Niles Road, St. Joseph, Michigan. 1040 p.p.

Evans, R. G. 1991. Frost protection techniques for trees in the northwest. In: *Proceedings Frost Protection Strategies for Trees and Grapevines.* December 5, 1991, Visalia, California. California Agricultural Technology Institute, California State University-Fresno. (Invited Paper) p.p. 111-147.

Evans, R.G. 1993. "Designing and operating overtree evaporative cooling systems for apples. Part 1." *Good Fruit Grower,* Yakima, Washington, June Vol. 44(11):23-27.

Evans, R.G. 1993. "Designing and operating overtree evaporative cooling systems for apples: Assessing the mechanics of evaporative cooling. Part 2." *Good Fruit Grower,* Yakima, Washington, July Vol. 44(12):29-32.

Evans, R. G. and T. W. Ley. 1992. "Pressurized Irrigation Systems for Orchards and Vineyards." *Inland Farmer-Stockman* (115(4):8,24-28) and Pacific Farmer-Stockman (117(3):46-47, 55).

Halverson, A.R. and A. I. Dow, 1975. *Interpretation of chemical analysis of irrigation water.* Wash. State Univ Col. of Agric. Cooperative Extension Mimeo 3522. Pullman, Washington. 5 pp.

James, L. G., J. M. Erbenbeck, D. L. Bassett, and J. E. Middleton. 1988. *Irrigation requirements for Washington—Estimates and methodology.* Wash. State Univ. College of Agric. and Home Ec., Cooperative Extension Bulletin EB 1513. Pullman, Washington. 37 pp.

Parsons, L.R. and P.H. Tucker. 1984. "Sprinkler Irrigation for Cold Protection in Citrus Groves and Nurseries During an Advective Freeze." *Proc. Fla. State Hort. Soc.* 97:28-30.

Pumping system design, evaluation, and improvement

Thomas W. Ley, P.E. and Terry R. Henderson

Extension Irrigation Engineer, Washington State University, Prosser, and
Irrigation Specialist for FloSonics, Inc., Hermiston, Oregon, respectively

High levels of pressurized irrigation system performance while minimizing pumping costs are attainable. To achieve this goal, irrigation pumping systems must be designed and maintained to operate at peak energy efficiency levels. Power consumption, and thereby pumping cost, increases as pumping plant efficiency decreases. A properly designed irrigation pumping system will be carefully matched so it delivers the flow and pressure requirements of the irrigation system at or very near peak efficiency. When pumps are operated outside of a fairly narrow peak efficiency range, irrigation system performance is adversely affected because the pump is not producing adequate pressure and/or discharge.

General design considerations for irrigation pumping systems are summarized. A review of irrigation pumping efficiency fundamentals is provided. Pump curves are discussed and the relationships between flow, pressure and efficiency analyzed. General factors which have been found to cause low pump efficiencies and some suggested solutions are discussed. The focus of this presentation is on electric-powered pumps. However, many of the fundamentals generally apply to any pumping plant installation.

DESIGN CONSIDERATIONS

Professional irrigation designers and consultants are the best source of information for pumping plant design. Choose a reputable consultant who specializes in the type of irrigation system to be used to do the design work.

An analysis of peak period crop water requirements balanced against the usable water in the crop root zone should be performed to determine the peak period irrigation interval, the peak period daily water requirement and subsequently the peak period net required irrigation depth. This analysis requires information on the soil types, crops to be grown, climate and layout of the farm. Irrigation system components including pumps, conveyance and distribution pipes, fittings, and valves are sized based upon this analysis.

The total crop irrigation requirement for the season, the typical pattern of use during the season and the peak period water requirement must also be evaluated in terms of the water supply, i.e., the total water volume available, the rate, duration and timing of deliveries, as well as system and delivery constraints. For pumping considerations information such as the delivery pressure (if water is delivered under pressure), the pumping lift from a well (including drawdown), or the pumping lift from a sump (and the variation of water levels in the sump), are critical in determining the total dynamic head at which a pump will operate. This analysis will also help indicate if on-farm storage may be needed and additional pumping capacity required. Pumping requirements and sizing considerations for frost protection and crop cooling are discussed elsewhere in these proceedings.

Electrical equipment installation should be completed by a licensed electrician. In most areas, new and re-designed installations must meet State code inspections prior to start-up.

PUMPING PLANT EFFICIENCY

Pumps are remarkable pieces of equipment. Within constraints governed by physical size, pumps can be forced to operate over a wide range of operating pressures and flow rates. There is, however, a fairly narrow range of flow and pressure in which a given pump will operate at peak efficiency. This is illustrated in Figure 1, which shows generalized sets of

curves relating pump discharge with pressure (head), efficiency and brake horsepower. Pressure is a measure of potential energy in the irrigation water being pumped and is often expressed in pounds per square inch (psi), while head is the height to which a column of water would rise above a point in a pipe line and is usually expressed in feet. Pressure and head are related by: 1 psi equals 2.31 feet of head.

The head-discharge curve shown in Figure 1 might represent a given size of pump at either a specific operating speed or for a specific impeller diameter. Published pumps curves show a family of such curves on the same graph, each representing a different impeller size or speed of rotation.

The pump in Figure 1 can realistically be forced to operate anywhere along the head-discharge relationship shown, from zero flow and a shutoff head of 200 ft to a flow of 1400 gpm and head of about 60 ft. Pump efficiency ranges from a low of 20 percent to a maximum of 80 percent over this range of flows. The maximum efficiency occurs at a discharge of 800 gallons per minute with head of 175 feet.

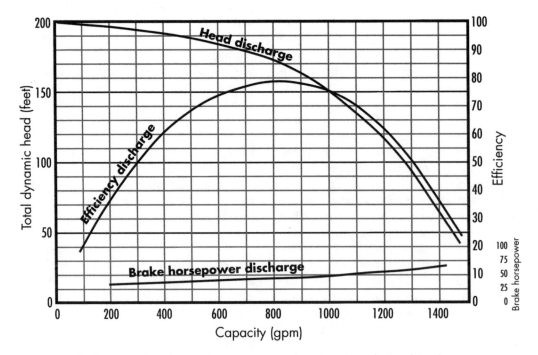

FIGURE 1. A generalized set of pump curves showing the relationships between pump discharge and head, efficiency and brake horsepower.

It is often recommended to match a pump with an irrigation system's flow and pressure requirements slightly to the right of the peak efficiency point. As the pump and irrigation system age (particularly steel pipelines) and wear, total dynamic head often increases due to increasing friction losses. This causes the pump operating point on the head-discharge curve to move up and back to the left towards peak efficiency. In the case of Figure 1, assuming other constraints are also met, this pump would be a good match for an irrigation system requiring a flow of 1000 gpm at a head of 150 ft.

Brake horsepower requirements, the power that must be delivered to the pump shaft to produce the given flow and head, generally increase as flow rate increases. Operating to the right of the peak efficiency point slightly increases the brake horsepower required.

One might ask, since horsepower required is lower, why not choose and operate a pump to the left of the peak efficiency point? The answer lies in the analysis of total power consumption compared with overall pumping plant efficiency.

The pump efficiency curve shown in Figure 1 is the ratio of the water horsepower (WHP) the work produced by the pump to the brake horsepower (BHP), or energy input required at the pump shaft:

Equation 1:
$$\text{Pump efficiency} = \text{WHP} / \text{BHP}$$

Modern irrigation pumps will typically have peak pump efficiencies in the range of 75 to 82 percent. Water horsepower produced is determined using the pump flow in gallons per minute (GPM) with pumping head (TDH) divided by a units conversion factor (3960) in the following relationship.

Equation 2:
$$\text{WHP} = (\text{GPM} \times \text{TDH}) / 3960$$

The input horsepower (IHP) or horsepower rating of the pump power unit is the ratio of the brake horsepower to the power unit efficiency. For instance, for electric motor-pow-

ered pumps, the motor efficiency is used. Electric motor efficiencies are dependent upon size and operating conditions, but typically will be in the range of 85 to 89 percent for smaller motors (less than 25 horsepower) and 88 to 93 percent for larger and high efficiency motors.

Equation 3:
$$\text{IHP} = \text{BHP} / \text{power unit efficiency}$$

Finally, overall pumping plant efficiency (OPE), also known as wire-to-water efficiency for electric powered pumps, is the ratio of water horsepower to input horsepower.

Equation 4:
$$\text{OPE} = \text{WHP} / \text{IHP}$$

Electric-powered pumping plants practically can attain maximum overall pumping efficiencies in a range from about 65 to 77 percent depending upon size and operating conditions.

With the appropriate conversion factors to change the units and considering only electrically-powered pumps, the relationship for overall pump efficiency can be rearranged to give a direct comparison between power consumption in kilowatt-hours (kWh) per unit of water pumped per unit of pumping head or pressure and overall pumping plant efficiency.

Equation 5
$$\text{kWh consumed per acre-ft per ft of head} = 1.024 / \text{OPE}$$
$$\text{or,}$$
$$\text{kWh consumed per acre-inch per psi of pressure} = 0.197 / \text{OPE}$$

An acre-foot of water is the volume of water needed to cover an acre of land to a depth of one foot; an acre-inch is the volume of water needed to cover an acre with a depth of one inch. Pressure is expressed in units of pounds per square inch (psi) in the second part of Equation 5. These relationships show that low overall pumping plant efficiency results in increased power consumption, and thus pumping costs, and vice versa.

By multiplying kWh consumption by different average electric energy costs, the effects of overall pumping plant efficiency on pumping costs can be seen in Figure 2. The average electric energy cost is primarily based on local electric utility power rate structures, total power consumption, size of pumping plant and hours of operation. It pays to operate near maximum overall pumping plant efficiency.

As an example, assume the pump in Figure 1 is operating at a peak efficiency of 80 percent and it is coupled with a high efficiency motor having an efficiency of 93 percent. The overall pumping plant efficiency is 0.93 x 0.80 = 0.74. If pump efficiency was 50 percent, plant efficiency drops to 0.93 x 0.50 = 0.47.

Using Figure 2 and an average electric energy cost of $0.08 per kilowatt hour, the cost of pumping one acre-foot of water against a foot of head increases from about $0.11 at 74 percent OPE to about $0.18 at 47 percent OPE. This is a 64 percent increase in pumping costs caused entirely by poor pumping efficiency!

Common reasons for low overall pump plant efficiency

Irrigation pumping plant efficiencies have been measured and documented in a number of studies and energy conservation programs throughout the western United States. Causes of low overall plant efficiencies generally fall into one or more of the following four categories:

1) poor match of pump with irrigation system either in original design or because of inconsistent operating conditions,
2) poor design and installation of fittings on the suction and discharge sides of the pump,
3) water pump wear caused by abrasion or to cavitation,
4) poor maintenance practices.

The effect of a poor match of pump with irrigation system flow and head requirements was previously discussed. This type of prob-

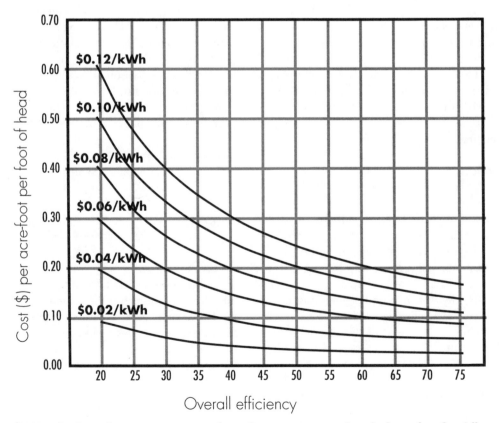

FIGURE 2. Cost of pumping one acre foot of water against a head of one foot for different average electric power costs as a function of overall pump plant efficiency.

lem is avoided by utilizing the services of a competent, experienced irrigation system designer. Irrigation system operating conditions can change over the years without consideration of the pump. More land may be brought under irrigation, laterals or sprinkler heads added or vice versa. Conditions at the water source may change, such as a change in water level at the delivery site or falling water tables. These changes may significantly alter where the pump will operate along its head-discharge curve and thus the operating efficiency. Any of these changes in an irrigation system will increase pumping costs because of reduced efficiency.

The irrigation system's performance will suffer because the delivered flow or pressure is not according to design. Irrigation uniformity may be reduced and runoff and deep percolation losses increased. The need to make pump system adjustments should be investigated any time irrigation system operating conditions are changed. There will be a benefit by keeping pumping costs lower.

Major plumbing problems on the suction and discharge sides of a pump often occur. Pumps and motors vibrate, and if not firmly anchored on a solid base, can result in misalignment of pipes, valves and fittings, as well as subsequent leaks. The pump and motor should be well anchored on a solid and level base. All suction and discharge piping should be well-supported and not allowed to "hang" off their connections to the pump.

Pump efficiency is adversely affected by turbulent, swirling flow conditions at the suction inlet. Ideally flow velocity into the impeller should be no more than two to four feet per second. Suction pipe sizing should be at least two to three nominal pipe sizes larger than the pump casing inlet size. Table 1 gives recommended suction pipe sizes for steel suction pipe for various flow rates which generally result in suction pipe flow velocities less than 4 feet per second. Shaded lines in Table 1 are flow rate/pipe size combinations for which the flow rate should not be exceeded for the given pipe size.

Fittings, bends, reducers and suction pipe sizing and layout should all be designed and selected to minimize friction losses, turbulence and potential for entrapped air pockets. Friction losses on the suction side of pumps are of critical importance in determining whether or not a pump will operate cavitation-free. Eccentric or offset reducers should be used to reduce from the suction pipe size to the pump inlet size. The highest point of the suction piping installation should be at the top of the inlet to the pump casing.

Minimize the use of fittings or other equipment which are potential air leaks into the pump suction system. Remember a vacuum is created on pump suction. Air entry at this point of the system reduces pump capacity and efficiency. Hand-operated primers for centrifugal pumps should not be located on the suction side of the pump. Not only is this a potential air entry point, it is also ineffective in completely flooding the impeller, which is really the primer's purpose.

Suction inlets must be adequately submerged to avoid vortexing of water around the inlet and possible pump cavitation. Trash and other debris as well as living organisms should be screened from the suction inlet to avoid plugging of the foot valve (if installed), the pump impeller and the sprinkler nozzles.

Water velocities on immediate discharge from the pump may range anywhere from 10 to 30 feet per second. Friction losses in piping and fittings such as valves, elbows and expansions are proportional to the velocity squared. Design of the discharge installation is critical to avoid losing significant portions of the head the pump is being operated to produce. Ideally pump discharges should be designed with no fittings such as valves or elbows until the discharge pipe has been expanded to the mainline size and flow velocities have been reduced to recommended maximum pipeline velocities of about 5 feet per second.

This can be accomplished with a gradual concentric expansion installed immediately at the pump discharge. Valves and other fittings are expensive at mainline sizes, but the payback in reduced pumping costs and better irrigation system performance is well documented. Table 2 gives discharge pipe sizes for PVC pipe for various flow rates which result in mainline flow velocities in the range of 5 feet per second. Shaded lines in Table 2 are

FIGURE 3. A pumping plant installation with many problems.

FIGURE 4. A clean, well-maintained, efficient pumping plant installation.

flow rate/pipe size combinations for which the flow rate should not be exceeded for the given pipe size.

Pressure and flow measurements at the pumping system installation are invaluable for water management purposes and are also necessary for monitoring pumping efficiency. With a knowledge of the pumping pressure and discharge, a simple test can be performed using the electric utility power meter to determine overall pumping plant efficiency. This simple test should be done at least annually to

monitor pump performance and guide pump maintenance decisions.

Figures 3 and 4 illustrate "the good, the bad and the ugly" of pump installations relative to pump suction and discharge design. The pump in Figure 3 has a vertical discharge, an immediate 90 degree bend, a small gate valve, an abrupt expansion and then another 90° bend into a buried mainline. This poor design wastes energy and money. With a little creativity in the layout of the system these problems can be removed. The only good

TABLE 1. Recommended suction pipe sizing for steel pipe for various pumping flow rates.

GPM	Pipe Size	FPS	Loss in ft/10 ft	GPM	Pipe Size	FPS	Loss in ft/10 ft	GPM	Pipe Size	FPS	Loss in ft/10 ft
\multicolumn{12}{c}{Suction Pipe Sizing Table for Steel}
25	2.0	2.55	0.28	200	5.0	3.27	0.15	800	10.0	3.27	0.07
30	2.0	3.06	0.39	250	5.0	4.09	0.23	900	10.0	3.68	0.08
35	2.0	3.57	0.52	300	6.0	3.40	0.13	1000	10.0	4.09	0.10
40	2.0	4.09	0.66	400	6.0	4.45	0.22	1200	12.0	3.40	0.06
50	3.0	2.27	0.14	450	8.0	2.87	0.07	1300	12.0	3.69	0.07
75	3.0	3.40	0.30	500	8.0	3.19	0.08	1400	12.0	3.97	0.08
100	4.0	2.55	0.12	600	8.0	3.83	0.12	1500	12.0	4.26	0.09
150	4.0	3.83	0.26	700	8.0	4.47	0.16	1600	12.0	4.54	0.10

Shaded areas = not to exceed pipe size   *By FloSonics, Inc. 1994*

TABLE 2. Recommended discharge sizing for PVC pipe for various pumping flow rates.

GPM	Pipe Size	FPS	Loss in PSI/100 ft	GPM	Pipe Size	FPS	Loss in PSI/100 ft	GPM	Pipe Size	FPS	Loss in PSI/100 ft
\multicolumn{12}{c}{Discharge Pipe Sizing Table for PVC}
25	1.5	4.45	2.30	200	4.0	5.11	0.91	800	8.0	5.11	0.41
30	1.5	5.45	3.22	250	4.0	6.38	1.38	900	8.0	5.74	0.51
35	1.5	6.35	4.28	300	5.0	4.90	0.65	1000	10.0	4.09	0.21
40	2.0	4.09	1.35	400	5.0	6.54	1.11	1200	10.0	4.90	0.29
50	2.0	5.11	2.05	450	6.0	5.11	0.57	1300	10.0	5.31	0.34
75	2.5	4.90	1.46	500	6.0	5.67	0.69	1400	12.0	3.97	0.16
115	3.0	5.22	1.33	600	8.0	3.83	0.24	1500	12.0	4.26	0.18
150	4.0	3.83	0.54	700	8.0	4.47	0.32	1600	12.0	4.54	0.21

Shaded areas = not to exceed pipe size   *By FloSonics, Inc. 1994*

thing about the pump in Figure 3 is that an eccentric reducer was used on the pump inlet; however, even it was rotated too far and the bottom of the offset was nearly on top!

Figure 4 is a pumping installation closer to the ideal. A mitered 90 degree bend and eccentric reducer were employed on the suction line. On the discharge side, expansion to the mainline size is accomplished in two stages, with a butterfly valve installed between expansions. This pump installation is clean, shaded, well-anchored and well-drained.

Sediment and other particulate matter contained in irrigation water can have a highly abrasive action at the high pressures and flow velocities generated inside the pump volute casing. Pump impellers wear under these conditions reducing pump efficiency. Pump life and efficiency can be extended by designing sumps which allow sediments to settle out before being pumped.

Impellers in centrifugal pumps may also be heavily damaged by cavitation. Cavitation is a process in which water vaporizes (boils) at ambient temperature under extremely low pressure conditions. Such a low pressure zone is created in the eye of the pump impeller. If there is inadequate head available at this point, vapor pockets form. They will then migrate outward along the radial vanes of the impeller into higher pressure zones. Eventually the vapor pockets will implode, collapsing upon themselves with tremendous force damaging nearby surfaces. Over periods of time entire impeller surfaces may be eaten away.

To avoid cavitation, design pump installations and select pumps so that the net positive suction head available (NPSHA) exceeds the net positive suction head required (NPSHR). NPSHR is a characteristic of the pump determined through testing and is usually reported with the other information on pump curves. NPSHA has a maximum value at sea level equal to one atmosphere of pressure, 14.7 psi or about 34 feet of head. NPSHA at a specific location is determined by accounting for atmospheric pressure (at the site elevation), the suction lift, and suction piping system friction losses. Water temperature also plays a role.

Friction losses occur and may push NPSHA below NPSHR under these conditions:

- if suction pipe sizing is too small or partially plugged (e.g., at the foot valve);
- if the pipe length is too long and installed so that air pockets can form at high points; and
- if the fittings are too numerous or inappropriate.

The result is cavitation, reduced impeller life and poor overall pump performance.

Maintenance of a pumping plant installation is a key factor to preserving high levels of overall pumping plant efficiency. Suction systems should be maintained to ensure screens, foot valves, and other critical parts are clean. Potential air intake due to a vortex above the foot valve in a sump and all leaks in fittings should be eliminated. Packing glands or seals should not be overtightened. Leaks in fittings and valves at the pump discharge should be eliminated, they are costing you money. Motors should be kept clean and well-vented.

The differences between the two installations in Figures 3 and 4 illustrate additional important maintenance practices. The water-cooling of the motor in Figure 3 is unacceptable and poses an extreme safety hazard. The grass around the motor may be plugging air cooling vents and the motor is not shaded, both of which can elevate motor operating temperatures significantly above ambient air temperature and well above safe allowable operating temperatures. The motor in Figure 4 is shaded, clean and well-vented. Motor life and efficiency of operation are increased when motors are installed and maintained to operate at as cool a temperature as possible.

Safety considerations

Adhere to electrical safety standards. If uncomfortable working around electrical equipment, the services of an electrical service center should be contracted to provide worker safeguards.

Never operate electrical equipment in the presence of puddled water or water sprayed from a system outlet or a leak. Do not stand in front of an electrical panel when turning on the system. Keep panel doors closed and latched. Keep panels clean and regularly maintained. Electrical panels should be shaded to avoid overheating.

When inspecting pumps and motors an open hand, palm down, should not be placed onto the pump and or motor unless it is verified that the machinery is well grounded.

Realizing the benefits of pumping plant efficiency

Figure 2 shows that by improving pumping plant efficiency, energy requirements and the cost of pumping each unit of water decreases. In order to realize these cost savings, however, it is important that water management also be improved or adjusted. Improvement of overall pumping plant efficiency in an existing installation will often lead to more water being pumped either because of greater pressures or discharges produced by bringing the pump efficiency back to specifications. The total power requirement may also increase.

If an inefficient installation is not providing sufficient water to meet peak crop requirements, system improvements will help to provide adequate water during peak use water periods and may improve crop production. Water management should be adjusted at other times of the season to avoid overwatering and excess pumping costs.

If the inefficient installation had been providing adequate water at peak use, water management needs to be adjusted all season long with a good irrigation scheduling program to avoid higher power bills, and thus, reep the benefits of saving energy costs.

Irrigation system evaluation and improvement

Thomas W. Ley, P.E.

Extension Irrigation Engineer

Irrigated Agriculture Research and Extension Center, Washington State University, Prosser

This chapter provides a summary of the primary considerations in evaluating existing irrigation systems and suggests guidelines for improvement. These considerations include a review of irrigation application efficiency and uniformity, water measurement, factors affecting uniformity and efficiency of sprinkle and micro systems, and examples of system evaluations and suggested improvements.

Sprinkle, micro (drip/trickle/microsprinkler) and surface irrigation systems are all used for irrigation of orchards in the Pacific Northwest (PNW). Sprinkle irrigation systems (solid set overtree and undertree impact sprinklers) used in orchards can be designed to apply water with high uniformity and efficiency and in easily measured and controlled amounts. Hand-line sprinkler systems are also used, but irrigation uniformity and efficiency for these systems are somewhat lower. Although they have been used on orchards in Washington, center-pivot sprinkler systems are not discussed here. Wheel-line sprinkler systems may be treated the same as handline sprinkler, but as they are not used in orchard situations, they will not be specifically mentioned.

Properly designed and managed micro-irrigation systems are capable of applying water (and nutrients) to individual plants in highly uniform and easily controlled amounts. Quality of the irrigation source water and changes in quality of the water with changes in pH, temperature and additions of chemicals (biocides, nutrients, etc.) must be considered from the beginning with any micro system. Chemical injection systems to control emitter clogging caused by water pH, algae and bacteria problems, as well as water filtration systems, are generally needed. Emitter plugging from poor planning, operation and maintenance of water treatment and filtration facilities is the most common cause of poor performance of micro-irrigation systems.

Surface irrigation systems (rill or furrow) require careful design, operation and management for efficient irrigation. Typically, these systems have low uniformity of application, especially on coarser-textured soils. Tailwater runoff is required to adequately irrigate the entire field. Tailwater catchment and re-use facilities are recommended to prevent runoff from leaving the field or farm being irrigated. Water management and control to achieve uniform application of a desired amount of water can be quite difficult. Because surface irrigation is used only to a very limited extent for orchard irrigation in the PNW, no further consideration of surface systems will be given in this chapter.

Water management

A fundamental factor in the operation and management of irrigation is knowing irrigation system capacity, or, how much water the irrigation system is capable of applying in a given time period. Generally, this requires an evaluation of the irrigation system to determine the gross application rate and any losses and/or non-uniformities that might be occurring during application.

A simple relationship can be used for any irrigation system to determine the average gross amount of water being applied. In this context, the term gross means the amount that would be applied at 100 percent efficiency. This relationship states that the gross depth applied is equal to the flow rate of water in the irrigation system multiplied by the total irrigation time divided by the area being irrigated.

Equation 1:

$$\text{Inches applied} = \frac{\text{GPM} \times \text{Hours}}{453 \times \text{acres}}$$

Equation 2:

$$\text{Inches applied} = \frac{0.992 \times \text{CFS} \times \text{Hours}}{\text{acres irrigated}}$$

Equation 2 is often simplified with the approximation that one cubic foot per second for a one hour period is equal to one acre inch of water. Specific versions of these relationships will be given for different irrigation systems.

It is quite easy to measure the time of application and the area being irrigated. To measure the flow rate of water in the irrigation system requires some means of water measurement. Many irrigation-district water-delivery gates are equipped with some type of water-measurement device. For surface gravity-flow deliveries, a weir box may be used. Common types of weirs are the Cipoletti Weir, which is trapezoidal-shaped, has a horizontal blade-like crest and outward sloping sides; rectangular weirs, v-notch weirs; and broad-crested weirs.

A common but different type of device for measuring water delivery at the farm gate is a submerged orifice. For each of these devices, assuming they are properly installed and maintained, a measurement of the water depth of flow over the weir, or the number of points, can be translated easily to flow rate and used in one of the above formulas. An example of this for different sized Cipoletti weirs is given in Table 1.

Table 1 examples:

1) Application rate per acre:
   1.5 ft weir blade, 0.30 feet depth of

TABLE 1. Irrigation application rate and amount for different size Cipoletti weir blades.

Water Flow Rate through a Trapezoidal Weir in Acre-Inches per Hour or Cubic Feet per Second			
Flow Depth (ft) over the Weir Blade	Width of Weir Blade		
	1.5 ft	2.0 ft	3.0 ft
0.10	0.16	0.21	.32
0.15	0.29	0.39	.59
0.20	0.45	0.60	.90
0.25	0.63	0.84	1.26
0.27	0.71	0.95	1.42
0.30	0.83	1.11	1.66
0.33	0.96	1.28	1.92
0.35	1.05	1.39	2.09
0.37	1.14	1.52	2.27
0.40	1.28	1.70	2.56
0.42	1.38	1.83	2.75
0.45	1.52	2.03	3.05

flow over weir, 5 acre field
flow rate = 0.83 acre-inches per hour (from table)
gross average application rate = 0.83 acre-inches per hour / 5 acres = 0.17 inches/hour.

2) Gross depth of application:
2.0 foot weir blade, 0.40 feet depth of flow over weir, 10 acre field, 24-hour set.
flow rate = 1.70 acre-inches per hour (from table)
gross depth applied = (1.70 acre-inches per hour x 24 hours) / 10 acres = 4.1 inches

Some irrigation districts deliver water under pressure in a pipeline. In such cases, a water meter or orifice plate is often employed for water measurement. Irrigation districts using any type of water delivery and measurement structures should be able to provide tables or charts of flow rate versus water level or head for those structures. Once a flow rate is known, an estimate of the gross depth applied to a given field area can be found, assuming all the water going over the weir blade is going to that field.

A water meter is recommended for water measurement in all pressurized on-farm sprinkle and drip/trickle irrigation systems. In some cases, it may be necessary to measure and monitor flows in several locations of an irrigation system. Flow measurement is an essential piece of information for irrigation scheduling. Water applications are impossible to manage unless the amount to be managed is known.

Water meters are available that give reliable readings of the rate of flow in the pipeline, measure cumulative volume of flow, or both. These must be carefully installed in straight sections of pipe (no fittings, valves, etc.) within a minimum pipe length upstream and downstream of the water meter equivalent to six pipe diameters.

Successful water measurement requires maintenance of the measurement system. Debris must be screened out of the water to avoid problems. These problems may include reduced capacity of an orifice due to partial blockage by submerged debris or sedimenta-tion, submergence of a weir blade due to poor downstream flow conditions, and fouling of meter movement for meters with mechanical parts installed in the stream of flow.

APPLICATION EFFICIENCY AND UNIFORMITY

Water application efficiency

Irrigation application efficiency is defined as the ratio of the amount of water beneficially used to meet crop needs to the average gross amount of water applied. Beneficial uses in this context include water made available to the plant for consumptive use and water used for leaching purposes to maintain a favorable salt balance in the crop root zone. Application efficiency also provides a measure of the losses occurring during application.

These losses include runoff, deep percolation of water below the root zone of the crop, evaporation and wind drift. Application efficiency depends on the uniformity of irrigation and system management. It will vary during the season depending on environmental factors at the time of each irrigation such as wind speed, temperature, and humidity. For instance, under cool, moist conditions (such as in the spring) sprinkle-irrigation efficiency is going to be near maximum. On the other hand, under hot, dry and windy summer conditions sprinkle-irrigation efficiency will be much lower.

Potential seasonal average irrigation-application efficiencies of various, well-designed and well-managed irrigation systems are given in Table 2. The gross irrigation depth is multiplied by the decimal value of the efficiency to estimate the net irrigation depth. This net depth is the estimated amount of water that is beneficially used.

When water supplies are tight and canal deliveries are at much reduced rates, there may be a tendency to irrigate with frequent, light applications to try to keep up. On the average, this strategy will not be as efficient as irrigating with less frequent and larger applications. This occurs because the percentage of applied water which is lost to evaporation under light, frequent irrigations is greater than for less frequent, larger irrigations.

Irrigation uniformity

Irrigation uniformity is a general term used to describe how evenly an irrigation system distributes water over the irrigated area. It is affected by the type of system (sprinkle, rill, drip, etc.), the design of the system, the equipment that makes up the irrigation system, environmental conditions, and irrigation management practices. Ideally an irrigation system should apply water so that all points in the field receive equal amounts. It is possible to engineer a system to achieve very high levels of uniformity, but this is often not economically feasible. A compromise between the cost of achieving high uniformity and an acceptable minimum level of uniformity is sought in irrigation-system design.

A closer look at some technical definitions of irrigation uniformity reveals why it is so important, and how it is related to irrigation efficiency.

Two commonly used terms for describing irrigation uniformity are the **Distribution Uniformity (DU)** and **Christiansen's Uniformity Coefficient (UCC)**. Each of these should be evaluated to obtain a more complete picture of water distribution under an existing system.

Each of these measures of uniformity is based upon measurements of individual depths of water applied from throughout an irrigated field. For sprinkle systems, this means an analysis of the depths caught in individual catch cans set out on some predetermined pattern under the system. For rill irrigation, it means an evaluation of the depths of water infiltrated at equal increments along the length of run. These data are usually available from measurements of the time that water is in the rill at given points along the run and the soil intake characteristics. For micro-irrigation systems a random sampling of emitter flow rates is usually taken and evaluated. For the cases of sprinkler and rill irrigation systems, the variation of depths of irrigation water applied across the field or block is evaluated. For micro-irrigation systems, the variation of flow rate from one emitter to the next is evaluated since these systems are typically not designed to provide coverage of the entire field area.

Distribution Uniformity (DU) gives a comparison of the average depth of water applied on the quarter of the field receiving the least amount of water to the average depth applied to the entire field. A simpler way to view this is by an example.

Assume there are 100 individual measurements of water applied at different points in a field, with each measurement representing an equal area. The average of the lowest 25 depth measurements is divided by the average of all 100 measurements to find DU. The result is multiplied by 100 to obtain a percentage. DU values that are smaller than 70 percent indicate problems: one quarter of the field is

TABLE 2. Potential seasonal average irrigation application efficiencies for various irrigation methods used in PNW orchards.

Method	Efficiency (%)
Sprinkle systems:	
Solid set overtree impact	.65 to 75%
Solid set undertree impact	.75 to 85%
Hand-line	.60 to 70%
Microirrigation systems:	
Drip/trickle (above ground)	.85 to 90%
Drip (subsurface)	.90 to 95%
Microsprinklers	.75 to 85%
Surface/gravity systems:	
Rill	.45 to 60%
Rill with tailwater re-use	.70 to 85%
Surge flow	.60 to 70%
Surge with tailwater re-use	.75 to 90%

receiving less than 70 percent of the average depth applied to the whole field. One of two situations usually results: 25 percent of the field is being seriously underirrigated, or realizing there are distribution problems, a grower irrigates until all of the field is adequately irrigated resulting serious overirrigation on up to 75 percent in the field.

The consequences of these situations are discussed below.

Christiansen's Uniformity Coefficient (UCC) is similar to DU in that a number between zero and 100 percent results, but it has more of a statistical basis. UCC accounts for the average difference of all the individual applied depth measurements from the average applied depth. Because of the numerous factors that affect the distribution of water under an irrigation system, the differences in application depths from the average depth tend to be distributed symmetrically about the average. This means that irrigation depths can be thought of as normally distributed. Classical statistics provides a number of useful analyses for data that are normally distributed.

For example, Figure 1 shows three curves which represent UCC values of 70 percent, 80 percent and 90 percent for actual irrigation water distributions in a sprinkle-irrigated field. We could easily take the 100 individual depth measurements from our previous example and create a similar curve. It is necessary first to rank the depths from highest to lowest and then plot them, in that order, versus the percentage of the total field area that each depth represents. The result is a bar chart. A smooth curve can be drawn through the bars to obtain curves like those in Figure 1. Using the statistics that form the basis of these curves, a number of important factors can be determined.

Referring to Figure 1, the following conclusions can be drawn about different levels of irrigation uniformity (UCC values).

1) Suppose we want to apply an irrigation such that 90% of the total field area receives at least 1 inch. To do this, an irrigation system having a UCC of 90 percent will have to apply an average depth of about 1.2 inches (this is the depth applied on at least 50% of the area). For an irrigation system having a UCC of 80 percent, an average depth of about 1.5 inches must be applied. And for a UCC of 70 percent, an average depth of about 1.9 inches must be applied.

2) For the same situation, Figure 1 shows that the variation in depths of water applied from the 10 percent of the field receiving

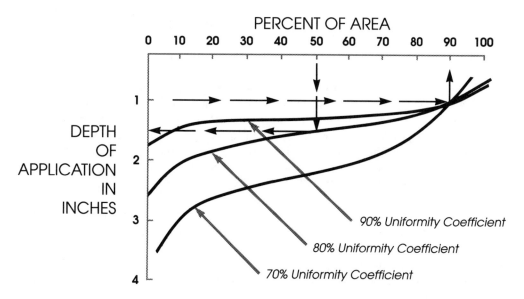

FIGURE 1. Comparison of 70, 80, and 90 percent coefficients of uniformity.

the lowest amount to the 10 percent receiving the most water is: 0.8 inches to 1.5 inches for UCC of 90 percent, 0.8 inches to about 2 inches for UCC of 80 percent and 0.7 inches to 3.1 inches for UCC of 70 percent.

For general irrigation, a UCC of 80 percent is considered the minimum acceptable value. Some irrigation systems are readily designed to this level and higher without incurring excess system costs. Systems used for frost protection and chemigation require levels of 85 percent and higher to ensure good coverage.

Consequences of poor uniformity

The consequences of poor irrigation uniformity are fairly obvious. Referring again to Figure 1, the 70 percent UCC irrigation system required applying considerably more water compared to uniformities of 80 percent and 90 percent to ensure that 90 percent of the field is adequately irrigated.

In reality, the statistical analysis shows that an improvement from 70 percent to 90 percent uniformity means that 38 percent less water is needed to do the same job, or perhaps more importantly, the irrigated area could be increased by 62 percent without increasing the water supply. Improvement from 70 percent to 80 percent means that 24 percent less water is needed or that irrigated area could be increased by 31 percent.

All three systems were operated to assure that 90 percent of the field was getting at least a one-inch desired depth of application.

Extra applied water for the lower UCC values is expensive. First, there is the cost of the applying the water. If it was pumped, then excess energy is being used and power bills are higher than necessary. There are probably excessive labor costs associated with this as well. Second, the excess water applied is leaching through the soil profile carrying nutrients such as nitrate nitrogen and sulfur, and possibly other agricultural chemicals out of the crop root zone. Or, the excess water may be running off the surface and possibly eroding the topsoil. Both reduce productivity, increase overall production costs, and have a negative impact on water quality.

Crop yields and quality may be negatively affected by low uniformity values. With a UCC of 70 percent there was a variation of as much as 3.1 inches in the wetter areas to 0.7 inches in the drier areas, more than a 400 percent change.

This localized overirrigation and underirrigation does not promote uniform, high quality yields of any crop. The effects of underirrigation are obvious. However, attempts to adequately irrigate the dry areas simply causes further overirrigation in the wet areas. This results in wasted water, money, time, energy, and fertilizers. Less than adequate results are obtained with fertigation. Localized waterlogging of the soil occurs, which reduces crop yields and can cause salinity to build up in the soil profile.

A certain amount of applied irrigation water must pass through the crop root zone on an annual basis in order to maintain a favorable salt balance in the root zone. Generally in eastern Washington, this annual leaching requirement is about five to ten percent. In other words, the amount of water to apply in addition to the amount needed to satisfy the net irrigation requirement (crop consumptive use minus effective growing season rainfall) ranges between five and ten percent. For irrigation systems with poor irrigation uniformity, the drier areas may see a salt accumulation caused by inadequate water applications. Thus the crop in these dry areas may undergo water stress as well as stress induced by higher soil salinity levels.

Under drip irrigation, salts generally migrate to the periphery of the wetted soil volume under the emitter. Under rill irrigation, salts may migrate laterally and upward in the dry strip between adjacent wetted furrows. In certain instances, it may be desirable to completely flush these zones of accumulated salts using sprinkle irrigation.

Importance of high irrigation uniformity

The importance of achieving high levels of irrigation uniformity cannot be stressed enough. Although improvement of irrigation uniformity generally may require the installation of more expensive irrigation systems and greater management costs, important benefits of the upgrade are realized which include the following:

1) more uniform crop yields and crop quality;
2) reduced irrigation pumping costs;
3) reduced irrigation labor costs,
4) better soil salinity management;
5) environmentally sound irrigation with runoff and erosion minimized and leaching constrained to amounts necessary for maintaining a favorable root zone salt balance. This conserves soil and water resources and helps reduce water-quality degradation, the positive benefits of which are significant to sustainable, efficient agriculture;
6) reduced localized waterlogging and drainage problems; and
7) more uniform water coverage, translating to better protection from irrigation systems used for frost protection and better chemical distribution for systems used for chemigation.

IMPROVING IRRIGATION UNIFORMITY

In order to improve irrigation uniformity, the factors affecting it for the various irrigation systems must be reviewed. These are discussed in detail in the following sections. Each system should be treated on a case-by-case basis. Further assistance with measuring uniformity of irrigation and assessing where the problems lie can be obtained from local Cooperative Extension offices or local Soil Conservation Service office.

Sprinkle systems that are designed with overlapping patterns to wet the entire orchard floor are discussed first. These include solid set overtree and undertree impact sprinkler systems and possibly some microsprinkler systems. Micro-irrigation systems designed for point-source or line-source applications are discussed in another section. These include drip and trickle systems both above ground and subsurface, as well as microspray and microsprinkler systems that are designed without overlapping patterns.

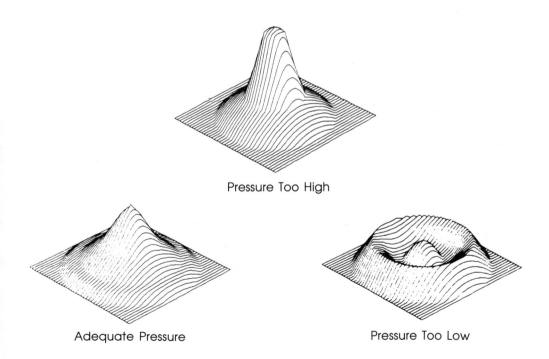

Pressure Too High

Adequate Pressure

Pressure Too Low

FIGURE 2. Individual sprinkler distribution patterns under operating pressures which are adequate (left), too high (center) and too low (right).

Factors affecting sprinkle system uniformity

In general, sprinkle irrigation systems are designed to wet most or all of the soil surface. For uniformity considerations the main concern is the evenness of this artificial precipitation across the irrigated field. A number of general factors affect how an individual sprinkler distributes water. These include: the type of head and nozzle, the sizes of droplets; the operating pressure, age and condition of the nozzle; and environmental conditions such as wind and evaporative demand. How individual sprinklers are arranged and operated in the sprinkle system further determines how much water reaches the ground and where. Factors include sprinkler-head spacing, height above ground surface, set time, crop interference and topography.

Pressure

Under low or no wind conditions, sprinkler operating pressure and the nozzle type have perhaps the largest effect on the distribution pattern of an individual sprinkler. For conventional round-orifice, conical shape nozzles used extensively in sprinkle systems, proper operating pressure is critical for obtaining a range of droplet sizes that will result in an acceptable distribution pattern.

Figure 2 illustrates three individual sprinkler distribution patterns under pressures that are too low, correct, and too high. Pressures that are too high cause excessive breakup of the sprinkler jet. This results in small water droplets that have low momentum, and thus, do not travel very far from the head causing excess water deposition close to the head, and a smaller wetted pattern. On the other hand, low pressures do not provide enough breakup of the sprinkler stream. Large droplets with greater momentum form. These tend to travel to the perimeter of the pattern causing a wet and dry doughnut-like effect. Adequate pressure results in a range of droplet sizes that effectively fill in the pattern in a smooth conical shape, as seen in Figure 2. It is much easier to achieve a uniform water distribution from overlapping patterns of this shape than those resulting from pressures that are too high or too low.

Incorrect operating pressures create additional distribution problems. The small droplets formed by pressures being too high are more susceptible to wind drift, because of their smaller mass, and overall evaporation losses are higher because of the greater surface area exposed. The net effect is less water ends up on the ground in the intended application area.

The large droplets created by pressures being too low have large mass and thus a considerable amount of energy when they strike the ground or soil surface. The doughnut pattern results in these droplets being somewhat concentrated in a narrow band. The net effect is the potential breakdown of soil surface aggregates and puddling of the soil. Considerable runoff and erosion problems may result, and uniformity may be further reduced. On cropped surfaces, lodging or other types of crop damage may result. This is a problem with the big gun type of sprinklers when used on many of the soils in the Pacific Northwest.

Allowable pressure variation between sprinklers on a system (whether it is a block of solid-set sprinklers or a hand-move lateral) should be constrained to plus or minus 10 percent of the desired or average operating pressure of the heads. Another way to look at this is that we want to allow only a 20 percent change in operating pressure from highest to lowest in any given block or lateral. This generally results in no more than a 10 percent change in sprinkler flow rates from highest to lowest.

Topographical changes and hydraulic friction losses are the two main causes of pressure variation in a pipe distribution system. Careful design should be undertaken to keep pressure variations within the above limits. Many systems have been designed with pipe sizes too small. This causes excessive pipe friction losses and consequent pressure losses from point to point.

Often, sprinkler pipe distribution systems and pumps are designed with little or no accounting of the effect of elevation changes on pressure within the system. Each foot of elevation gain or loss is equal to 0.43 psi. With many orchards situated on slopes to take advantage of air drainage for frost protection purposes, this is a major contibutor to poor uniformity. Pressure regulators and multiple pipe sizing are two means of working with excessive pressure variation.

Pressure-compensating nozzles deliver relatively even flow rates over a wide range of pressures above some minimum pressure. These are applicable in situations where there may be considerable elevation change or friction losses causing wide operating pressure variation in an existing irrigation system. They should also be considered for new systems where elevation changes are large. However, they may have different distribution patterns under different operating pressures, i.e., throw patterns and droplet sizes will be different even though the flow rate remains fairly constant.

As a result of increasing pumping costs, low- or reduced-pressure nozzles and sprinklers were developed through the late 1970s and 1980s. These include the spray-type sprinkler heads used on center pivots and nozzles having various orifice shapes for use on the traditional impact sprinklers.

The general concept of the low-pressure nozzles is to cause breakup of the sprinkler jet under low pressure by passing it through some irregular orifice shape. Most are effective at doing this, but often at the expense of reduced throw-pattern diameter.

Low-pressure nozzles used on hand-lines require closer head spacing or the use of a lateral offset program. Lateral offsetting is a procedure where at alternate irrigations, the lateral position is midway between set positions of the previous irrigation. Low-pressure nozzles on solid set systems require closer sprinkler head spacing to obtain acceptable uniformity levels.

Wind

The effect of wind on sprinkler irrigation uniformity and application efficiency can be devastating. The obvious visual evidence is that sprinkler streams or sprays are bent back against themselves under moderate and higher wind conditions (less than seven to 10 mph). Less water is deposited upwind and much more deposited downwind or lost outside the application area because of evaporation or wind drift. There is no completely effective means of battling the wind. Factors that can help to reduce wind drift and evaporation loss include:

1) Avoiding irrigation at windy times. Wind tends to have diurnal fluctuation with some periods of the day being less windy than others. Unfortunately, most systems do not have the luxurious system capacity that irrigating only at non-windy times might require. An alternative is to be sure that a particular point in a field gets irrigated at various times of day rather than always at the same time of day. With solid set systems and hand-lines on 12-hour sets, always alternate between day and night sets at a given location.
2) Using lateral offsets on hand-line systems.
3) Using the lowest possible mounting height and jet angle possible without getting crop interference with the pattern. Sprinkler spray losses increase with increasing height of the head and stream above ground. Spray losses in excess of 50 percent have been measured on overtree solid set systems on windy, warm days. Depending on application rates, up to 100 percent evaporation losses may occur during the hottest part of the day under overtree systems.
4) Being certain pressures are not too high. Small droplets have little wind-fighting capability.

Sprinkler spacing

A certain amount of overlap of single sprinkle distribution patterns is required to obtain even distribution under the system as a whole.

A general set of conservative or safe spacing recommendations for different wind conditions follow:

Under 0 to 5 mph winds, the maximum spacing in one direction should not exceed 60 percent of the wetted pattern diameter (most sprinkler manufacturers' catalogs contain these data), and the sum of the two spacings (solid-set and set-move type systems) should not exceed 105 percent of the individual sprinkler wetted diameter. The larger of the two spacing distances should be parallel to the prevailing wind direction.

Under 5 to 10 mph winds, maximum spacings in one direction should not exceed 50 percent of the wetted pattern diameter, and the sum of the two spacings should not exceed 85 percent of the individual sprinkler wetted diameter. Again, the larger of the two spacing distances should be parallel to the prevailing wind direction.

Other less conservative rules of thumb are sometimes used. For example maximum spacing on the lateral should be such that water is thrown from one sprinkler to the next (this is the equivalent of 50 percent of the wetted pattern diameter), and maximum lateral spacing should be such that water is thrown at least two-thirds of the way across to the next lateral (67 percent of the pattern diameter) under low wind conditions. It is generally safe to assume that sprinkler spacing in any direction needs to be about 50 percent of the pattern diameter under the Pacific Northwest's sometimes windy conditions in order to obtain good uniformity of application. This applies to any sprinkle irrigation system, regardless of system type, type of head, nozzle, or pressure.

System maintenance

This is often a major factor in why systems test out with poor uniformity levels. There is a general perception that if a sprinkle system looks like it's working okay, it isn't broken. There are several items that require attention and are easily checked.

1) Nozzle size. Are correct size nozzles installed in all sprinklers? It is often easy and convenient to replace a nozzle with whatever is handy in the pickup. Handlines and solid-set systems should all be equipped with a single-size nozzle throughout the system. At the same pressure, a nozzle size difference of only 1/64 inch equates to a flow rate difference of 25 percent. On systems with too much pressure variation it is often attempted to even out application rates by mixing nozzle sizes. This is not a good solution, because invariably the wrong nozzle size gets used in the wrong place. Use pressure-compensating nozzles instead.

2) Sprinkler heads. Use one type of sprinkler head throughout a block wherever possible. Don't mix double-nozzle and single-nozzle sprinklers within the same block. Some older systems use double-nozzle sprinklers; usually one is smaller than the other. Sometimes one of the nozzles will be capped. Make sure the two nozzle sizes on double-nozzle sprinklers are the same for the same nozzle locations on every sprinkler throughout the block.

3) Nozzle wear. Sediment in irrigation water is very abrasive as it passes through the nozzle at very high velocities. Depending on the amount of sediment, nozzles may hardly wear at all, or wear out in less than a season. Under high rates of wear, it pays to replace nozzles every year or two. Excess nozzle wear translates to increased pumping costs and large decreases in irrigation uniformity. Nozzle wear should be checked annually. This is easily done using a pair of vise grips and set of new drill bits. Insert the shank end of the drill bit (of the same size as the nozzle) into the nozzle while it is operating. Flow will be completely stopped in a new or unworn nozzle. Leakage and spray will occur around the drill bit when nozzles are worn. When the leakage and spray squirts out to 10 feet or more, it is time to replace nozzles. Pumping costs will be saved and irrigation uniformity increased.

Soil problems

Sprinkle systems are designed with application rates less than or equal to soil intake rates. If this is not the case, excessive runoff and soil erosion losses occur. Often soils within a field or block will be variable having different intake rates as well as different slopes and different available water holding capacities due to texture or depth. Systems are designed for one application rate and one depth applied for a given set time. If soils are too variable, inefficiencies occur. Some areas may have runoff, while other areas may be overirrigated.

Where economically practical, valving and blocking of a solid-set sprinkle system for each major soil type should be considered to overcome these problems. The installation of valves on each sprinkler riser can offer significant management flexibility, although labor input increases as well. In years when water supplies are tight, being able to turn individual sprinklers on and off according to soil or other conditions can stretch available water much further. Areas having different requirements compared with an average field or block can be much more efficiently irrigated. Changing nozzle sizes within a set to match soil types is not recommended because of the effects this will have on pressure variation and hydraulics within the system.

Uniformity of irrigation under sprinkle systems should be routinely checked with catch can tests. These tests will yield data for calculating the uniformity coefficient or distribution uniformity for the conditions of the test. The information obtained goes a long way towards assessing the performance of the system. Indications of possible pump, pressure, nozzle, sprinkler head or other problems are usually spotted.

For sprinkle systems with stationary laterals, catch cans are set on a square grid pattern, no greater than 10 feet by 10 feet, on both sides of the lateral and for at least two heads along the lateral. The test should be run for several hours. Wind speed and direction should be monitored during the test. Evaporation suppressants (kerosene or diesel) should be used in the cans or catch containers designed to minimize evaporation should be used. Containers should be at least four inches in diameter, able to hold the expected depth applied, and should not be shielded by the crop. Depths caught in the catch containers should be recorded immediately upon completion of the test.

Sprinkle system evaluation examples

A number of simple measurements can be made on set-move sprinkle systems to get a handle on how the system is operating. WSU Extension publication EB1305: *Sprinkler Irrigation-Application Rates and Depths* provides a procedure for making these measurements. Basic tools needed are a container of known volume such as a five gallon bucket or

one gallon milk jug, a short section of hose with diameter large enough to fit loosely over the sprinkler nozzle, a set of new drill bits, a pair of vice grips, a tape measure, a stop watch or wrist watch with second hand, and a Pitot tube pressure gauge. This last item is available at local sprinkler irrigation dealers and allows the pressure at each sprinkler nozzle to be measured. The following measurements should be made on several sprinkler heads while the system is operating under normal conditions.

Sprinkler flow rate

Measure sprinkler flow rates to evaluate gross water application rates and amounts. An accurate estimate of the overall average water application rate (or depth) requires that several sprinklers throughout the entire system be measured and an average determined. place a hose over an operating sprinkler nozzle to direct the water from the sprinkler into the five-gallon bucket or other container. The time it takes to gather this known volume of water should be measured. The volume and time can be easily converted to the sprinkler flow rate in gallons per minute. For instance, five gallons collected in 45 seconds equals (five gallons x 60 sec/min divided by 45 sec) 6.7 gpm. For best uniformity, the difference in flow rates from one head to another operating at the same time on the system should be no more than 10 percent.

Sprinkler flow rate is used to determine the sprinkler application rate and the depth applied. Measurements of the sprinkler spacings on the lateral and the lateral spacings on the mainline (both in feet) are needed. This applies to all types of spacings equally: square, rectangular and diamond. The average gross application rate under one sprinkler (inches per hour) equals:

Equation 3:
Inches per Hour =
$$\frac{GPM \times 96.3}{Sprinkler\ Spray \times Lateral\ Spacing}$$

Multiply this by the set time in hours to find the gross depth applied. The gross depth is multiplied by the application efficiency to find the average net depth applied. This is the field or block average amount of water made available to the crop in the root zone as a result of irrigation when it is based on a representative sample of sprinklers.

Sprinkler pressure

Measure sprinkler pressure using the Pitot tube pressure gauge. The end of the Pitot tube should be held in the center of the sprinkler jet about 1/16 inch from the nozzle. A fan-shaped plume of water around the tube is created. The energy in the jet is directed up into the base of the pressure gauge causing the needle to register a reading.

There should be no more than a 20 percent difference in pressures between any two sprinklers operating at the same time in the same block. Excessive pressure variation is a large problem. It is caused by poor hydraulic-design, system wear, poor system management and elevation differences on the system.

It is clear that sprinkler operating pressure is important to achieve uniform, efficient irrigations. Systems with traditional round orifice nozzles on 3/4-inch sprinklers should generally have at least 50-55 psi at the sprinkler, while 1/2-inch sprinklers should have at least 35 pounds per square inch (psi) at the sprinkler.

Figure 3 shows the results of a test of overtree sprinkler flow rate and pressure variation in a 10-acre block near Mattawa, Washington. Nine heads equally spaced around the block were measured. All nozzles were equal size. Sprinkler flow rates ranged from 4.45 gpm to 4.95 gpm, while pressures ranged from 56 psi to 64 psi. The pressure variation in this block was calculated to be 14.3 percent, which is acceptable. The gross application rate was 0.175 inches per hour. During a 12-hour set the system applied a gross depth of 2.1 inches of water.

A catch can test was conducted between four adjacent sprinklers in the same block, as given in Figure 3. The test was conducted in a relatively open area where the trees were quite small, so there was minimal vegetative interference. Twenty-five catch cans were placed on the ground on approximately a 10 feet by 10 feet square grid pattern between the four sprinklers.

The test was conducted on a windy (5-10 mph average wind speed with gusts to 20 mph) and hot (95°F) July afternoon. Results are given in Figure 4 as the measured net application rate at each catch can in inches per hour. The overall average net application

LATERAL 15	LATERAL 8	LATERAL 1
SPRINKLER 18 60 psi 4.59 gpm 0.17 in/hr	SPRINKLER 18 57 psi 4.55 gpm 0.17 in/hr	SPRINKLER 18 56 psi 4.45 gpm 0.165 in/hr
SPRINKLER 9 62 psi 4.86 gpm 0.18 in/hr	SPRINKLER 9 61 psi 4.86 gpm 0.18 in/hr	SPRINKLER 9 61 psi 4.62 gpm 0.17 in/hr
SPRINKLER 1 64 psi 4.89 gpm 0.18 in/hr	SPRINKLER 1 64 psi 4.67 gpm 0.17 in/hr	SPRINKLER 1 64 psi 4.95 gpm 0.18 in/hr

9/64" nozzle on 48 ft x 54 ft head spacing
Average sprinkler flow rate = 4.72 gpm
Average gross application rate = 0.175 inches per hour
Maximum pressure variation = (64 - 56) / 56 * 100 = 14.32%
Gross application depth in 12-hr set = 2.10 inches

Figure 3. Results of sprinkler flow rate and pressure tests on an overtree impact sprinkler system near Mattawa.

rate (depth caught in one hour) was 0.09 inches per hour. This system was measured to have a gross application rate of 0.175 inches per hour. The ratio of these two numbers, a measure of application efficiency, is 50 percent, indicating evaporation and wind drift losses of 50 percent of the applied water. The uniformity coefficient of this system under the conditions of this test was 71 percent. An average application efficiency of nearly 95 percent for a night time set was measured in the same block during May.

Nozzle inventory and nozzle wear

An annual inventory of nozzles sizes installed on a system is important. If more than one size is found, there will be problems with uniformity and efficiency.

The set of system test results given in Figure 5 is a good illustration of the effects of mixing nozzles size, having worn nozzles and considerable topographic variation. The data were collected on two laterals of an undertree solid set impact sprinkler system in the West

Valley area near Yakima, Washington. One of the laterals (no. 1) had a large drop in elevation over its length. The other was relatively flat. Sprinkler flow rate, pressure, nozzle size and nozzle wear were measured on three heads of each lateral: near the submain connection, in the middle and near the end. Worn nozzles, effects of the elevation drop and different size nozzles all contributed to measured application rate differences of more than two to one.

Nozzle wear was evaluated by determining the difference in flow rate as measured with the bucket test and as obtained from tables of nozzle discharge for new nozzles operating at a given pressure. Drill bit tests on the nozzles confirmed the these results. Flow rate measurements were repeated on the first lateral after replacing the nozzles with pressure-compensating nozzles. No differences in flow rate were found even though the pressure variation was still 34 psi at the top and 50 psi at the bottom.

S						S
	0.10	0.07	0.09	0.11	0.10	
	0.13	0.10	0.04	0.03	0.09	
48'	0.11	0.14	0.10	0.08	0.09	
	0.14	0.13	0.09	0.01	0.00	
	0.07	0.08	0.09	0.09	0.11	
S						S

54'

S indicates sprinkler location, sprinkler spacing = 48' x 54'
Average depth caught in one hour = 0.09 inches
Average system gross application rate = 0.175 inches per hour
Estimated application efficiency (ratio of depth caught to applied) = 50%
Uniformity coefficient, UCC = 71%

FIGURE 4. Results of catch can test conducted on a hot, windy July afternoon in the same overtree sprinkler block as given in Figure 3. Values at each grid point are depths caught in one hour.

Factors affecting micro-irrigation system uniformity

Micro-irrigation systems include drip/trickle irrigation systems and micro-spray or micro-sprinkler systems. Since the entire orchard floor is generally not wetted under most of these types of irrigation systems, the critical irrigation uniformity concern is ensuring that the flow rate from one emitter orifice to the next is as even as possible. This applies equally to drip emitters and micro-sprinklers where water is applied at discrete points, and to line source emitter systems, drip tubing which has pre-installed or pre-fabricated orifices on some interval (or continuously) along the length of tubing. Some orchard micro-sprinkler systems are designed for irrigation coverage of the entire orchard floor. Many of the factors discussed previously for impact sprinkle systems will apply to these systems, as well as the factors discussed below. It is important to realize that microsprinkler orifices are closer in size (and some are even smaller) than the typical drip emitter orifice size. Thus, water quality considerations for these systems are extremely important. In addition, few microsprinklers are pressure-compensating.

The major factors affecting micro-irrigation uniformity are those that affect the amount of water discharged through each orifice. These include: 1) the hydraulic design and amount of pressure variation from point to point in the system, 2) the quality of emitter manufacturing, and 3) irrigation water quality and clogging of emitter orifices.

Similar to the previous discussion on allowable pressure variation in a sprinkle irrigation pipe distribution system, it is desirable to maintain an envelope of operating pressures throughout a micro-irrigation system as well. Operating pressures for micro-irrigation emitters are generally considerably less than for sprinklers, often in the 10 psi to 25 psi range. A general rule of thumb is that allowable pressure variation throughout a zone or block of emitters operating simultaneously should be within five percent of the desired or average operating pressure in the zone. Another way to look at this is that only a 10 percent change in operating pressure from highest to lowest in any given zone should be allowed. This generally results in a maximum five percent change in emitter flow rates from highest to lowest.

Factors such as topography, lateral pipe sizing and friction losses in fittings must be carefully accounted for to be sure pressure losses are not too great. Because of the narrow range within which pressures must be kept, micro-irrigation systems should be designed by qualified, experienced professionals. Pressure-regulating devices may be used to help maintain pressures within the allowable range. Pressure-compensating emitters, which generally produce a relatively constant flow rate for a wide range of pressures, may be necessary in instances where topographic variation is large.

Lateral No.	Sprinkler No.	Nozzle Size (in)	Pressure (psi)	Rated Flow rate (gpm)	Measured Flow rate (gpm)	% Wear	Gross Applic. Rate (in/hr)
1	Top	3/32	34	1.5	1.5	0	0.10
	Mid	3/32	42	1.7	1.7	0	0.11
	Bot	7/64	50	2.5	3.2	28	0.21
2	Top	7/64	42	2.3	2.7	17	0.18
	Mid	3/32	46	1.8	1.8	0	0.12
	Bot	7/64	40	2.3	2.9	26	0.19

Undertree impact sprinklers on 36 ft x 40 ft spacing.
Rated flow rate taken from manufacturer's tables using nozzle size and measured pressure.
Measured flow rate determined using 5 gallon bucket.
% wear determined using the ratio of measured flow rate to rated flow rate.

FIGURE 5. Results of flow rate, pressure, nozzle wear tests on an undertree sprinkler system in the West Valley, Yakima, Washington, area.

The quality of emitter manufacturing is described by a term called the manufacturer's coefficient of variation, (C_v). This term describes variation in flow rate tests for a sample lot of identical emitters. The American Society of Agricultural Engineers (ASAE, 1989a) classifies C_v as excellent for point source type emitters when it is less than 0.05, and average when it is between 0.05 and 0.07, marginal when between 0.07 and 0.11 and poor when greater than 0.11. For line-source emitters, C_v is good when it is less than 0.10, and average when it is between 0.10 and 0.20. Problems can be avoided by selecting high quality emitters from reputable manufacturers who use quality control checks in their manufacturing processes. The Center for Irrigation Technology at California State in Fresno, California, publishes the results of their emitter manufacturing variation tests.

Emitter clogging caused by improperly filtered and/or treated water is perhaps one of the larger sources of non-uniformity in micro-irrigation systems. Clogging can be caused by organic debris (weed seeds, insect parts), mineral particles in the water (sand, silt and clay particles), chemical precipitates (calcium and magnesium carbonates, or fertilizers) and biological growths (algae or bacterial slimes) that develop in the system. A properly designed, maintained and managed water filtration and treatment system, based on water quality analyses of the source irrigation water, is the only solution to this problem. This must be accompanied by a rigorous field maintenance program which includes routine filter backwashing, periodic flushing of lateral lines, random sampling of emitter flow rates, and checks of residual chlorine in the lateral lines.

Typical laboratory irrigation water quality analyses are discussed more thoroughly in another chapter. In summary, analyses should include determination of electrical conductivity and total dissolved solids, levels of concentration of individual cations and anions including calcium, magnesium, manganese, sodium, carbonate, bicarbonate, nitrate, chloride, iron and sulfate. In addition, boron levels, the water pH and the sodium adsorption ratio (including the adjusted sodium adsorption ratio) should be evaluated.

Water quality evaluation for micro-irrigation systems must include assessment of physical, chemical and biological contaminants that contribute to orifice plugging. Table 3 provides a summary of the plugging potential of irrigation waters used for micro-irrigation.

In general, for Pacific Northwest conditions where water is being drawn from a surface source (e.g., canal, stream, pond), a sand media filtration system is recommended. Sand media filters have large capacity for filtering organic contaminants without frequent filter backflushing. Groundwater used in micro-irrigation systems must also be tested.

TABLE 3. Plugging potential of irrigation waters used for micro-irrigation. (adapted from Nakayama and Bucks, 1986).

Type of Problem	Little	Some	Severe
Physical			
Suspended solids (ppm)	<50	50-100	>100
Chemical			
pH	<7.0	7.0-8.0	>8.0
Dissolved solids (ppm)	<500	500-2000	>2000
Manganese (ppm)	<0.1	0.1-1.5	>1.5
Iron (ppm)	<0.1	0.1-1.5	>1.5
Hydrogen sulfide (ppm)	<0.5	0.5-2.0	>2.0
Biological			
Bacteria populations (max. number per milliliter)	<10,000	10,000-50,000	>50,000

Bacteria, iron content, pH level and other parameters must be checked to ensure that chemical or biological precipitates will not form in the system.

Groundwater may need special treatment including acid injection for pH control, oxidation for iron precipitation, injection of biocides to control bacteria, etc. It may also require extensive filtration if considerable precipitates form as the groundwater undergoes temperature or pH changes.

All micro-irrigation systems should have a chlorine injection system for control of algae and bacterial populations and their by-products such as gelatinous slimes. Chlorine (either chlorine gas or sodium hypochlorite) should be injected continuously to maintain a free residual chlorine concentration of one ppm at the lateral ends. Large doses of chlorine may also be used, injecting to achieve a maximum 20 ppm free residual chlorine concentration level at the lateral ends for the last 30 to 60 minutes of an irrigation. Be careful never to exceed 20 ppm free residual chlorine. Free residual chlorine may be checked with a DPD color indicating test kit. Test kits that measure total chlorine will give misleading readings and algae or bacteria control will be inadequate. All injection should occur upstream of filters.

Calcium and magnesium carbonate precipitate problems are most often treated by injecting acids to maintain irrigation water pH between 5.5 and 7.0, thereby keeping these materials in solution. Iron precipitates and iron bacteria problems are generally treated by injection of chlorine. Chlorine should be injected at a rate of approximately 0.64 times the iron content of the water to cause iron to precipitate out. Injection well upstream of the filter system is mandatory. Elbows, valves and other pipe fittings which cause turbulence and mixing will help formation of iron oxide precipitates. Automatic filter backflushing should be considered. Maintenance of a one ppm free residual chlorine concentration at lateral ends should control iron bacteria problems. Iron concentrations greater than five ppm may be difficult to treat by the above approach. Although "double pumping" of the water is required, a more effective approach is to aerate the irrigation water by pumping into a settling basin with baffles causing the iron to oxidize and settle out, before pumping into the irrigation system.

Hydrogen sulfide bacteria are controlled by injecting chlorine at a rate of four to nine times the hydrogen sulfide concentration in the irrigation water. Manganese problems are controlled by injecting chlorine at a rate of 1.3 times the manganese concentration in the irrigation water.

Ideally all microirrigation systems should have accurate flow meters and pressure gauges installed at strategic locations throughout the system. These should be monitored frequently and readings evaluated to help determine if emitters are becoming plugged. Refer to Chapter 14 on fertigation and chemigation systems for more information on calibration of chemical injection systems.

Micro system evaluation examples

Flow rate variation in drip/trickle/microsprinkler irrigation systems can be evaluated in a manner similar to that described for sprinklers. Use a graduated cylinder or measuring cup and measure the time it takes to catch a certain volume of water from each of several emitters throughout a system. Ideally flow rate variation should be within five percent of the average measured flow rate. The average system emitter flow rate is balanced with the individual plant water requirements and the number of emitters per plant to assist irrigation management decisions.

Pressure variation within micro systems is not so easily assessed as with sprinkler pressures unless it has been planned for in the original design. It is generally recommended that pressure measurement taps be installed at various strategic points throughout a micro system. At a minimum, each zone or subunit should have a pressure tap at the control valve. In addition, pressure taps at the pump system, at the ends of mains and submains, and at the ends of manifolds are desirable. Pressure increase with about the same flow rate is an indicator of possible emitter plugging.

Drip/trickle and some microsprinklers systems may be designed such that the wetted patterns of the individual emitters do not overlap in the row middles. In this case, there should be at least one emitter or microsprayer per tree. The wetted soil surface area is limited to that under the canopy of the tree. For irrigation management purposes, the daily crop evapotranspiration in inches per day is translated into an equivalent amount of water to be supplied to each tree in gallons per tree per day using the canopy area of the tree and the tree spacing.

Equation 4:

Gallons per tree per day =

$$0.623 \times \frac{ET}{efficiency} \times area \times \% \ cover$$

For example, an orchard is planted with trees on a 10 feet by 14 feet spacing. During the peak of the growing season, the trees provide 70 percent shading of the ground. How long should the system operate to apply a 0.35 inch gross depth (crop ET divided by the application efficiency)? Assume first that a drip system with four one-gph emitters per tree is being used. Using the above relationship, the gallons per tree for the 0.35 inch gross application is 0.623 x 0.35 x (10 x 14) x 0.70 or 21.4 gallons. The drip system should be operated for about five hours and 20 minutes to apply this volume. Now assume spray type microsprinklers providing 10 gph and a five feet wetted diameter are installed between every tree. In this case, the cover crop area between rows will not be well irrigated. At 10 gph per head, the system should be operated daily about two hours and 10 minutes to apply the required volume. Or, irrigate 4.33 hours every two days, 6.5 hours every three days and so on. The maximum duration of an individual irrigation should be carefully evaluated with respect to soil water holding capacity to be sure that set duration is not too long and causing deep percolation.

Microsprinkler systems may also be designed to have overlapping patterns. Microsprinklers with medium to large throw pattern diameters should be used. The design then becomes very much like the design of an undertree impact sprinkler system. Where tree spacings range from 10 by 14 feet, up to 14 by 20 feet, and microsprinklers with at least a 20- to 25-foot throw diameter are used, there typically should be one head placed midway between adjacent trees (or midway between every other tree if sized large enough) down each row. This arrangement may give fully or nearly fully overlapping patterns and the entire orchard floor will be irrigated. This is an important consideration if maintenance of a green cover crop is important.

The orchard as above with trees planted on a 10 by 14 feet spacing could be taken as an example. Microsprinklers are installed one per tree, deliver 20 gph and have a throw pattern of 16 feet diameter. There is overlap along the tree row and some overlap in the row middle. A cover crop is maintained between rows. How long should the system operate to apply the same gross depth of 0.35 inch? On a 10 by 14 feet spacing there are 311 trees per acre. The 0.35 inch gross depth translates to 9,503 gallons per acre (there are 27,152 gallons per acre-inch). This equals about 31 gallons per tree, or 31 gallons per head. Each head delivers 20 gph, so the system should operate about 1.5 hours to apply the equivalent of 0.35 inch. This example assumes the 0.35 inch gross depth is the combined requirement of the trees and cover crop divided by the system application efficiency. With the microsprinklers providing nearly full coverage of the orchard floor, the cover crop will be maintained. When the gross irrigation requirement is 0.35 inches per day, the irrigation frequency with this system is 1.5 hours every day, three hours every two days, six hours every four days and so on.

Uniformity of application can be high when microsprinkler systems are designed for limited wetting of the surface. In this case, uniformity is measured as the variation in flow from individual heads and is not based on the evenness of coverage of the orchard floor. Levels of 85 to 90 percent are achievable with proper design and adequate water treatment and filtration. Uniformity of microsprinkler systems with overlapping patterns can be variable. Tests of a system with overlapping patterns near Prosser, Washington, showed a uniformity of only 33 percent (see

Figure 6). Estimated water application efficiency calculated as the average depth caught, divided by the average depth applied to the entire orchard floor was 58 percent. Using just the catch data within 2.5 feet of the tree, adjusted application efficiency of 85 percent and adjusted uniformity of 75 percent are computed. These results indicate the microsprinklers are spaced too widely to achieve uniform orchard-floor coverage. However, the water applied to the row middles is adequate to keep the cover crop green, while the uniformity and efficiency of application in the tree rows are good.

SUMMARY

This chapter has provided an in-depth review of irrigation application efficiency and uniformity with respect to sprinkle and micro-irrigation systems used in the Pacific Northwest.

Irrigation is absolutely essential to the production levels currently being achieved in PNW orchards. Sustained, cost-effective production of high quality, high yielding fruit in the future will require that irrigation water is applied as uniformly and efficiently as possible. Competing demands for water will likely reduce available irrigation supplies. High density plantings and earlier production requires uniformity in all cultural practices including irrigation.

Agriculture's impact on the environment is increasingly in the public eye. Wise stewardship of water and soil resources used in irrigated agriculture requires efficient, uniform irrigation applications to minimize deep percolation and potential leaching of ag chemicals into groundwater supplies and to minimize soil erosion and runoff.

S							T					S
	2.80	1.59	0.20	0.52	1.57		1.59	0.15	0.39	1.70	2.82	
	1.61	0.34	0.09	0.04	2.61		4.41	0.36	0.20	1.18	1.41	
T							S					T
	2.11	0.66	0.10	0.14	2.89		1.03	0.64	0.30	1.52	2.65	
	3.55	1.45	0.25	0.55	2.07		3.36	1.00	0.88	1.41	3.42	
S							T					S

S indicates microsprinkler location
Catch can spacing = 4 feet x 4 feet
Tree spacing = 14 feet x 20 feet offset
Sprinkler spacing = 14 feet x 20 feet offset
Average depth caught = 1.40 inches
Estimated application efficiency (ratio of depth caught to applied) = 58%
Uniformity coefficient, UCC = 33%
Average depth caught within 2 ft of tree trunk = 2.05 inches
Adjusted application efficiency (ratio of depth caught to applied) = 85%
Adjusted uniformity coefficient, UCC = 75%

T indicates tree location
Microsprinkler flow rate = 17.9 gph
Gross application rate = 0.10 in/hr
Gross application in 24 hr = 2.40 in

FIGURE 6. Results of an undertree microsprinkler system catch can evaluation near Prosser, Washington. Catch values are depth caught in inches.

REFERENCES

ASAE. 1989a. "Engineering Practice EP405.1: Design and Installation of Micro-Irrigation Systems." *ASAE Standards, 36th Edition,* ASAE, St. Joseph, Michigan.

Ley, T.W. 1987. *Sprinkler Irrigation Application Rates and Depths.* EB 1305, Washington State University Cooperative Extension, Pullman, Washington.

Nakayama, F.S. and D.A. Bucks (eds). 1986. "Trickle Irrigation for Crop Production: Design, Operation and Management." *American Society of Agricultural Engineers,* St. Joseph, Michigan.

Ley, T.W. 1988. *Determining the Gross Amount of Water Applied—Surface Irrigation.* CO912, Washington State University Cooperative Extension, Pullman, Washington.

Vomocil, J.A. and J. Hart. 1990. "Irrigation Water Quality." *Fertilizer Guide 76,* Oregon State University, Corvallis, Oregon.

GLOSSARY

ABSCISIC ACID (ABA) - a naturally occurring plant hormone which causes the separation of plant parts.

ABSCISE; ABSCISSION - The natural separation of plant parts.

ABSORB; ABSORPTION - The process by which one substance is taken to and included within another substance, as the absorption of water by soil or nutrients by plants.

ACID SOIL - a soil with a pH below 7.0.

ACIDIC - a pH of less than 7.0

ACTUATOR - A device which causes motion or action.

ADSORPTION - the process by which ions are attracted to and held on the surface of soil particles through electrical bonds.

AERATE/AERATION - the process of creating channels or pores to allow free exchange of ambient air. Also refers to circulation of air for purification. In soils, soil air is replaced by atmospheric air.

AGROMETEOROLOGICAL - refers to the application of weather data. These climate data are used for agricultural decisions such as frequency of irrigation or for calculating pest growth models.

AGRONOMIC - refers to soil and plant sciences which relate to soil management and crop production.

ALKALINE SOIL - a soil with a pH above 7.0.

AMELIORATE - general term for improvement. For example, if a soil condition exists which inhibits plant growth, steps are taken to modify that condition to improve plant growth.

AMINO ACID - the fundamental structural units of proteins. There are 20 common amino acids in plants and animals with the basic structure based upon an amine group, NH_3.

ANAEROBIC - the absence of molecular oxygen in soils or organisms.

ANALOG - Chemically related structures.

ANION - A negatively charged ion; an ion which gains electrons.

ANTIOXIDANT - A chemical which inhibits the loss of electrons from a chemical reaction with molecular oxygen.

ANTITRANSPIRANT - A chemical which inhibits the loss of water through plant parts or organs.

APERTURE - An opening; can also refer to an orifice for pumps.

APOPLASTIC - Refers to movement of water through channels outside the cell walls in plant roots.

ARSENIC (AS) - a nonessential plant element; phytotoxic in general to fruit trees.

ARTESIAN - describes water that rises to the soil surface by internal hydrostatic pressure.

AVAILABLE WATER - The amount of water in soil that can be absorbed by plant roots; the amount of water between field capacity and permanent wilting point.

ATRAZINE - An herbicide usually commonly in row crop production.

ATTENUATION - The reduction in strength, force or amount; can also refer to decrease in density of a compound.

AUGER - A special drill for preparing deep holes in soil; these holes are generally for post installation or tree planting.

AZINPHOS-METHYL - The chemical name for an insecticide marketed as Guthion.

BACKFLOW PREVENTION DEVICE - A combination of check valve, vacuum breaker and low pressure drain installed between the point of chemical injection and the water source to prevent pollution of the water source by the injected chemical.

BICARBONATE - An negatively charged compound, HCO_3^-, present in water and soil.

BIOCIDES - Chemicals which kill or suppress growth of an organism.

BIOTA - A total ecological unit of a region which encompasses all plant and animal life found in that region.

BISULFITE - The inorganic acid group, HSO_3^-, or any chemical which contains this group.

BEST MANAGEMENT PRACTICES, BMP - A collection of agricultural practices which are safe for the environment and are cost-effective and efficient.

BORON, B - An essential plant micronutrient.

BROMACIL - An herbicide which inhibits photosynthesis, or the production of carbohydrates by the plant.

CALCIUM - An essential plant nutrient that is needed for tree growth and fruit quality. Low calcium in fruit is associated with bitter pit of apples and cork spot and alfalfa greening in pears.

CALCIUM CARBONATE, CaCO₃ - Generally referred to as "lime". It is an insoluble compound that forms white deposits on leaves and fruit when it occurs in high concentrations.

CALCARIOUS, SOIL - soil containing sufficient free calcium carbonate or calcium-magnesium carbonate to effervesce visibly when treated with cold 0.1N hydrochloric acid.

CALYX - the outer part of the floral envelope composed of sepals.

CARBARYL - An insectide, marketed commercially as Sevin. Also used as a thinning agent of apple fruit.

CALCIUM SULFATE, CaSO₄ - An inorganic compound which is formed when calcium carbonate combines with elemental sulfur; commonly called gypsum.

CARBOHYDRATES - Metabolites, such as sugars, made of carbon (C), hydrogen (H) and oxygen (O).

CASPARIAN STRIPS - barriers in plant roots which are suberized or covered with a corky layer. Water moves around these impervious areas via the symplast (see definition.)

CATIONS - A positively charged ion; one which loses electrons.

CAVITATION - Formation and collapse of low-pressure bubbles in liquids by means of mechanical forces, such as those of a pump or propeller.

CENTIBAR, Cb - Unit of measurement which refers to hydrostatic pressure; reflects the water content of a soil. A fully saturated soil is 0 Cb pressure.

CHELATE - an organic compound which forms ring compounds with metal cations. These ring compounds made the metals more soluble than they might normally be. Metal cations which are commonly chelated include calcium (Ca), copper (Cu), iron (Fe) and zinc (Zn).

CHLOROPLAST - A cellular plastic containing the gree photosynthetic pigment chlorophyll, in which solar light energy is absorbed and converted to chemical energy, and carbon dioxide is assimilated or fixed into simple sugar products (e.g., carbohydrates). Chloroplasts contain DNA and have the ability to produce proteins.

CHLOROSIS - The symptom of chlorophyll deficiency, which is exhibited by yellowing of leaves. It is often associated with high lime, water-saturated soils which induce iron deficiency.

CONVECTIVE - Refers to heat transfer which occurs in the atmosphere or a body of water. In meteorology, it refers to heat transfer by massive motion with the atmosphere.

CORTEX - A layer of tissue in roots and stems lying between the epidermis and the vascular tissue.

CUTICLE - The layer which covers the epidermis (skin) of plants. Generally composed of waxes and proteins.

CUTIN - A waxlike, water-repellent compound present in the walls of some plant cells, and forming the cuticle which covers the epidermis.

CYANIDE - A toxic compound, HCN, found in plants. It is generally not available as free cyanide, but as a chemically bound form with simple sugars, such as glucose.

CYTOKININ - A naturally occurring hormone, or a class of synthetic plant growth regulators, which promote growth and cell division. This hormone is also important in fruit growth and development.

CYTOPLASM - Refers to the cellular matrix in which plant organelles and plastids reside.

DIFFUSION - The movement of a chemical in the soil solution from zones of high concentration to zones of low concentration.

DISTRIBUTION UNIFORMITY - The ratio of the average depth of water applied to the quarter of the field receiving the least amount of water to the average depth of water applied over the entire field.

DIVALENT ION - An ion having two electrical charges.

DENITRIFICATION - Bacterial activity which makes nitrogen unavailable to the plant.

DESSICATION - The process of drying; generally in plants it is a harmful process in that water is lost.

DEWPOINT - The temperature at which air becomes saturated (with water) and produces dew.

DIURNAL - Refers to activities or processes that occur daily, during daylight hours.

EFFLUX - An outward flow or movement of water or a compound.

ELECTRODE - A solid electric conductor through which an electric current enters or leaves a medium such as an electrolyte, a nonmetallic solid, a molten metal, a gas, or a vacuum.

ELECTROLYTE - A substance that dissociates into ions in solution or when fused, thereby becoming electrically conducting.

ELECTROLYSIS - A chemical change produced in an electrolyte by an electric current.

ELECTROMAGNETISM - Magnetism arising from electric charge in motion.

ELECTROSTATIC - Of or pertaining to stationary electric charges.

EMBOLISM - An obstruction in a plant vessel caused by bubbles or solid deposits.

EUTROPHICATION - The process by which a body of water increases in mineral and organic nutrients to the point that dissolved oxygen is reduced, producing an environment that favors plant over animal life.

EVAPOTRANSPIRATION - The total loss of water from a plant by evaporation from the plant surface and epidermis, and transpirational loss of water from stomata.

FERTIGATION - The application of fertilizer materials with the irrigation water by injecting the fertilizer material directly into the irrigation stream prior to distribution to the field/orchard.

FIELD CAPACITY - The maximum amount of water in the soil after gravitational, freely-moving water leaves the soil profile.

FLOCCULATION - The process of forming lumps or masses in soil.

FLUX - The flow of energy or matter as a fluid; a continued flow or flood.

FPS - Feet per second; a measurement of flow.

GAUGE - A device or instrument for measuring pressure, vacuum, flow or other physical properties of matter.

GIBBERELLIC ACID, GA - A naturally occurring, or synthetic, plant hormone which affects cell elongation and fruit type.

GRADIENT - An increase or decrease in a per unit change of a material or process.

GRANULAR - Formulation of fertilizer or other farm chemical which is pelleted or formed into grains.

GRAVITATIONAL WATER - Water that moves into and out of soil in response to gravity.

GROUNDWATER - Water in a saturated zone or stratum beneath the surface of land or below a surface water body.

GUARD CELLS - Specialized cells of stomata or stomates. Two guard cells border each stomate, one on each side. When they absorb water because of changes in internal osmotic strength, they flex and the stomates open, allowing the inward and outward movement of gases and water vapor. When they lose water, the guard cells become flaccid and thus the stomate closes. Guard cells are generally open in light and closed during the dark.

HEAD-DISCHARGE - In pumps, the physical relationship of head (pressure) to flow rate (discharge) that is specific to the design and wear of each pump.

HEADLOSSES - Irreversible energy losses in fluid flow due to friction, elevation, velocity changes and changes in direction of flow.

HYDRAULICS - The physical relationships and behavior of water movement through closed and open conduits.

HYDROCOOLING - A practice of continuous application of water to fruit trees and fruit to enhance color development and decrease sunscald of the fruit.

HYDROLOGY - The science of the properties, distribution and effects of water on the earth's surface, in the soil and underlying strata, and in the atmosphere.

HYDROLYSIS - Decomposition of a chemical compound by reaction with water, such as the dissociation of a dissolved salt or the catalytic conversion of glucose to starch.

HYDROSTATIC - Pressure of water due to its depth (weight).

HYGROSCOPIC - Readily absorbing moisture, as from the atmosphere.

INDOLEACETIC ACID, IAA - A naturally occurring plant hormone belonging to the class of hormones known as auxins.

INFILTRATION - The downward movement of water into the soil.

INTERLOCKING CONTROLS - Electrical, electronic or mechanical devices which cause the chemical injection device on a fertigation or chemigation system to shut down in the event the irrigation pump shuts down or mainline operating pressure drops below an acceptable level.

ION - An electrically charged element or combination of elements resulting from the breaking up of an electrolyte in solution.

KAOLINITE - A component of kaolin, a clay with fine particles. Composed primarily of aluminum oxide and silicon oxide.

K_c-ET_o - Crop coefficient specifically related to the reference evapotranspiration of grass.

K_c-ET_r - Crop coefficient specifically related to the reference evapotranspiration of alfalfa.

K_c-PAN - Crop coefficient specifically related to evaporation from a Class A pan.

K_{oc} - Soil sorption index (organic carbon partition coefficient) used to classify mobility (leaching potential) of chemical through a soil.

kPa - Kilopascals; metric unit of pressure. 6.9 kPa = 1 pound per square inch (psi).

kWh - Kilowatt hours; a unit of energy usage.

LEACHING - The removal of materials in solution from the soil. Leaching occurs as excess water drains through the soil profile.

LIME - A soil amendment consisting principally of calcium carbonate but including magnesium carbonate and perhaps other minerals. Used to furnish calcium and magnesium as elements for plant growth, and to neutralize soil acidity.

LYSIMETER - A device for measuring percolation and leaching losses for a column of soil under controlled conditions.

MANOMETER - A device for measuring the pressure of liquids and gases.

MANUFACTURER'S COEFFICIENT OF VARIATION - A term describing the variation in flow rate for a water application emitter used in a micro-irrigation systems. It is used to rate and rank emitters according to the quality of manufacturing and how uniformly water will be delivered from the emitter.

MASS FLOW - Mass movement of water and nutrients into roots and through the xylem system; typically driven by diffusion.

MATRIX - A general description of the soil-water interface; a binding substance.

MEMBRANE - A thin, pliable layer composed of lipids (fats) and proteins which covers connecting plant cells. It is generally selectively permeable to chemical compounds, particularly nutrients and metabolites.

MERISTEM - An area of plant cells that is actively or can potentially undergo cell division. The meristem not only perpetuates the formation of new tissue it also regenerates itself. Undifferentiated cells which are rapidly dividing and forming new tissues or organs.

METABOLISM - The physiological processes of cells which maintain life.

METABOLITE - A chemical product of metabolism.

MICROIRRIGATION SYSTEM - Any drip, trickle, microsprinkler and micro spray or other system which applies water to individual plants or groups of plants at low volume and low pressure.

MICROBIAL - Relating to microbes, bacteria or microorganisms; generally associated with those organisms causing plant disease.

MICRONUTRIENTS - Nutrients that plants need in trace amounts, usually less than 100 parts per million (ppm).

MICROORGANISM - An animal or plant of microscopic size, particularly a bacterium or protozoan.

MICROSPRINKER - A type of sprinkler which applies water to individual plants or groups of plants at low volume and low pressure.

MONOVALENT ION - An ion having a single positive or negative electrical charge.

MUCIGEL - A gummy and slimy substance produced by plants or bacteria.

MYCORRHIZAE - Refers to symbiotic fungi which colonize plant roots, either externally or internally. Associated with the uptake of certain plant nutrients, such as phosphorus.

NEUTRAL SOIL - a soil with a pH of 7.0

NITRIFICATION - Biological oxidation of ammonium (NH_4^+) to nitrite ($NO_2^=$) and nitrate ($NO3^-$), or a biologically induced increase in the oxidation state of nitrogen.

NEMATICIDES - Agricultural chemicals used to control plant parasitic nematode populations.

OSMOSIS - Diffusion of fluids through a semipermeable or permeable membrane in response to a difference in solute concentrations on each side of the membrane; solutes move from an area of low concentration to the area of high concentration.

OUTFLOW - Water leaving a device (e.g., sprinkler or dripper), a field, or a farm.

PARTS PER MILLION, ppm - A notation for indicating small amounts of materials. Generally refers to milligrams/liter or milligrams/kilogram.

PERCOLATION, SOIL WATER - The downward movement of excess water through the soil profile.

PERMANENT WILTING POINT - The amount of water in the soil at which plants wilt and cannot recover.

pH - The negative logarithm of the hydrogen ion concentration; below 7.0 is acid; pH 7.0 is neutral, and above pH 7.0 is alkaline (or basic).

PHOTOSYNTHESIS - The process all green plants use to intercept solar light energy for the uptake and conversion of carbon dioxide (CO_2) and water (H_2O) into sugars. The sugars produced by photosynthesis are used either for respiration or the formation of other metabolites, such as starch. The sugars can also be used for the formation of nonliving structures such as cell walls.

PHYTOTOXIC - Toxic or harmful to plant tissues.

PLASMALEMMA - The outer membrane of the plant cell.

PLASMODESMATA - Channels between cells which allow transport of solutes, nutrients and water.

PLASTID - Specialized disc-shaped bodies in the cytoplasm and peculiar to plant cells (such as chloroplasts).

PRESSURIZED IRRIGATION - Irrigation systems that require greater than atmospheric pressure to operate, such as sprinkle and trickle systems.

REGULATED DEFICIT IRRIGATION, RDI - A technique for managing irrigation of fruit trees which conserves water during periods of tree and fruit growth.

RESPIRATION - The oxidation of sugars with the uptake of oxygen (O_2)in plants for the release of chemical energy for metabolism and the release of carbon dioxide (CO_2)

RHIZODERMIS - The outer covering or epidermis of a woody root.

RHIZOSPHERE - The surrounding soil matrix in which a root is embedded and growing.

ROOT CAP - The specialized root tip structure.

ROOT HAIR - The elongated tubular extension of an epidermal cell of developing root tips through which water and nutrients are absorbed.

ROTATORS - A low-volume, low pressure irrigation nozzle which delivers water in a circular pattern.

SALINE/SALINATION - Refers to accumulation of sodium (and also chloride) in a soil or body of water.

SAR - Sodium adsorption ratio; used to describe the potential sodium hazard to soil infiltration and structure as a ratio of sodium content to calcium and magnesium in water or saturated soil extracts.

SEMIPERMEABLE - Refers to a membrane which selectively allows passage of nutrients, solutes or other compounds. Requires metabolic energy to maintain this state of selectivity.

SENESCE/SENESCENCE - The physiological aging of tissue which leads to deterioration and death.

SIPHON - A pipe or tube fashioned in an inverted U shape and filled until atmospheric pressure is sufficient to force a liquid from a reservoir in one end of the tube over a barrier higher than the reservoir and out the other end.

SLURRY - A combination of soil and water, or another solid material with water. Usually the consistency of thick cream.

SMOLTS - Young hatchling fish.

SODIC - Refers to salt or salinity.

SOLUBILITY - Refers to the ease with which a chemical dissolves in water.

SORBITOL - A six-carbon sugar alcohol. The primary transport carbohydrate product of photosynthesis in fruit trees. May have a role in stress tolerance such as drought tolerance or winter hardiness.

STELE - The central core of vacular tissue in a plant stem.

STOMATE - Small openings or pits in the epidermis of leaves. Water vapor is lost through the stomates in the process of transpiration, oxygen is absorbed in the process of respiration, and carbon dioxide is taken up in the process of photosynthesis.

SUBERIN - A corky substance that covers roots; compound contained in tree bark. Imprevious to water.

SUBIRRIGATION - A water application method that occurs below ground or controls shallow water tables to affect irrigation by upward water movement.

SUNSCALD - An physiological disorder, or injury, caused by extreme light, temperature and moisture stress to a plant organ, such as a fruit.

SURFACTANT - A material added to reduce the surface tension of water, allowing better wetting of a surface by a solution.

SYMBIOSIS - A mutually beneficial relationship between two different types of living organisms.

SYMPLAST - Refers to the living portion of the cell in which water and nutrients move.

TAIL WATER - Water leaving a field that may be discharged back into a surface-water system or collected in a pond for reuse on the farm.

TELEMETRY - The science and technology of automatic measurement and transmission of data by wire, radio, or other means from remote sources, to a receiving station for recording and analysis.

TENSIOMETER - A device used to measure soil water potential (as a negative pressure). It consists of a ceramic cup filled with water and connected through a water-filled tube to a vacuum gauge.

THERMODYNAMICS - Refers to the inter-relationships of heat and other forms of energy, as well as the movement of heat through gases, liquids and solids.

TORTUOSITY - Refers to the extent of the indirect path that water must travel in and around soil particles. Much higher in clays than sands.

TRANSPIRATION - The loss of water vapor from plant surfaces, mainly through the stomates.

TURGOR - The pressure within a cell caused by absorbed water pressing against the cell wall.

VA MYCORRHIZAE/VESICULAR-ARBUSCULAR MYCORRHIZAE - Certain fungi which form a symbiotic relationship with plants. Generally inhabit the roots (either internally or externally) and may assist in the uptake of plant nutrients such as zinc, copper and phosphorus.

VAPORIZATION - The evaporation or changing of a substance from liquid to vapor.

VENTURI INJECTOR - A passive chemical injection device which operates on the principle of a venturi, i.e., mainline flow (or a portion of flow) is caused to pass through an engineered constriction in the pipeline having specific entrance and exit conditions. Velocity of flow increases, creating a low-pressure zone at the constriction. Suction is created on a port at the constriction pulling chemical into the water flow.

WATER APPLICATION (OR IRRIGATION UNIFORMITY) - A measure of how evenly water is applied by an irrigation system during an irrigation period. Usually is a number between 0 and 100%, with 100% indicating perfectly even distribution. It is affected by the method of irrigation, the system design and layout, environmental conditions at the time of irrigation and irrigation management.

WATERLOGGED - Saturated soil, which induces anaerobic conditions and leads to plant death in severe cases.

WEIR - A structure placed across a river or canal to raise or divert water to measure and/or to regulate the flow of water.

XYLEM - The principal water-conducting tissue in vascular plants. Specialized cells and tissue through which water, nutrients and solutes move upward from the soil through plants.

GOOD FRUIT GROWER BOOKS

Professional growers throughout the world recognize *Good Fruit Grower* magazine as one of the most comprehensive and authoritative periodicals in the industry. First published in 1946, the magazine has been an essential part of their operations for a half century. A not-for-profit, grower-owned business, its sole purpose is the education of deciduous tree fruit growers, irrespective of region or nationality.

In recent years, Good Fruit Grower has expanded its educational offerings by teaming with university experts to produce high-quality, low-volume books that present in detail subjects vital to the industry. Pest management and identification, high density orchard systems, tree fruit nutrition, pollination, and irrigation and water issues all have been covered extensively in separate books. By reading the magazine and using the in-depth manuals for reference, growers remain competitive in the increasingly complex tree fruit industry. Each year we add a title or two to our catalogue to keep it comprehensive.

Readers interested in either a subscription to *Good Fruit Grower* magazine or a current listing of Good Fruit Grower book titles may call 1-800-487-9946 or write:

Good Fruit Grower
P.O. Box 9219
Yakima, WA 98909
U.S.A.